DIFFERENTIAL DIAGNOSIS OF … S

(For diagnosis of mushr… intoxications, see Chapter IX.)

Dieffenbachia IIA	Wisteria IIB	Saponin IICa	Resin IICb	Taxine IICc	Protoanemonin IICd	Misc. G.I. IICe	Toxalbumin IIDa	Solanine IIDb	Oxalate IIDc	Colchicine IIDd	Digitalis IIIA	Aconite IIIB	Veratrum IIIC	Veratrine IIID	Nicotine IV	Atropine V	Cicuta VI	Cyanide VII	Akee VIII	Lantana X
X		(X)	X		X					X										
X		X											X		X		X			
	X	X	X	X	X	X					X	X	X	X	X		X	X		
							X	X	X	X									X	X
		X	X	X	X	X	X	X	X	X	X									
		X	X		X	X	(X)	X	X	X										
				X												X				X
											(X)		X			X				
							X		X					X					X	X
								X	X		X	X								
			X									X		X						
												X					X	X	X	
																X				
				X	X											X				
																X				
															X	X				
											X	X	X	X						
							X						X	X						
				X							X	X								
								(X)								X				
												X				X		X		

Plant Toxicity and Dermatitis

"PROBABLY NO FIELD OF SCIENTIFIC ENDEAVOR EXISTS IN WHICH IT IS MORE DIFFICULT TO SEPARATE FACT FROM FICTION THAN IN THE STUDY OF POISONOUS PLANTS. EXAMINATION OF THE PERTINENT LITERATURE WILL REVEAL CONFUSION TENDING TO MASK AN EVEN GREATER AMOUNT OF IGNORANCE. INDEED, ALMOST ANY PLANT MAY BE JUDGED AS TOXIC, QUESTIONABLE, OR EDIBLE, DEPENDING UPON THE REFERENCE CONSULTED."

Edward P. Claus and Varro E. Tyler, Jr.
Pharmacognosy, Fifth Edition
Lea & Febiger, Philadelphia, 1965

ILLUSTRATIONS BY GERTI ANTAL

Plant Toxicity and Dermatitis

A MANUAL FOR PHYSICIANS

KENNETH F. LAMPE, Ph.D.
Professor of Pharmacology, School of Medicine, University of Miami

RUNE FAGERSTRÖM, Pharm. Dr.
Director, Central Hospital Pharmacy, Uddevalla, Sweden

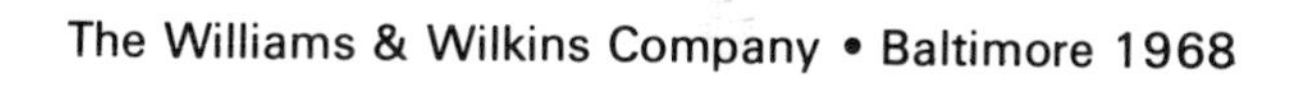
The Williams & Wilkins Company • Baltimore 1968

428 E. Preston Street
Baltimore, Md. 21202 U.S.A.

Made in the United States of America

LIBRARY OF CONGRESS CATALOG CARD NUMBER 68-14278

Composed and printed at the
Waverly Press, Inc.
Mt. Royal & Guilford Avenues
Baltimore, Md. 21202 U.S.A.

PREFACE

Intoxications from plant ingestion are responsible for about 4 per cent of all accidental poisonings in the United States. In most cases the victim is a small child. Occasional cases of poisoning result from misidentifying poisonous plants as edible fruits or vegetables or by the use of plants in home medicine. Self treatment with plants is no longer a common practice in the United States. An exception to this is the serious and sometimes fatal intoxications which result from attempts to secure abortion. Usually a careful history will reveal the offending material. Secondary poisoning, that is, drinking milk obtained from cows who have eaten poisonous plants or eating honey made from oleander blossoms, are infrequent, bizarre events which have been recognized only because they affected a large number of people during the specific episode.

Ingested plant intoxications may result in either gastroenteritis or systemic reactions. In the category of the non-ingested plant intoxications are the asthmatic reactions (hay fever) and the topical reactions, which may be either allergenic in nature or the result of vesicant materials.

The production of asthmatic effects is too broad in scope for coverage in this text. The reader is referred to the many fine detailed treatises for coverage of plants and fungus spores responsible for this response.

Plants selected for inclusion in this manual are restricted to those which have been reported to have produced human poisoning or, in a few instances, have, in our judgment, the potential to do so. An analysis of the fatal plant poisonings in recent years in the United States shows that mushrooms were responsible for 50 per cent of these deaths. The remaining fatalities are associated with a limited number of plants. The most prominent of these are Poison Hemlock (*Conium* spp), Water Hemlock (*Cicuta* spp), and the Castor Bean (*Ricinus communis*).

Since it may be of considerable importance in determining the prognosis to know of previous poisonings, especial effort has been made to give the outcome of known cases. In many instances this will simply be a statement as to whether or not the patient has survived. A real service could be performed by physicians if they report cases of plant poisoning to their regional Poison Control Center. In each case, an effort to identify the offending plant material should be made. Since many physicians have only the most scanty knowledge of botanical terminology, we have prepared extensive illustrative material rather than relying solely on physical descriptions of the plants.

The physician only rarely is able to use a specific treatment or antidote in plant poisoning. In most cases his approach must be symptomatic. He is interested, however, in what symptoms to anticipate and to have a general idea of the probable duration and prognosis of the poisoning. It is on this basis that this book was written.

K. F. L.
R. F.

ACKNOWLEDGEMENTS

We wish to thank Warren Lindau, M.D. for reviewing the section on emergency and supportive care. We are indebted to Mary Ann McCann for help in the preparation of many portions of the manuscript, particularly the chapter on plant dermatitis, and to Philip Frost, M.D. and Walter Edmundson, M.D. for their critical comments on that section. We also wish to thank Dr. Varro Tyler, Jr. for his aid in the preparation of the text on poisonous mushrooms. We are also grateful for the cooperation of Drs. Finn Sandberg, Gunnar Samuelsson and Bo Holmstedt.

Without the generous help of the library staff, it would have been impossible to prepare this manual. Therefore we wish to express our gratitude to Isabel Cabellero, Mary Dillon, Cyril Feng and Joy Richmond, of the Medical Library at the University of Miami. Similarly we wish to thank Carl Elwin, Gloria Francke, Charlotte Kenton, Joy Stiller and Ellen Wells, of the National Library of Medicine.

We are grateful for the cooperation of the Apothecaries' Society who so kindly furnished financial support for Dr. Fagerström's replacement at the Central Hospital Pharmacy in Uddevalla and to Bertil Holtzberg and Karl-Eric Linder of the Uddevalla Pharmacy for their approval of his sabbatical stay in the United States and to Bengt Sjöberg, who was instrumental in securing Bo Lundberg as his replacement for the second year and to Torsten Aronsson, who so ably replaced him during the first year.

The botanical nomenclature, spelling and capitalization, for the most part, follow that given in *Hortus Second* by L. H. and E. Z. Bailey (Macmillan, 1964) and *Weeds* by W. C. Muenscher, (Macmillan, 1955). We wish to thank Dr. Daniel Ward and Mr. John Beckner for checking the botanical descriptions.

We wish to thank Corinna Bourbeau for her patience in typing and retyping the text.

The preparation of this manuscript was supported by Public Health Service Research Grant No. DS 00249.

CONTENTS

I EMERGENCY AND SUPPORTIVE CARE

Following ingestion of plant material and prior to the advent of symptoms, the physician is faced with the following questions:

Is the plant poisonous?
How poisonous?
What will be the symptoms?
When should I expect these symptoms to appear?
What should I do in the meantime?
If symptoms of systemic poisoning have already appeared, how should I proceed?

If ingested plant material is not available and can not be described, or if the plant can not be identified, even though symptoms are not evident, one should proceed on the assumption that the plant may have been poisonous. If no more than 2 or 3 hours have passed since ingestion, one begins by removing the stomach contents. If systemic reactions appear it is sometimes possible to identify the toxic material based on their nature; for this a special table has been prepared which is shown inside the front and back covers.

The treatment of symptoms produced by toxic materials does not usually differ from normal medical care of such symptoms regardless of cause. No attempt is made in this chapter to give highly detailed discussions on the management of acid/base balance, renal failure, or cardiac arrythmias. Rather we have attempted to present sufficient material to institute emergency supportive care for the toxicological emergency. It is left to the physician to then provide the usually accepted medical treatment thereafter. It is also assumed that the physician will seek the assistance of such specialty services as are indicated by his judgment in anesthesiology, cardiology, pediatrics, dermatology, gastroenterology, etc.

A. EMPTYING THE STOMACH

Induced Emesis

Vomiting may be induced by mechanical stimulation of the posterior pharyngeal wall to elicit the gag reflex. Emesis is said to be more effectively produced if the patient's stomach is first distended with a large volume of water.

The use of syrup of ipecac is probably the most efficient method of promoting emesis. The dose of syrup of ipecac is 4 to 8 ml orally, but up to 20 ml have been given to children without encountering significant toxicity. The average latent period is 19 minutes.

Gastric Lavage

Gastric lavage is an alternative method for emptying the stomach. Since lavage usually requires special facilities, emesis is commonly attempted first, but unless vomiting has been profound the subsequent employment of lavage is probably indicated.

To remove unabsorbed poison, a tube is used alternately to empty and fill the stomach with liquid, several of these cycles are necessary for effective mechanical washing. Finally the lavage tube can be used to introduce an appropriate antidote which is allowed to remain in the stomach.

Most patients are lavaged without anesthesia. With young children physical restraints are required, however, even with a frightened and uncooperative patient intubation rarely leads to significant trauma.

Use as large a stomach tube as possible, so that the wash solution will flow freely and the procedure can be carried out quickly. A tube with a diameter between $^{5}/_{16}$ and $^{1}/_{2}$ inches (24 F or greater) is usually satisfactory in an adult patient; an 8 to 12 F catheter is appropriate in infants. The tube should be inserted for a distance equal to that measured between the bridge of the nose and the tip of the xiphoid process. This distance can be measured off on the tube and marked with a small patch of adhesive tape. The tubing should be lubricated with water or a water soluble jelly. It is sometimes desirable to chill the catheter.

For the introduction of the lavage tube in adults and older children the nasal route is usually used, whereas the oral route is easier in infants and young children. For nasal intubation choose the nostril with the wider lumen to minimize the chance of nosebleed. First remove dentures and any other foreign objects from the mouth. During intubation the patient is positioned on his side with his head hanging over the edge of the bed, face down. Make certain the end of the tube lies in the stomach. If the tip enters the larynx instead of the esophagus, violent coughing and dyspnea are usually induced, but these signs may be absent in a deeply narcotized patient. Whenever in doubt, test by submerging the free end of the tube just below a water surface at the moment of expiration. In all cases aspirate before instilling water or antidote.

In most cases the composition of the wash fluid is less important than its volume or the promptness of lavage. Tap water is often as good as any vehicle, and it is never contraindicated. In some cases a solution of 1:10,000 potassium permanganate is used to chemically inactivate or detoxify the unabsorbed poison.

The use of tannic acid solutions or tea has been generally discontinued since they have been found, in some instances, to facilitate absorption of the poison. Alcohol is contraindicated since it markedly increases absorption.

The technique of the lavage is dependent upon the diameter of the stomach tube. With relatively small bore tubing a 50 or 100 ml syringe is used to force 30 to 90 ml of fluid down the tube. The fluid and gastric contents are then aspirated with the same syringe. The procedure is repeated 10 to 15 times or until the washings are clear. If the conventional glass syringe becomes plugged with solid particles, a rubber bulb or an ear syringe may prove satisfactory. With large bore stomach tubes, the stomach is filled by gravity. Pour no more than 500 ml water (generally 300 to 360 ml) into a funnel attached to the stomach tube and then elevate the funnel above the patient. As soon as the fluid reaches the stomach, turn the patient to promote mixing within the stomach and to wash all the mucosal surface. Promptly remove the washing by stomach pump or by gravity siphoning. Repeat 10 to 15 times (at least 3 liters) or until the returns are clear.

Several choices are open at the completion of lavage. The stomach may be left empty, or activated charcoal (3 to 4 tablespoons suspended in water) may be instilled through the tube and allowed to remain.

Remove the tube carefully to avoid the gag reflex. Pinch the tube or maintain suction while it is being withdrawn.

Catharsis

To facilitate the rate of elimination of toxic materials saline cathartics may be given, e.g., sodium or magnesium sulfate, 15 to 30 g in water. Cathartics are contraindicated in instances of irritant poisonings. Enemas are seldom warranted.

B. GASTROINTESTINAL AND HEPATIC SYSTEMS

General Management of Gastroenteritis

Nothing is permitted by mouth as long as nausea and vomiting persist. Then light fluid such as tea, bouillon or broth with added salt may be given.

Suction, endotracheal tubes, laryngoscopes, and bronchoscopes, all should be on hand in case the patient should vomit and aspirate or becomes apneic.

Persistent Vomiting

If emesis persists, intravenous infusion of 5% dextrose and sodium chloride in water are administered to prevent dehydration and its consequences. Potassium should be added when necessary. Blood or plasma is indicated in severe cases if the patient exhibits shock. Vomiting can usually be controlled by sedation with sodium phenobarbital, 30 to 100 mg subcutaneously 3 or 4 times/day, alone or with scopolamine, 0.5 mg subcutaneously or by injections of an anti-emetic, such as, thiethylperazine maleate (Torecan) 10 to 20 mg/day or trimethobenzamide hydrochloride (Tigan) 100 to 300 mg intramuscularly 4 times daily.

For severe abdominal cramps meperidine (Demerol) 50 mg IM every 4 to 6 hours if necessary or an antispasmodic, e.g., atropine, 0.3 to 1.2 mg SQ, may be given.

Persistent Diarrhea

If after 12 to 24 hours, moderate diarrhea persists in the absence of severe systemic symptoms or respiratory depression, 5 ml of paregoric may be given orally every 4 hours.

When warm liquids are well tolerated, the diet may be increased gradually to include cooked bland cereals and puddings, soft boiled eggs, etc.

Abdominal Distension

In simple paralytic ileus, gastric decompression is a useful prophylactic and therapeutic measure which, if begun promptly, obviates other treatment. An 18 F plastic Levine tube is appropriate for nasogastric intubation in adults. Abdominal pressure is usually effected within 12 to 18 hours but suction may have to be continued prophylactically for several days. As long as it is maintained, the hypochloremic alkalosis and potassium loss must be corrected by parenterally administered salts.

Liver Damage

Fortunately, liver damage induced by plants is infrequently encountered, in this country being associated only with the *Amanita phalloides* group of mushrooms and with the immature fruit of the akee. In poisoning from either of these, a daily evaluation should be made of liver function particularly in respect to serum transaminase levels. There is no general agreement that any particular dietary regime is effective in reversing progressive hepatocellular destruction or in promoting repair. The generally accepted practice for the management of liver damage is to control emesis, to increase the carbohydrate intake, and to carefully monitor fluid and electrolyte balance. The administration of thioctic (α-lipoic) acid, discussed in the chapter on *Amanita phalloides* poisoning, might be considered. See also the review by Brown.

C. CENTRAL NERVOUS SYSTEM

Depression

Central nervous system (CNS) depression may be manifested by headache, inability to concentrate, vertigo, excitement, delerium, drowsiness, stupor, coma, and finally, respiratory paralysis. The patient with severe CNS depression requires prompt and intensive management. The prevention or correction of anoxia is of primary importance. An adequate airway must be maintained. Oxygen administration and assisted respiration may be necessary. If anoxia can be minimized, cardiovascular collapse can often be avoided. Mild degrees of hypotension may be ignored, but severe circulatory failure requires prompt attention with vasoconstrictor agents. Dehydration and electrolyte disturbances must be corrected. The periodic intake of even small amounts of glucose or other carbohydrate is usually sufficient to prevent ketosis and acidosis. If coma persists a program of parenteral alimentation is instituted. The patient should be examined repeatedly for signs of urinary retention, and if the bladder is distended, it should be emptied by catheterization. To prevent hardening of the colonic contents and fecal impactions and occasional oil retention enema is desirable. Defects in temperature regulation have to be compensated. The parenteral administration of a wide-spectrum antibiotic is no longer considered an advisable prophylactic measure, but overt infection must be treated promptly and rigorously.

Delirium

Delirium usually results from CNS depression in combination with some degree of anoxia. Circulatory disturbances, electrolyte imbalance and pain are lesser causes. General supportive treatment therefore should be directed primarily at the maintenance of oxygenation.

Another important objective is to manage uncontrolled behavior that might lead to injury or serious exhaustion. A delirious patient should be given constant nursing care. Sedatives, because of their inherent respiratory depressant effects, should be avoided, if possible. Prolonged manic excitement may be allayed by the administration of chlorpromazine (Thorazine) 25 to 50 mg, I.M.

Coma

The comatose patient who is reactive to a painful stimulus, whose swallowing and cough reflexes are intact, has no need of an analeptic drug and none should be given. The use of such an agent to raise the general level of reflex excitability has proven of little value; far better results are obtained with intensive nursing care.

Pain

Prior to the application of drugs for the control of pain, an assessment should be made of the etiology. Thus visceral pain, which is encountered most commonly in plant poisoning, should be treated with antispasmodic drugs. Pain may also be produced from muscle spasm secondary to tremors or convulsions. In this instance simple physical measures such as heat-packs and exercise are indicated. Localized cutaneous mucosal lesions may be managed with topical anesthetic lotions. The use of narcotics for pain associated with plant intoxication is rarely indicated. When necessary, meperidine (Demerol) 50 to 100 mg I.M. is usually satisfactory.

Convulsions

The most important consideration in the management of the convulsant patient is adequate oxygenation. Convulsive episodes are always accompanied by periods of apnea. During the actual seizure the patient is unconscious and experiences laryngeal spasm, thereby preventing oxygen from reaching the lungs. Between paroxysms the larynx is relaxed but the patient may have a continued loss of consciousness due to apnea or exhaustion. During the inter-seizure period, respiration may be maintained artificially. In many instances where the convulsion is of short duration (1 to 10 seconds) and the interval between seizures is sufficient (10 to 20 seconds) to allow adequate oxygenation, the convulsions may be controlled by the use of oxygen alone.

If the patient has severe, sustained convulsions, then 40 mg (2 ml) of succinylcholine chloride (Anectine) can be given intravenously to paralyze the patient, relax the spasm of the cords of the larynx, and permit oxygenation. In these instances the patient is unconscious from the convulsion and since the duration of the action of succinylcholine chloride is 4 to 5 minutes, he is unaware of the total paralysis. Artificial respiration must be maintained until the apnea of the period of depressed respiration from either the toxic plant or the succinylcholine is over. Convulsions may also be arrested by the administration of a 2.5% solution of thiopental (Pentothal) intravenously in 50 mg (2 ml) increments. The disadvantage of a barbiturate is that it will add to a pre-existing depression of the medullary centers and may result in prolonged apnea. Thiopental, particularly when administered rapidly, has the added inherent danger of producing severe hypotension and laryngospasm. Therefore, this technique should only be employed when oxygen is available.

If facilities are not available to administer oxygen by intermittent positive pressure, or if persistent convulsions and tremors are leading to serious exhaustion of the patient, a longer acting barbiturate, such as pentobarbital sodium (Nembutal) 5 per cent, may be given intravenously or intramuscularly in increments of 0.2 to 0.5 g (4 to 10 ml or 3 to 7 mg/kg).

Convulsions due to tetany, such as those caused by the oxalic acid containing plants, are preferentially treated by the administration of calcium.

Disturbances of Body Temperature

Hot weather and a mild elevation of body temperature appear to enhance the toxicity of exogenous toxins and vigorous efforts to hold the temperature at a normal or even subnormal level are warranted. Various cooling applications are used; these include sponging the skin with tepid water or with alcohol, the application of cold compresses on the forehead and neck, the use of thermal blankets or, when not available, immersion in baths of cool water. Water temperatures below 78°F. are rarely used, not only because they are sometimes painful but also because they generate reflex vasoconstriction which impairs their effectiveness. Ice packs, ice water baths, and ice water enemas are unnecessarily violent and dangerous and may produce shock in very young children. Antipyretic drugs are ineffective and in some cases are potentially dangerous.

If a severe depression in body temperature is evident, the presence of shock must be ruled out. If the disturbance in temperature regulation is apparently due to hypothalamic depression, the patient should be made comfortable with blankets, warming packs, or heating pads.

D. CARDIOVASCULAR SYSTEM

Hypotension and Shock

Plant toxins can produce either neurogenic or oligenic shock. Neurogenic shock develops as a result of loss of central or peripheral nervous control of peripheral resistance. The characteristics of this type of shock are hypotension, weak pulse, and little or no change in cardiac rate during or prior to the development of hypotension. The treatment of neurogenic shock requires that adequate oxygenation be established followed by the administration of vasoconstrictor agents such as phenylephrine (Neo-Synephrine) 2 to 10 mg I.V. to re-establish vascular tone.

Secondary shock is the result of fluid loss which may occur during gastroenteritis as a result of violent and persistent vomiting and diarrhea or from hemorrhage from intestinal lesions. The characteristics of secondary shock are hypotension, a marked increase in pulse rate, pallor and cold skin which result from cutaneous vasoconstriction, and perspiration. The treatment of oligenic shock requires replacement of the circulating blood volume with whole blood or plasma. Since the arterioles are constricted in this form of shock, nothing is to be gained by the administration of vasoconstrictor drugs.

Disturbances in Cardiac Physiology

Disturbances in cardiac rate, rhythm, conduction, or effort occur with only a limited number of plant toxins. It should be recalled that many disturbances in cardiac function are secondary to extreme hypotension and anoxia or electrolyte imbalance and that normal cardiac function will be restored if these conditions are corrected. In the absence of life-threatening situations, the exact nature of the plant should be identified so that specific therapy can be instituted.

The ability to manage disturbances in cardiac function will depend upon both the physician's experience and the facilities of the treatment center. In general, it is well to start with more conservative measures, since, contrary to dealing with established pathology, once the toxin is eliminated a normal sinus rhythm should reappear.

If digitalis or aconitine containing plants are responsible for the rhythm or conduction defect, specific therapy should be instituted as indicated in the text, otherwise the following therapeutic methods may be considered for the management of cardiac arrythmias.

Sinus bradycardia	Atropine
Sinus tachycardia	Sedatives
Supraventricular tachycardia	Digitalis
Premature atrial contractions, atrial flutter, or atrial fibrillation	Digitalis or Procainamide

Premature ventricular contractions or paroxysmal ventricular tachycardia	Potassium chloride or Quinidine sulfate, or Procainamide
Paroxysmal ventricular fibrillation	Electric shock; Quinidine or Procainamide prophylactically
Heart block, sinus arrest	Atropine may improve

E. RENAL SYSTEM

Specific damage of the proximal tubules, which sometimes proceeds to necrosis, may result from the local action of various nephrotoxic agents. It usually appears 2 to 4 days after exposure then slowly regresses as the damaged tubular cells regenerate. There is no convincing evidence that a simple water diuresis speeds the excretion of any toxic substance. On the other hand, urine flow induced by an osmotic diuretic may promote the excretion of any solute, toxic or otherwise, that is normally resorbed by the renal tubular epithelium. Furthermore, there are at least theoretical advantages in maintaining a dilute tubular fluid during the excretion of a primary nephrotoxic chemical. On this basis it may be advisable as a prophylactic measure to administer intravenously mannitol or some similar osmotically active diuretic drug. In the adult probably no more than 1 liter of 10 per cent mannitol in water should be given and then only if the infusion can be started soon after the toxic exposure.

Although a transient phase of polyuria is sometimes noted, the first objective evidence of renal injury is expected to be oliguria. Early in the clinical course, however, it may be difficult to distinguish between oliguria due to dehydration or other hemodynamic abnormality and oliguria due to injury of the renal tubules. If there are clinical signs of dehydration, 500 ml of 5 per cent dextrose in water (or in saline if there is evidence of a salt deficit) should be given intravenously over a one hour period. If dehydration is the sole cause of oliguria, an increase in urine flow promptly ensues. Similarly, if oliguria is due to a reduction in the glomerular filtration rate caused by hypotension, then therapy for shock can be expected to accelerate the flow of urine.

Oliguria may persist for a period ranging from a few hours to 3 weeks (average 10 to 12 days), but as the renal tubules begin to regenerate, oliguria is gradually replaced by a phase of polyuria. Although the onset of diuresis signals probable recovery, the polyuric phase is also associated with a high mortality (25 per cent) and demands scrupulous vigilance for a period of at least one week. Normal renal function is not regained for some time, as evidenced by the fact that the blood urea level often continues to rise for another 5 days. Urine volumes during the stage of polyuria may reach as high as 3 to 5 liters daily, especially if the prescribed loss of body weight was not attained during the oliguric phase. Even if overhydration was avoided, some degree of polyuria is inevitable and under these circumstances the daily losses of water and of electrolytes (now including both sodium and potassium) must be replaced to avoid serious states of depletion.

Miscellaneous clinical problems that may arise during acute renal failure include the following gastrointestinal disturbances: anorexia, nausea, vomiting, diarrhea, and abdominal distension. The diarrhea, which usually occurs late in the oliguric stage, may be profuse and persistent. These intestinal losses of water and electrolytes (exclusive of potassium during the phase of oliguria) must be replaced in like measure through parenteral routes. The most common mental symptom in acute renal failure is somnolence; to attempt its correction by drugs is generally unwise. Indeed, any drug therapy must be conducted with caution, since renal excretion is normally a major mechanism for disposing of medicinal agents. In the presence of renal damage, therefore, drugs should either be avoided or used only sparingly. A rapidly developing anemia, which is usually normochromic and normocytic, is a constant feature of renal insufficiency. Apparently it is self-limiting and usually well tolerated, in contrast to the blood transfusions which are sometimes used to correct or ameliorate it. Transfusions are hazardous because of the ease with which congestive heart failure can be precipitated in these patients.

F. ALLERGIC RESPONSES

All allergic reactions subside after removal of the source of allergen. Thus, in mild cases, no treatment is warranted.

Dermatitis

Topical reactions associated with a great deal of discomfort and itching may be benefited by the application of 1/8 to 1 per cent hydrocortisone, preferably as a lotion or spray rather than as an ointment. Topical ointments of hydrocortisone, prednisolone and adrenocorticoids are available for inflammations of the conjunctiva. Antihistamines such as cyproheptadine (Periactin) or trimeprazine (Temaril) may be of benefit for id reactions and intractable pruitus. Systemic cortisone therapy should be reserved for severe and extensive reactions. Additional details are given in Chapter XI.

Systemic Allergic Reactions and Anaphylactic Shock

Severe anaphylactic reactions are occasionally encountered. The response may vary in its characteristics and may easily be confused with toxic reactions of a non-allergenic type. The signs and symptoms of an anaphylactic reaction may include generalized and laryngeal edema, pallor, restlessness, pruritus, bronchial asthma, "giant hives", apprehension, tachycardia, vomiting, muscular spasm, convulsions, and coma. The subcutaneous administration of epinephrine, 0.2 ml of 1:1000 aqueous solution, will, at least temporarily, minimize or abolish these effects. For more prolonged control it may be necessary to administer adrenocorticoids.

REFERENCES

Brown, H. Treatment of Hepatic Failure and Coma. J. Am. Med. Assoc. *201:* 547, 1967.

Gleason, M. N., Gosselin, R. E., and Hodge, H. C. *Clinical Toxicology of Commercial Products*, 2nd ed., Section IV. The Williams & Wilkins Company, Baltimore, 1963.

Gosselin, R. E., and Smith, R. P. Trends in the therapy of acute poisonings. Clin. Pharm. Therap. *7:* 279, 1966.

II PLANTS WHICH ARE GASTROENTERIC IRRITANTS

In order to facilitate the identification of plants whose activity is generally limited to the gastroenteric tract, a somewhat arbitrary classification system has been developed based on the following presenting symptomatology:

A. **Irritation chiefly of mouth and throat.** These plants produce immediate pain when placed into the mouth and are rarely swallowed.

B. **Irritation chiefly of gastric mucosa.** These plants produce spontaneous emesis shortly after ingestion and are rarely absorbed in sufficient quantity to produce serious systemic intoxication.

C. **Irritation chiefly of the intestinal mucosa.** Ingestion of plants from this group produce relatively immediate emesis, abdominal pain and diarrhea. Some of these, if eaten in sufficient quantity, may produce systemic reactions.

D. **Plants producing delayed gastroenteritis.** After eating these plants there is a symptom-free period varying from one hour up to two days. The first sign of intoxication is usually a severe gastroenteritis with both vomiting and diarrhea. Many of the plants in this category are associated with fatalities.

A. PLANTS PRODUCING IRRITATION PRIMARILY OF THE MOUTH AND THROAT

Toxicology

The plants in this category contain water insoluble calcium oxalate in bundles of fine, needle-like crystals packed in cells and surrounded by a mucilaginous liquid. Bundles of this character, called raphides, have the property of ejecting the individual needles on contact with water. When eaten raw, these plants produce a painful burning sensation in the mouth.

It is suspected that some of these plants may contain other toxic materials, see particularly Barnes (11) and Manno (50), but the question is largely academic since the intense pain produced in the mouth deters the individual from swallowing a significant amount of material.

The medical aspects of exposure to *Dieffenbachia* have been reported in greatest detail. The signs and symptoms produced by the other members as well as the clinical management of intoxications may be considered similar (13, 25, 29, 42, 46).

Plants belonging to the resin-containing (for example, *Daphne*) and the protoanemonine groups can produce vesication and edema of the lips, tongue, and pharynx as well as dysphagia. Since these plants do not produce immediate pain when placed in the mouth, the material is usually swallowed and systemic reactions produced. Both of these are treated in the next section.

Members of the Group

Alocasia spp	
Arisaema triphyllum	Indian turnip, Jack-in-the-pulpit, etc.
Arisaema dracontium	Green dragon, Dragon root
Caladium spp	Caladium
Colocasia spp	Elephants ear, Dasheen
Dieffenbachia spp	Dumb cane
Monstera spp	Ceriman
Philodendron spp	Philodendron
Symplocarpus foetidus	Skunk cabbage
Xanthosoma spp	Malanga
* *Zantedeschia aethiopica*	Calla lily
* *Calla palustris*	Wild calla, Water arum

(See also, *Hippomane mancinella*, Chapter X)

* *Zantedeschia* is the Calla of gardeners; it is a popular greenhouse plant and is grown outdoors in warm regions. The true Calla is a small northern herb (*Calla palustris*). This latter should not be confused with *Caltha palustris*, which is treated in the protoanemonin group. The black Calla (*Arum palaestinum*) or red Calla (*Sauromatum guttatum*; formerly *Arum cornutum*) are discussed with the resin containing plants under *Arum* spp.

Symptoms

An intense burning sensation and increased salivation occurs after chewing the stem or leaves. Severe edema of the buccal mucosa, tongue, palate, and face appear, and bullae may be seen on the edematous surface of the tongue and mucosa. The speech becomes thick and unintelligible and in certain cases there is a total loss of voice, hence the common name Dumb Cane for *Dieffenbachia*. The edema and pain leads to dysphagia or to complete inability to swallow. The plant is dangerous because, in some instances, contact may not produce immediate irritation. Ingestion of the plant has rarely been reported but edema of the pharynx may be anticipated together with serious gastroenteritis (56).

Contact with the sap will produce dermatitis in susceptible individuals. Entry of the sap into the eye has produced permanent corneal opacification. Toxic reactions to the calcium oxalate contained in Dumb Cane, and other plants of this group, has not been reported to produce kidney injury or symptoms of tetany.

Treatment

The intense pain produced in the mouth requires meperidine (Demerol) for relief. Rinsing the mouth and swallowing, when tolerated, of a solution of aluminum magnesium hydroxide, 1 ounce every 2 hours, may be of benefit.

Corticoids may be helpful, but the experience with antihistamines has been disappointing. Intravenous fluids will be required. If no plant material was swallowed, a diet of liquids and puréed foods may be instituted about the second or third day and the diet should remain so restricted until all symptoms are abated.

Prognosis

The edema usually begins to lessen in about 4 days and becomes minimal in about 12. The pain regresses more slowly and remains severe for about eight days. Superficial necrosis may be expected on the tongue and buccal mucosa. Severe corrosion must be anticipated in the esophagus and stomach if portions of the plant are swallowed.

Botanical Descriptions

All the genera described in this section belong to the family Araceae. Characteristic is the "flower" shown in figures 1 and 3. This consists of an envelope, the spathe, and an axial spike, the spadix. The true flowers, and later the fruit, form on the spadix.

Most are tropical plants which are hardy outdoors in southern Florida and Hawaii but are commonly grown as potted plants throughout the United States because of their luxuriant tropical appearance. Native northern species, like the Jack-in-the-pulpit and skunk cabbage, are usually restricted to wet, woody areas.

Alocasia spp. There are many species and varieties with leaves ranging in length from a few inches to many feet. These are usually shaped in the form of an elongated valentine heart. Each is attached perpendicularly to an individual stalk.

Arisaema triphyllum (figure 1). Jack-in-the-pulpit, Indian turnip, three-leaved Indian turnip, pepper turnip, wild turnip, bog onion, brown dragon, starchwort, wake robin. This plant usually has two stalks standing about three feet high each bearing three 7 inch leaflets. The spathe is green striped with purple and arched over the spadix. The fruit forms as a cluster of globose red berries 1 cm in diameter each with one to three seeds. The plant is native in moist or wet wooded areas from Canada to Florida and westward to Texas and Minnesota.

Arisaema dracontium. Dragon-root, dragon arum, green dragon, dragon-tail. This plant is generally similar to *A. triphyllum* in distribution and appearance except that the leaves are divided into 7 to 13 leaflets and the berries are orange-red. The common names are derived from the spadix which extends, like the tail of a disappearing dragon, beyond the length of the spathe.

Caladium spp. These plants are similar to the *Alocasia* spp but the leaves are generally marked in many colors or patterns. As house plants these often are incorrectly called colocasias.

FIG. 1.
Jack-in-the-Pulpit
(*Arisaema triphyllum*)

FIG. 2.
Dumb cane
(*Dieffenbachia sequine*)

FIG. 3.
Skunk cabbage
(*Symplocarpus foetidus*)

FIG. 4.
Wild calla
(*Calla palustris*)

Colocasia spp. Elephants ear, dasheen. These are large plants, the leaves 2 feet or larger and the leaf stalks (petioles) up to 5 feet in length. The *Colocasia esculenta* (taro) has an edible tuber, often served as poi in Hawaii and other Pacific islands.

Dieffenbachia spp (figure 2). Dumb cane. These plants have large oblongated leaves splotched with ivory colored marbling. These and the *Philodendron* species constitute the chief decorative plants to be found in hotel lobbies, office waiting rooms, and restaurants.

Monstera spp. These are woody-stemmed climbers which are similar to the *Alocasia* except that the thick leaves are often perforated with irregularly shaped and placed holes.

Philodendron spp. Two leaf styles may be encountered. The first is similar to the *Alocasia* but differs in the pronounced irregular notching about the entire margin. The other form encompasses the vines frequently sold in variety stores. In these the leaves are heart shaped or oblong, sometimes variegated, and usually not notched.

Symplocarpus foetidus (figure 3). Skunk-cabbage, polecat weed. All parts of the plant have a strong and unpleasant odor. The spathes, which appear before the leaves, are about 3 to 6 inches high and may be green, purple brown, or striped and spotted with both colors. The leaves eventually reach 3 feet in length and 1 foot in width. The plant ranges from Quebec and Nova Scotia to North Carolina and westward to Iowa and Minnesota.

Xanthosoma spp. These plants are similar to the *Alocasia*. The leaves often have a pronounced spear-head appearance.

Zantedeschia aethiopica. Calla lily. This plant has arrowhead shaped leaves, sometimes mottled with white, borne individually on long stalks (petioles). The showy spathe which flares out like a lily is white in this species but in others may be pink or yellow.

Calla palustris (figure 4). Water arum, wild calla. This is a small plant with leaves about 4 to 6 inches in length which may be found in swampy areas in Quebec to Alberta and southward to New Jersey, Ohio, and northern Indiana and Minnesota. The spathe is inconspicuous, about 2 inches long. The berries are red and borne in thick clusters.

B. IRRITATION CHIEFLY OF GASTRIC MUCOSA

Emesis with minimal diarrhea following plant ingestion suggests that the toxic agents have only a limited direct irritant effect on the mucosa and may act primarily due to a stimulant action on the emetic zones of the central nervous system. This central emetic mechanism has been established for the alkaloid lycorine which is contained by all the plants in the Amaryllidaceae group, and may also apply to the wisteria.

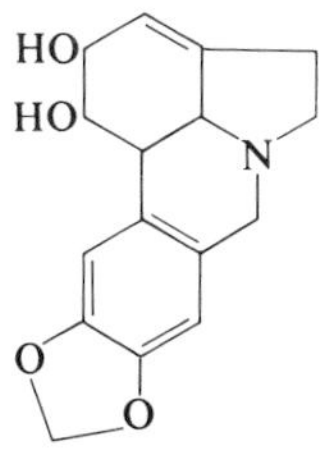

HO
HO
N
O
O

Lycorine

Plants containing digitalis glycosides also have a central emetic action but are treated separately in the section on cardioactive plants.

Wisteria

Toxicology

The poisonous substances contained in wisteria have not been identified. Intoxications occur most frequently in children following the ingestion of beans or the whole pods of the wisteria vine. One or two seeds are apparently sufficient to cause a severe response.

Symptoms

The predominant effect is gastric irritation evidenced by nausea, abdominal pain, and repeated vomiting. The vomitus may contain blood and bile-stained mucus. Abdominal distention may appear but diarrhea is usually slight or absent (26, 40, 66).

Treatment

The stomach should be lavaged as soon as possible after ingestion if spontaneous vomiting has not been adequate to remove the plant material. The use of antiemetics, such as chlorpromazine, is recommended. Younger children may require fluid replacement.

Prognosis

Despite the severity of the poisoning there are no fatalities reported. The patient usually becomes asymptomatic within 24 to 48 hours.

Botanical Description

The *Wisteria* are woody twiners with pendulous racemes of fragrant flowers similar in shape to the sweet pea. The flowers are generally in shades of blue but there are some less common varieties in white or pink. The plant generally flowers before the leaves are fully expanded. The seeds are contained in flat pea-shaped pods which vary in length, according to the variety, from 2 to 5 inches. Family: Leguminosae.

Amaryllidaceae

Toxicology

Over 70 different alkaloids have been isolated from the members of the subfamily Amaryllidaceae. Without exception, all of the 26 genera in this group contain the heat-stable alkaloid lycorine, which is probably responsible for most of the observed clinical response in acute intoxications. Each plant has an additional 4 to 8 alkaloids, and are listed by Wildman (71) for individual plants.

Many of the cultivated lily-like plants belong to this group, which is composed, in part, of the following genera: *Amaryllis*, *Clivia*, *Crinum*, and *Narcissus*. All of these are potential intoxicants, but only one instance of poisoning has been recorded involving the daffodil (*Narcissus pseudo-narcissus*). Poisoning was the result of mistaking a daffodil bulb for an onion (73).

Symptoms

In mild poisoning, the intoxication is limited to severe emesis and shivering. In the case cited above, two of the five affected individuals also experienced diarrhea.

Severe poisoning has not been observed in humans, but animal data suggests that narcosis, convulsions and pronounced hypotension and, perhaps, hepatic degeneration might occur (71).

Treatment

If emesis has been insufficient to evacuate the stomach, gastric lavage should be instituted and simple care given for the gastroenteritis. There is too little experience to suggest other than symptomatic care for complications involving the central nervous system and liver.

Botanical Description

The subfamily of Amaryllidaceae contains a variety of showy flowers commonly cultivated in home gardens throughout most of the United States and in vast quantities commercially for florists. Among this large group are the narcissus, jonquil, snowdrop, amaryllis, tuberose, daffodil, spider lily, atamasco lily, and snowflake. Each of these plants has onion-like bulbs similar to those of the true lily.

C. IRRITATION CHIEFLY OF INTESTINAL MUCOSA

The plants in this category produce emesis, colic, and diarrhea within one hour of ingestion. If only small amounts are ingested or if only limited quantities of the toxic material are absorbed through the intestine, these may be the only signs of intoxication.

Although this section has been divided into various groups according to the chemistry of the irritant principle:

a. Saponin Group
b. Resin Containing Plants
c. Taxine Group
d. Protoanemonin Group
e. Miscellaneous Gastroenteritis-producing Plants

these categories are of somewhat limited usefulness from a clinical standpoint since the overall effect is generally similar. In the event plant identification cannot be made, the clinical management of all is essentially:

1. Gastric lavage in the absence of severe and effective emesis.
2. The administration of demulcents such as milk and egg white followed by the usual dietary care for simple gastroenteritis.
3. Scrupulous attention to fluid and electrolyte balance.

a. Saponin Group

Toxicology

The saponins are steroidal glycosides which can be found in almost any variety of plant, but not necessarily in toxicologically significant concentrations. The saponin content of any plant varies considerably with the conditions of growth, the maturity of the plant, and the plant part. Thus many plants in which the foliage is toxic to range animals are not a concern in human intoxication due to the low saponin content in the fruits, flowers or seeds which may be attractive to children. Human fatalities ascribed to the seeds of the corn cockle (*Agrostemma githago*) and bouncing bet (*Saponaria officinalis*) in wheat are no longer to be feared since the implementation of screening machines (46).

The nearly ubiquitous presence of saponins in conjunction with their rather non-specific toxic manifestations complicates the assignment of the active ingredient in any plant which, as one of actions, produces gastroenteritis. The rain tree (*Samanea saman*), for example, contains an alkaloid (48, 70) which in animals produces clonic convulsions, an increase in barbiturate sleeping time, changes in respiratory pattern, and a lowering of body temperature. To what extent this alkaloid may contribute to human toxicity by this species is not known. On the other hand, the nausea and emesis produced in intoxications with digitalis-containing plants is known to be a joint contribution of the central emetic action of digitalis together with the local irritant effects of saponins.

Considerable argument has been expended on the selection of the toxic principle in the horse chestnut (*Aesculus hippocastanum*). Various authorities have selected alkaloids, glycosides, and saponins for this role (46). Considerable attention has been directed toward the saponin glycoside aesculin (6-β-glucosido-7-hydroxycoumarin), but the evidence is inconclusive. In any case, ingestion of either the kernel of the immature nut or the green husk has produced fatalities (26, 60).

The saponins act as irritant substances which produce cellular damage and modifications in tissue permeability. Severe gastroenteritis is the most common, and usually the only, consequence following the ingestion of saponin-rich plant parts. Absorption of most saponins through an intact mucous membrane is usually very poor, thus systemic intoxications are rare. However, some types may produce sufficient damage to the intestinal wall to facilitate absorption of toxic quantities. The severity of systemic intoxications appears to be directly related to the degree of resulting erythrocyte hemolysis (62).

Members of the Group

Botanical Name	*Common Name*	*Part of Plant Toxic*
Aesculus hippocastanum	Horse chestnut, Buckeye	Nut (60)
Caulophyllum thalictroides	Blue cohosh*	Berry (25)
Duranta repens	Golden dewdrop, Pigeon berry	Fruit (53)
Hedera helix	English ivy	Berry, leaf (21, 52)
Momordica charantia	Balsam pear	Orange body of fruit (53)
Pachyrhizus erosus	Yam bean	Seed (14)
Poncirus spp	Mock orange†	Fruit (51)
Pongamia pinnata	Pongam	Seed and root (53)
Samanea saman (*Pithecellobium* or *Inga saman*)	Rain tree, Monkey pod	Seed (51)
Sapindus saponaria	Soapberry	Fruit (14)

* Saponin in the root of the blue cohosh is an orally active smooth muscle stimulant and oxytocic (20).

† This should not be confused with the southern mock orange (*Prunus caroliniana*), the toxic principle of which is a cyanogenetic glycoside.

Symptoms

Topical: Dust from saponin containing plant material may produce lacrimation and painful inflammation of the eyes, violent sneezing, and nasal secretion.

Gastroenteric: The clinical picture is dominated by the local irritant effect of the saponins, manifested by increased salivation, nausea, emesis, abdominal pain, and gastroenteritis. In severe cases, deep tissue damage may be produced.

Systemic: If absorption of saponin occurs, the toxic effect is generally proportional to the degree of hemolysis (62). The patient experiences anxiety and headache and may complain of fever and thirst. Mydriasis and a face rash may appear. In severe poisoning, the patient exhibits muscular weakness and incoordination. Circulatory disturbances and convulsions are usually terminal events.

Case History

The importance of gastroenteric erosion by a saponin to facilitate its own systemic absorption is illustrated in a case report presented by Schweitzer (60).

A 4 1/2-year-old boy became suddenly ill at the end of the day and throughout the night was restless and could not sleep. On the following day he was exhausted and in deep sleep. Upon questioning the child admitted to his mother that he had eaten horse chestnuts. Two of the boy's playmates had also eaten horse chestnuts and developed symptoms of intoxication limited to vomiting, headache, and fever.

Two days after this ingestion the child was lively and appeared healthy. Upon returning from a walk, the mother found evidence that he again had eaten horse chestnuts. During the night the child was very restless. The following morning the mother noted a unilateral facial distortion. The child was sleepy, ataxic, ate little, and during meals froth came from the mouth.

The following morning he became unconscious and was hospitalized. On admission there was a left-sided facial paralysis and incipient respiratory paralysis. Shortly thereafter, about 48 hours after the second ingestion, the child died of respiratory paralysis.

Autopsy showed severe swelling of the intestinal epithelium and lymph follicles with some sloughing of the stomach, distal portion of the lower intestine, and of the entire colon.

Undoubtedly, in this case, the first saponin ingestion had inflamed the gastroenteric tract so that when a second challenge was presented absorption was greatly enhanced resulting in severe systemic poisoning and death.

Prognosis

Estimating the prognosis solely on the ingestion of saponin-containing plant material is not possible since the extent of saponin absorption, if any, cannot be predicted. However, if only gastroenteritis appears, the prognosis is quite favorable, the condition being limited to the rate of passage of the plant material through the intestine. If signs of systemic effects appear, the prognosis becomes quite grave.

Treatment

Since the saponins can produce intestinal erosion, the use of demulcents, such as egg white, seems indicated. Otherwise the treatment is the same as it is for simple gastroenteritis. Care should be exerted to avoid dehydration.

No specific inactivating substances are available against the detergent-like action of saponins which have entered the circulation. In extreme situations dilution of the active material by exchange transfusions seems to offer the only hope.

Botanical Descriptions

Aesculus hippocastanum (figure 5). Horse chestnut, buckeye. A large tree, hardy in the north temperate zones, with showy foot-long clusters of white flowers blotched with red and yellow. The serrated leaflets, commonly seven at the end of a stem, range in size from 4 to 7 inches. The name buckeye is derived from the seed which is a glossy brown with a white scar. It is contained in a green leathery pod covered with small bumpy spikes. Family: Hippocastanaceae.

Caulophyllum thalictroides. Blue cohosh. This is an herb which stands 1 to 3 feet tall with small clusters of yellowish green or greenish purple flowers on the top. The leaflets are attached to the main stems in groups of three. The seeds resemble blueberries in size and color. It is found in moist woods in Canada southward to Alabama and Missouri. Family: Berberidaceae.

Duranta repens (figure 6). Golden dewdrop, pigeon-berry, sky-flower. This is a small tree not greater than 18 feet. It has trailing branches, occasionally spiny, with small lilac-blue flowers in terminal racemes. The fruit is an orange-yellow berry about $1/2$ inch in diameter. In the United States it is found only in southern Florida. Family: Verbenaceae.

Hedera helix. English ivy. This is the climbing ivy commonly cultivated as a wall cover in the northeastern United States and found as a potted plant elsewhere. It is now escaped in some areas, particularly in Virginia. The leaves are dark green about 2 inches wide and 4 inches long with 3 to 5 lobes. The leaves on flowering branches are unlobed. The flowers are an inconspicuous green. The fruit is a small black berry. Family: Araliaceae.

Momordica charantia. Balsam pear, bitter gourd. This is a climbing or creeping vine with deeply lobed leaves, trailing tendrils, and tubular yellow flowers. The warty yellow-orange pear- to oval-shaped fruit contains a bright red pulp that is exposed when it bursts open at maturity. The vine can be found both wild and cultivated along the coastal plain from Florida to Texas. Family: Cucurbitaceae.

Pachyrhizus erosus. Yam bean. This twining vine has large tuberous roots and violet sweet-pea shaped flowers on racemes, producing 4 to 6 inch pods. It is cultivated in the southern Gulf states. Family: Leguminosae.

Poncirus spp. Mock orange. This is a small deciduous tree armed with stiff thorns up to $2\,1/2$ inches in length. It is used extensively as a source of root stock for citrus tree grafts and as a singly grown ornamental or pruned hedge plant in the south and in protected areas as far north as Philadelphia. The most common member, *P. trifoliata*, has 2 inch wide white flowers which form at the base of the thorns before the thin shiny leathery leaflets appear. The fruit resembles a small orange which has a pronounced aromatic odor but is filled with an acrid pulp. Family: Rutaceae.

Pongamia pinnata. Pongam, Poonga oil tree. This tree grows to a height of about 40 feet. The leaves are pinnately compound and the flowers are purplish pink to white, sweet-pea-like, borne on racemes. The seeds are con-

FIG. 5.
Horse chestnut
(*Aesculus hippocastanum*)

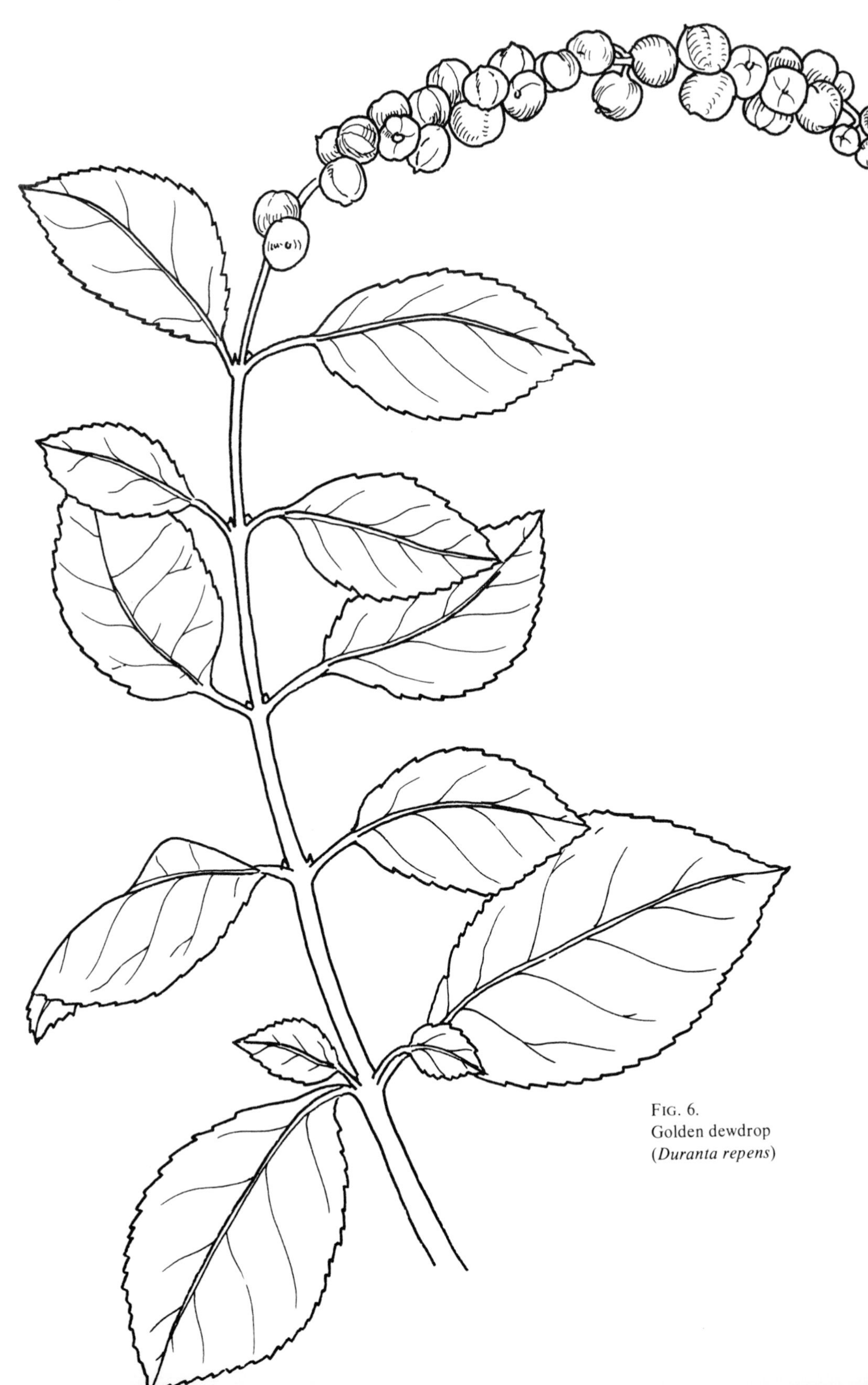

FIG. 6.
Golden dewdrop
(*Duranta repens*)

tained in woody, flat pods about 1 inch wide and 2 inches long. Despite the tree's somewhat offensive odor, it is sometimes grown as an ornamental in subtropical Florida. Family: Leguminosae.

Samanea saman. Rain tree, monkey pod (not identical to *Hura crepitans*). This tropical shade tree is rarely found in the United States except in the southern tip of Florida and Hawaii. It is of immense size, 80 feet high with a limb spread of over 100 feet. The leaflets are oval shaped, about 1 1/2 inches long, in groups of four. They are shiny above, downy underneath. The tree bears silky yellow flowers with long pink stamens. The pods are flat and about 6 to 8 inches long. Family: Leguminosae.

Sapindus saponaria. Soapberry. The soapberry is a tropical evergreen tree that grows to about 30 feet. It has narrow 4 inch long leaflets, white flowers in racemes and forms a shiny orange-brown berry up to 3/4 inch in diameter. Family: Sapindaceae.

b. Resin-Containing Plants

Resins are mixtures of polycyclic acids and phenols, alcohols and complex neutral substances. The resin-containing plants treated in this section all produce gastroenteritis and pronounced diarrhea as a common feature. *Melia azedarach* and *Cannabis sativa*, which also owe their pharmacological action to resins, are to be found in the section of plants affecting the central nervous system.

In this group, two plants deserve particular attention. The first is *Phytolacca americana* (Pokeweed) because of the high frequency of intoxication for which it is responsible. The other is *Daphne mezereum* and its relatives which belong among the most seriously toxic plants found in the United States.

On the basis of its chemical constituents, the *Arum* spp should not be assigned to this group; however, the close similarity between the nature and seriousness of the intoxications produced by these plants and the *Daphne* spp make this placement convenient.

Members Treated in this Group

Daphne spp, particularly *D. mezereum*	Spurge Laurel, Spurge Olive, Dwarf Bay
Arum spp, particularly *A. maculatum*	Lords and Ladies
Dirca palustris	Wicopy, Leatherwood
Phytolacca americana (*P. decandra*)	Pokeweed, Poke, Inkberry, Pigeon berry
Rivina humilis	Rouge Plant
Podophyllum peltatum	May Apple
Iris spp	Iris, Flag

Daphne spp

Toxicology

All parts of the *Daphne* are poisonous but most intoxications result from ingestion of the berries. One or two berries may cause severe poisoning in the child and the ingestion of about 12 berries is considered fatal to the adult. The juice from the berries or sap from the bark may be absorbed in sufficient quantity through abraded skin to produce systemic reactions. Toxicity is not abolished by drying.

Toxic Principles

Species of *Daphne* contain a vesicant resin mezereinic acid anhydride, which is probably responsible for the toxic effects, and daphnin which is a glucoside containing 7,8-dihydroxycoumarin as its aglycone. The similarity of this latter substance to the saponin glycoside aesculin, q.v., should be noted.

Symptoms

Topical contact with the sap results in erythematous swelling and blistering of the skin.

The ingestion of berries or chewing of the bark produces corrosive vesication and edema of the lips, tongue, and pharnyx, salivation, and dysphagia. This is followed by thirst, abdominal pain, emesis, and a persistent bloody and watery diarrhea. The kidneys are usually damaged, giving rise to hematuria, albuminuria, and strangury.

Both ingestion and absorption through the skin may produce fever, somnolence, headache, delirium, muscular twitching, and occasionally convulsions. Secondarily one may see evidence of shock due to excessive fluid loss and electrolyte imbalance (25, 26, 46, 67).

Prognosis

Poisoning by the *Daphne* should be considered as extremely serious. The mortality rate is approximately 30%. Even with successful management of the acute phase, symptoms may persist for several days.

Treatment

Gastric lavage should be instituted with appropriate caution depending on the extent of damage to the mucous membranes. This may be followed by the administration of saline cathartics to hasten evacuation and demulcents for the severe gastroenteritis. It may be necessary to institute parenteral feeding. Because of the possibility of shock due to fluid loss, care should be taken to maintain fluid and electrolyte balance.

Botanical Descriptions

Daphne spp. These plants are shrubs, sometimes evergreen, with clusters of white or lilac flowers which often precede the leaves. Most are hardy to New York and New England. Figure 7 shows *Daphne mezereum* (Spurge

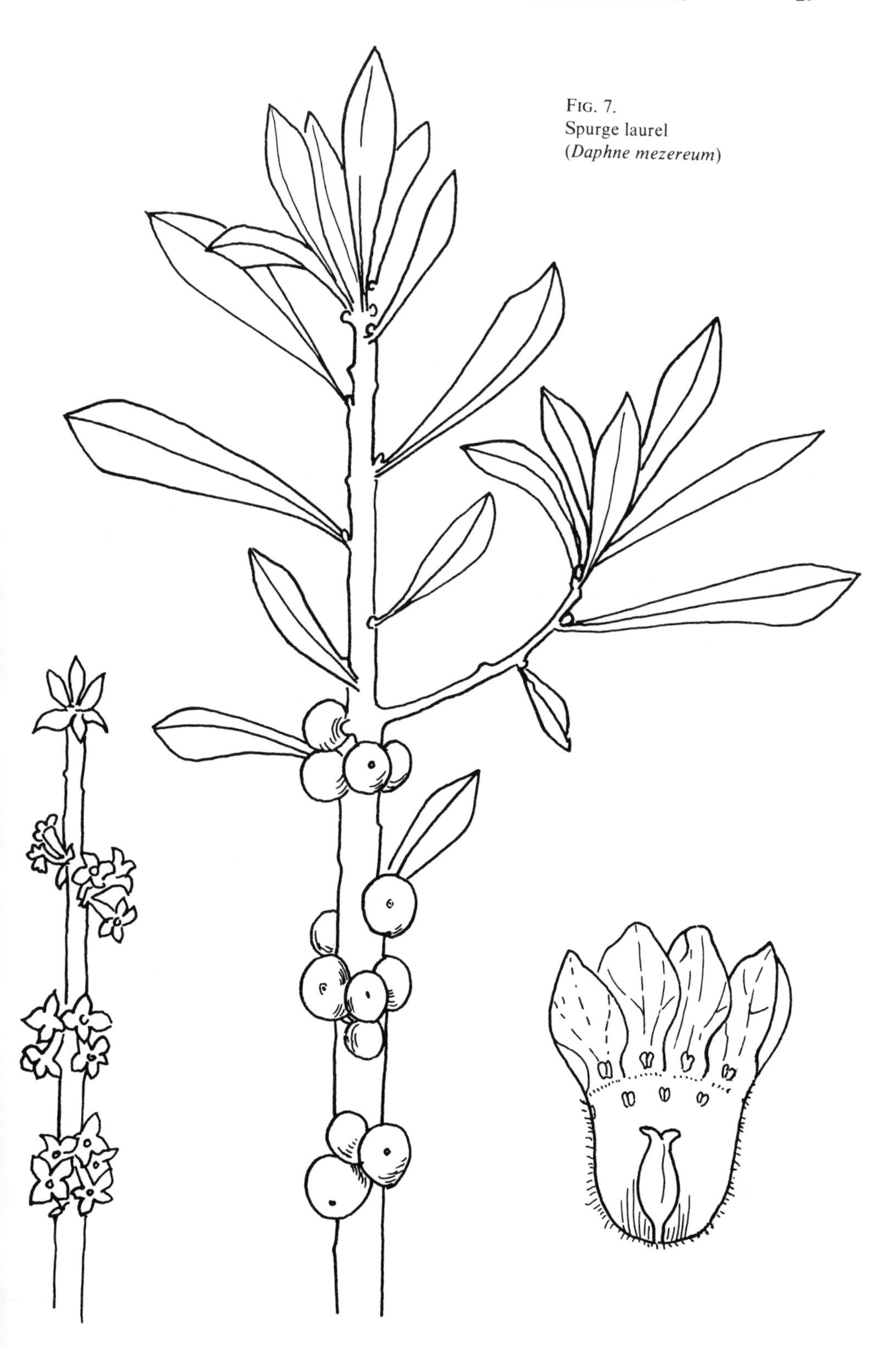

FIG. 7.
Spurge laurel
(*Daphne mezereum*)

laurel, Spurge olive, Dwarf bay, Lady laurel, Flax olive, Paradise plant, Mysterious plant, Wild pepper). This shrub grows to a height of about 4 feet. Its clusters of fragrant purple or carmine flowers appear along the previous year's branches prior to leafing. The leaves are 3 inches long, vivid green above and grayish underneath. The fruit is a scarlet berry. Family: Thymelaeaceae.

Arum spp

Toxic Principles

The whole plant, especially the fresh roots, contain aroin, a volatile compound of unknown structure which is destroyed by cooking or drying. A small amount of a cyanogenetic glycoside and saponins are also present, but these are without toxicological significance.

Toxicology

Intoxications among children have occurred after ingesting or chewing the leaves or berries. The sweet taste of the berries and the initial sour taste of the leaves may tempt children. The toxicity is stated to vary with different locations.

Topically the sap causes severe dermatitis with erythema and vesication.

Symptoms

About a half minute after ingestion of any portion of the plant there is a pronounced swelling and inflammation of the mucous membrane of the mouth, the lips, tongue, and epiglottis. The patient suffers from a burning pain in the mouth and pharynx. The voice becomes hoarse and there may be loss of speech. This is followed by a violent enteritis with salivation, vomiting, and diarrhea.

Very intense paresthesias described as a combination of a burning sensation with formication, affect the peripheral areas of the body such as the palm of the hand and may persist for several days. Red spots may appear over the entire body within minutes after ingestion.

The patient feels drowsy and a feeling of heaviness on the head may persist for several days after intoxication. Tachycardia and disturbances in the heart activity have been observed.

In severe cases there is mydriasis and bleeding from the gums, stomach and uterus. In fatal cases there are convulsions preceding death in coma (26).

Treatment

See *Daphne*, page 28.

Botanical Descriptions

Arum spp. This genus belongs to the family Araceae which was discussed extensively in the first part of this chapter. The species of particular interest here is the *Arum maculatum* (Cuckoopint, Lords-and-ladies). The plant varies considerably but may grow to about a foot high with 10 inch leaves. The "flower" (spathe) is about 10 inches long, green often spotted with purple. The fruits are a brilliant red. This species is a common house plant and is hardy outdoors in the South.

Dirca palustris

All parts of this shrub, but particularly the bark, contain a vesicant resin which produces effects similar to the daphne. Probably because ingestion is immediately accompanied by a burning, nauseous taste, no serious intoxications have been reported. The bark is also associated with severe dermatitis, especially during flowering and fruiting (25).

Botanical Description

Dirca palustris. Wicopy, Leatherwood. This is a branched shrub growing to 6 feet. The leaves are 2 to 3 inches long and elliptically shaped. Short stalked, small pale yellow flowers appear from the branches prior to leafing. The fruit is a green to reddish berry about ¼ inch long. The range of the leatherwood is from southern Quebec westward to Minnesota and south to Florida and Oklahoma. Family: Thymelaeaceae.

Phytolacca americana and *Rivina humilis*

Toxicology

Most serious intoxications have resulted from the misidentification of pokeweed roots (*P. americana*) for parsnips or horseradish. The berries are relatively nontoxic and have been used for the preparation of pies without adverse reactions. Nevertheless the uncooked berry may possess sufficient toxin to affect children. In certain sections of the southeastern part of the United States, the sprouts and stems are boiled and eaten after discarding the pot water. These cooked greens are known colloquially as "salads". Newcomers to the area have often prepared fresh salads from pokeweed, thereby precipitating cases of moderate to severe poisoning.

The toxicity of *Rivina humilis* is similar to that of *Phytolacca americana* (6).

Symptoms

Other than a transient burning sensation in the mouth, symptoms do not appear for about 2 hours and may be delayed even longer. These usually commence as a soreness of the mouth and throat accompanied by salivation, coughing, and thirst. A general feeling of lassitude with yawning may become pronounced. Usually there is a blurring of vision and possibly temporary amblyopia. A prodroma of warmth in the throat and stomach usually precedes nausea, severe gastric and intestinal cramping, persistent vomiting, and diarrhea. Both the vomitus and stools may be bloody.

In severe intoxications the patient may develop tremors and experience formication; however, convulsions are rare. There is profuse perspiration, salivation, dyspnea, and occasional cardiac arrythmia (30).

Case History

This case involves an adult who misidentified pokeweed for horseradish. Only a small amount was swallowed because of the exceedingly bitter and burning taste which it imparted. About 1 ½ hours later he remarked that "his throat was quite sore and he was in a condition of general lassitude. He examined his throat with the aid of a looking glass and noticed that the pharynx was considerably injected. The sensation in that region was dry and burning. Soon, yawning became incessant, vision appeared defective, a dry, hacking cough and salivation were noticeable and the general dull feeling was more pronounced. A decidedly warm sensation was also perceptible in the gastric region. A few minutes later he was seized with violent stomach cramps accompanied by retching and vomiting. The burning sensation now extended from the mouth to the stomach, and respiration became somewhat labored."

There were 5 or 6 additional recurrences of vomiting at intervals of 5 to 10 minutes. By a little over 2 hours after the initial ingestion it became impossible for him "to proceed any further as the vomiting and gastralgia had become very violent and exhausting, and vertigo with almost complete loss of vision had developed. The latter condition only lasted a short while. He was by this time unable to stand or even sit, but found great relief in the recumbent position. Other symptoms noticeable were: convulsive tremors and prickly sensations all over the surface of the body, the latter particularly noticeable in the palms of the hands, the insides of the arms, and the soles of the feet; great coldness followed by clammy perspiration; profuse salivation; sense of suffocation; and dull aching in the lumbar region. An attempt to swallow alcoholic stimulants caused pharyngeal pain and instant vomiting on this occasion of slightly blood-stained mucus."

By this time the patient was "in a state of extreme prostration; the pulse was weak, the respiration slow and labored. The skin was cold and bathed in clammy perspiration. The pupils were contracted. He was retching violently and bringing up small quantities of mucus stained with blood. As he had vomited freely, no emetic was given, but half a grain of morphine sulphate, with one-fiftieth of a grain of atropine, was administered subcutaneously. In a few minutes great relief followed, the pulse became stronger and the respirations stronger and less labored."

Emesis recurred almost hourly for the succeeding 11 hours. There was some diarrhea and a persistent bitter taste for about 48 hours, after which the patient was asymptomatic (22).

Treatment

If the patient is seen prior to the advent of emesis, the stomach should be emptied followed by the administration of demulcents. Therapy thereafter

FIG. 8.
Pokeweed
(*Phytolacca americana*)

should be directed to the management of the intense abdominal pain and to preventive support against the development of secondary shock.

Prognosis

Recovery is essentially complete within 24 hours. Fatalities are rare.

Botanical Descriptions

Phytolacca americana (*P. decandra*) (figure 8). Pokeweed, Poke, Pigeon berry, Inkberry, Scoke. The pokeweed is a strong smelling branching plant that may reach a height of 12 feet. The leaves appear singly and are 4 to 12 inches long. The flowers are greenish white to purplish, about $^1/_4$ inch wide, and appear on a vertical stalk. The dark purple berries are attached to the stalk by a short stem. The plant is found in fields and damp woods from Maine to Minnesota south to the Gulf of Mexico and in Hawaii. Family: Phytolaccaceae.

Rivina humilis. Bloodberry, Rouge plant, Baby-pepper, Pigeon berry, Pokeberry. This plant is usually seen as a small shrub about 3 feet high. The leaves are ovate approximately 4 inches long. The flowers appear on hanging sprays and are pinkish white. The fruit is a shining, bright crimson or orange berry. It is found in Hawaii, the southern United States from New Mexico to Florida, and it is popularly cultivated as a house plant elsewhere. Family: Phytolaccaceae.

Podophyllum peltatum

Toxicology

Intoxications from this plant source are most frequently encountered during its industrial processing, from use as a home remedy for its cathartic action, or from the injudicious medical application of various podophyllum preparations for condyloma acuminatum. The fruit, which is often ingested by children, is relatively non-toxic and may be eaten either without effect or with only slight catharsis.

Podophyllum contains a number of pharmacologically active constituents, the chemistry of which is given by Hartwell and Schrecker (36). From a toxicological standpoint, the most important are the purgative podophylloresin and the antimitotic podophyllotoxin group.

Symptoms

Industrial workers exposed to the powdered *Podophyllum* rhizome may develop conjunctivitis with ecchymosis, keratitis with erosion and desquamation of the epithelium, ulceration of the cornea, iritis, photophobia, and attenuation of the corneal reflexes (67).

The topical application of podophyllum ointment to the scalp may result in erythema, edema, crusting, tender kerion-like lesions and alopecia (61).

Ingestion of the whole plant or rhizomes or medical preparations from these as well as topical applications of podophyllum to mucous membranes (68) produces a similar pattern of systemic poisoning. This is characterized by abdominal pain, persistent emesis, and severe diarrhea, followed by vertigo, headache, respiratory stimulation, and elevation in body temperature. After a considerable latent period of 12 to 24 hours the patient becomes lethargic, then comatose (18). The respiratory and pulse rates are markedly elevated and the blood pressure is depressed. The deep tendon reflexes are absent. A case exhibiting extensive neurologic involvement, persisting for many months after acute podophyllum intoxication, is presented by Clark and Parsonage (17). There is abdominal distension and anuria with continued elevation of blood non-protein nitrogen.

Details of post-mortem findings are given by Ward (68).

Prognosis

Only one case of fatal poisoning is known as the result of ingestion of the plant. Cases involving children who have eaten the fruit are not considered serious.

Treatment

Normally no treatment is necessary. Severe cases associated with drastic purging require hospitalization so that measures may be instituted to support the blood pressure, and to manage the possible subsequent adynamic ileus, anuria, and coma. No specific therapy can be advised. Opiates may be of value to reduce the respiratory stimulation and diarrhea and phenothiazines may be employed for their antiemetic action (9).

Botanical Description

Podophyllum peltatum (figure 9). May-apple, Mandrake, Ground lemon, Wild lemon, Umbrella leaf. This perennial herb grows to 1 ½ feet tall with two large 5 to 9 lobed umbrella-like leaves sometimes 1 foot across. Between the stems of the leaves there is a single white, nodding flower with a 2 inch diameter. This forms into a yellowish green fruit about the size and shape of an egg. Sterile plants produce only a single leaf. The plant grows extensively in moist open woods in Quebec and southward to Texas and Florida. Family: Berberidaceae.

Iris spp

Toxicology

The rootstock (rhizome) contains an irritant resinous substance. This is, however, unpalatable and not likely to be eaten except when confused with the root of the non poisonous sweet flag (*Acorus calamus*) the chewing of which is considered in folk medicine as a cure for indigestion. The iris resin produces gastroenteric pain, nausea, vomiting and diarrhea (25).

Some individuals develop dermatitis on contact with the plant.

FIG. 9.
May apple
(*Podophyllum peltatum*)

Prognosis and Treatment

Intoxications are rare and not generally severe. Symptomatic management of the simple gastroenteritis should be all that is required.

Botanical Descriptions

Iris spp. Iris, Flag. There are approximately 200 species of iris which are easily recognized from their characteristic bloom and their flat, sword-shaped leaves. It is not known whether all forms are equally toxic. Reports have dealt with two species, the German Iris (*I. germanica*), which is a blue-purple bearded iris, and the Yellow Flag (*I. pseudacorus*), which as the name implies, has bright yellow flowers and its leaves are often veined purple. The iris is a popular garden flower throughout the United States. Family: Iridaceae.

c. Taxine Group

Toxicology

Members of the Yew family contain at least 10 alkaloids. The most important of these are Taxine A and Taxine B which occur in all parts of the plant with the exception of the fleshy aril which surrounds the seed (12, 28, 36, 65). Intoxications are most commonly encountered in children following ingestion of the red berries. If the seeds are swallowed whole, no absorption takes place because the seed coat is resistant to the digestive enzymes. Severe and fatal intoxications have occurred from the use of a decoction of the needles as a home remedy, generally for its supposed abortifacient property.

Taxine has an irritating effect on the mucosa producing a severe gastroenteritis. Systemic absorption affects cardiac conduction. Reports of a digitalis-like activity appearing in the older literature should be disregarded.

Members of the Group

Taxus baccata	English yew
Taxus brevifolia	Pacific or Western yew
Taxus canadensis	Ground hemlock, American yew
Taxus cuspidata	Japanese yew

Symptoms

Symptoms usually appear within an hour as dizziness, dry throat, marked mydriasis and colic usually accompanied by emesis. Muscular weakness and stupor develop. This is followed by loss of consciousness. Red spots may appear on the skin; there is marked facial pallor and a purple discoloration of the lips.

The primary systemic toxicity of taxine is its interference with the cardiac conduction system usually resulting in a slow, irregular pulse. Hypotension, then respiratory depression, appear secondary to the arrythmia (21, 26, 46).

Case History

This case involves an adult male who ingested a decoction of *Taxus* needles, apparently to evaluate its effects prior to its administration as an abortifacient for his girl-friend. The material was taken at approximately 2:00 a.m. "Somewhere around 3:00 a.m. his brother with whom he shared a bedroom, thought he heard someone talking. A little before 5:00 a.m. the brother awakened and noticed the patient was unconscious and had a rattling respiration.

"Upon admission to the clinic at 5:25 the patient was deeply comatose. No visible signs of injury by violence were evident. On his pajama top were some signs of spots of bloody discolored sputum. The patient was calm. Worthy of note was the infrequent, gasping respiration. The skin was covered with cold sweat and the face, neck, and entire thorax appeared blue from cyanosis but was otherwise pale. The pupils were alike on both sides, very wide and reactionless. The biceps, triceps patellar and achilles reflexes were not capable of being emitted. The Babinski sign was negative. The peripheral pulse was unperceptible, the heart action very weak with pronounced irregularities and great intervals, the blood pressure was no longer measurable. In spite of immediate therapy with circulatory drugs (catecholamines) the patient died about 5:35 of respiratory failure" (23).

Prognosis

In severe intoxications death can occur within a half hour after ingestion due to acute circulatory collapse; however, symptoms may persist for a 24 hour period prior to death from respiratory failure secondary to extreme hypotension. Terminal convulsions may appear.

Treatment

The plant material should be removed from the stomach. In serious intoxications, circulatory support may be required. This procedure should be monitored electrocardiographically in order to avoid precipitating catecholamine-induced ventricular tachycardia or fibrillation in the presence of the conduction defect. Preparation should be made for the support of respiration if required.

If hypotension is severe and prolonged, various sequelae from anoxia should be anticipated.

Botanical Descriptions

Taxus spp. Yew. There are about 7 species of yew in North America extending from northern Florida and California into Canada and Alaska. They are evergreens varying in height, leaf-shading and in density of branching. They have a characteristic bright red berry-like fruit. The illustration in figure 10 is of *Taxus baccata*. Family: Taxaceae.

Fig. 10.
English yew
(*Taxus baccata*)

d. Protoanemonin Group

Toxicology

Several plant members of the family Ranunculaceae contain a glycoside which, on enzymatic cleavage, liberates the irritant substance protoanemonin. The toxicity of this compound is abolished by drying or cooking. Severe topical effects have been produced by the use of these plants as compresses in home remedies for the treatment of frost-bite and arthritic pains. Intoxications have been reported from the use of the leaves in salads.

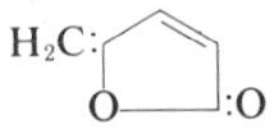

H_2C:

O :O

Protoanemonin

The unpleasant odor and the acrid taste of many of these plants tend to limit youthful experimentation. Systemic poisoning by the protoanemonin containing plants is so infrequent that their hazard has been generally considered negligible, nevertheless, the number of fatalities recorded in the foreign literature indicate that these plants are potentially dangerous (25, 26, 46, 57).

Members of the Group

Actaea alba (*A. pachypoda*)	White baneberry
Actaea rubra	Red baneberry
Actaea spicata	Black baneberry, Herb-Christopher
Anemone spp	Anemone, Windflower
Anemone patens	Pasque-flower, Prairie crocus
Caltha palustris	Marsh marigold, Cowslip
Clematis spp	Clematis, Virgins-bower
Ranunculus spp	Buttercup, Crowfoot, Spearwort

Symptoms

Prolonged contact with the protoanemonin-containing plants produces dermatitis. In severe cases vesiculation and a burning pain may result. The volatile constituents are intensely irritating to the mucous membranes of the eyes, nose, and respiratory tract, producing a painful conjunctivitis, lacrimation, sneezing, and nasal congestion.

After ingestion there is a burning sensation in the mouth and pharynx, copious salivation and stomatitis sometimes with blisters and ulceration. This is followed by emesis, a painful colicky gastroenteritis, and bloody diarrhea.

After absorption through the gut, dizziness, syncope and convulsions are seen. In severe cases of systemic intoxication a pemphigus eruption may occur about 48 hours after ingestion.

The toxic principles are excreted by the kidney. The initial irritation induces polyuria. Subsequently the inflammation of the urinary tract results in hematuria and considerable urethral pain during micturition. Renal damage may be produced resulting in oliguria.

In the case of *Actaea rubra* intoxication, visual hallucinations, severe headache, and incoherency were reported (see the Case History which follows), which suggests that other toxic materials may be present in this genera.

Case History

The following illustrates a non-fatal case of experimental self-intoxication produced by the ingestion of fruit from the Red Baneberry. The onset of symptoms began within 30 minutes.

"At first there was a most extraordinary pyrotechnic display of blue objects of all sizes and tints, circular with irregular edges; as one became interested in the spots a heavy weight was lowered on the top of the head and remained there, while sharp pains shot through the temples.

"Then suddenly the mind became confused and there was a total disability to recollect anything distinctly or arrange ideas with any coherency. On an attempt to talk, wrong names were given to objects, and although at the same time the mind knew mistakes were made in speech, the words seemed to utter themselves independently.

"For a few minutes there was great dizziness, the body seeming to swing off into space, while the blue spots changed to dancing sparks of fire. The lips and throat became parched and the latter somewhat constricted; swallowing was rather difficult; there was intense burning in the stomach with gaseous eructations, followed by sharp colicky pains in the abdomen and also pain across the back over the kidneys. The pulse rose to 125, was irregular, wiry, tense; the heart fluttered most unpleasantly.

"These symptoms lasted about an hour and were followed by a feeling of great weariness, but in three hours from the time of taking the dose all seemed to be again normal" (7).

Treatment

Gastric lavage should be instituted at once but with care in respect to the tissue damaging properties of protoanemonin. At the completion of lavage, demulcents such as egg white and milk may be instilled into the stomach. Appropriate measures should be instituted to prevent fluid and electrolyte depletion. Continual evaluation of renal output is necessary.

Botanical Descriptions

Actaea spp (figure 11). Baneberry, Cohosh. These perennial herbs, with compound leaves, hairy on the underside along the veins, grow to a height of 2 feet. They have small white or bluish white flowers and showy terminal clusters in the spring and attractive shiny berries in the summer and autumn,

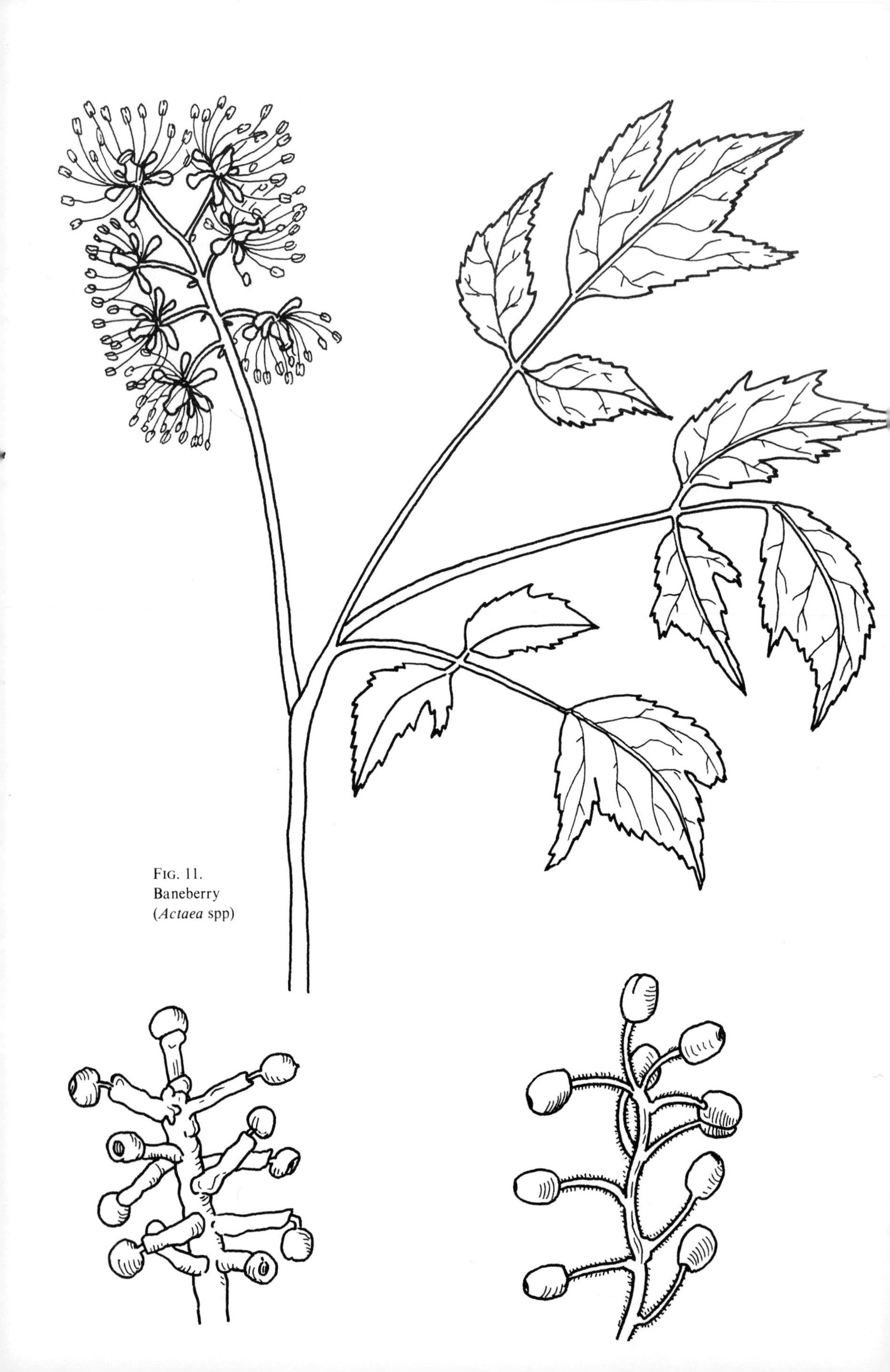

FIG. 11.
Baneberry
(*Actaea* spp)

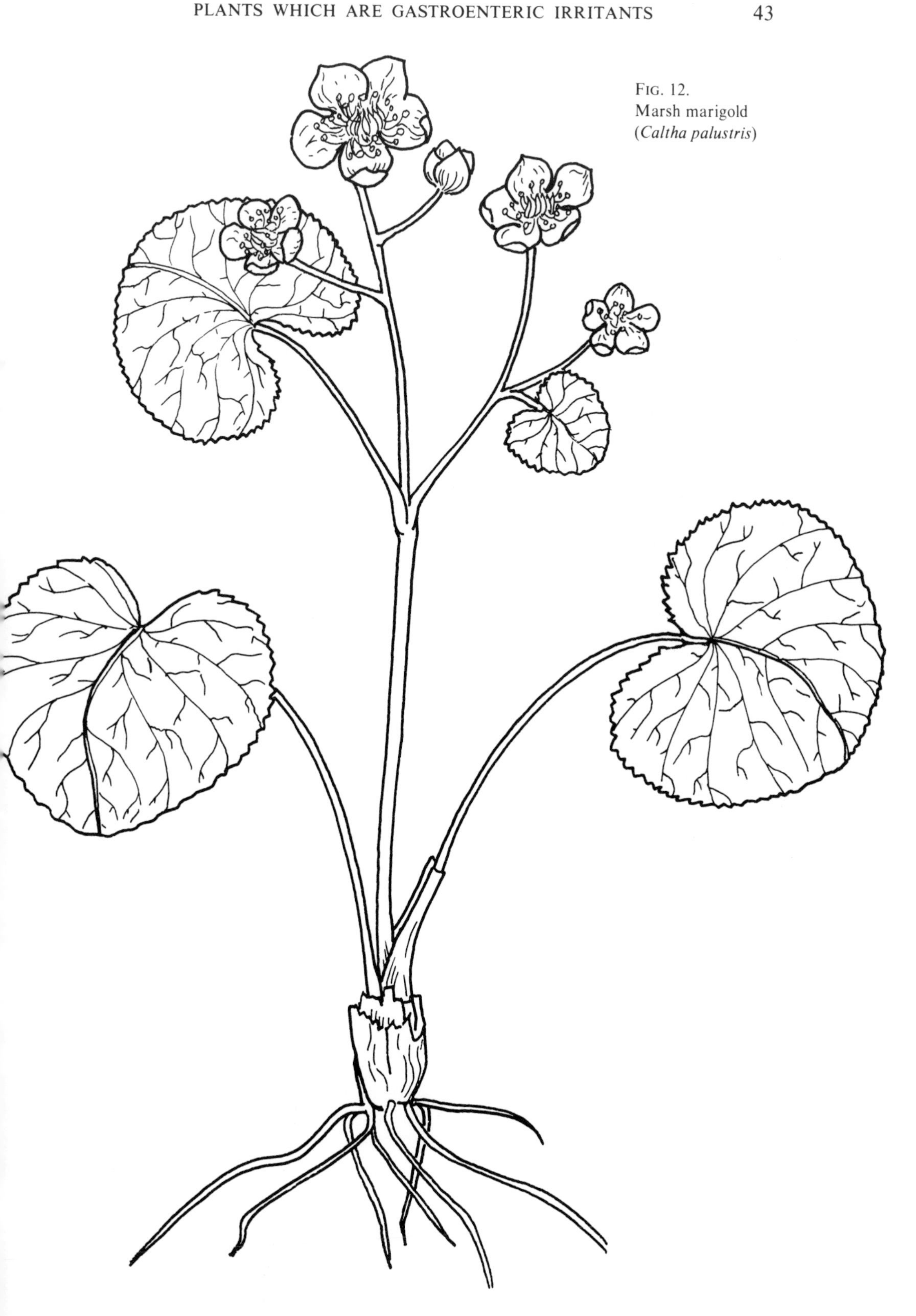

FIG. 12.
Marsh marigold
(*Caltha palustris*)

FIG. 13.
Buttercup
(*Ranunculus bulbosus*,
R. sceleratus, *R. acris*)

the color depending upon the species (*A. alba*, white; *A. rubra*, red; *A. spicata*, purplish black). The first two of these species are found from southeastern Canada to South Dakota, the third is cultivated as a garden plant in the northern part of the United States. Family: Ranunculaceae.

Anemone spp. Anemone, Windflower. These plants are attractive perennials which bloom white or red. There are about 100 species in the north temperate zone extending to the Arctic. Most of the plants are under 1 foot in height. The leaves are similar to those shown in figure 13. *Anemone patens*, Pasque-flower, Prairie crocus, is about 3 to 6 inches high when in bloom becoming 1 foot or more while fruiting. The leaves appear after flowering and are generally purplish but occasionally white, to 2 ½ inches across. It is distributed through the west from Alaska to Texas and on dry prairie land to Wisconsin and northern Illinois. Family: Ranunculaceae.

Caltha palustris (figure 12). Marsh marigold, Cowslip. This perennial herb is found in marshes and wet meadows and woods across Canada into Alaska, south to Virginia and westward into Iowa. The stems are hollow to 2 feet in length with 7 inch wide heart-shaped leaves. The flowers are a bright yellow to 2 inches across, usually appearing in masses. Family: Ranunculaceae.

Clematis spp. Clematis, Virgins-bower. This is a genera of more than 100 species of perennial herbs and woody climbing vines. The leaves are usually compound and sometimes have a resemblance to poison ivy. Species are available for cultivation in all climatic zones in the United States. Family: Ranunculaceae.

Ranunculus spp (figure 13). Buttercup, Crowfoot, Spearwort. These are annual or perennial herbs with yellow, white, or rarely, red flowers. Most grow in wet areas and may be found from Florida to northern Canada and Alaska. In general, there height does not exceed 3 feet and many varieties are only a few inches tall. Of the plants shown in figure 13, *R. acris* grows to 3 feet and has golden yellow flowers; *R. bulbosus* grows to 1 foot and has bright yellow flowers; and *R. sceleratus* grows to 2 feet.

e. Miscellaneous Gastroenteritis-Producing Plants

Plants placed into this category possess gastroenteric irritants or cathartics which, for the most part, have not been chemically identified. Of this group the Tung tree nuts have probably produced the greatest number of intoxications. Tourists traveling through the Southeastern states have eagerly climbed 8 foot fences to obtain the nuts of this tree under the impression that these were pecans or Brazil nuts.

Undoubtedly well over a thousand species of plants could be found which are capable of producing some degree of gastroenteric discomfort. In order to present a useful discussion, the remaining plants selected for inclusion in this section are restricted to those which produce drastic catharsis, and, in some instances, are associated with fatalities due to severe fluid and electrolyte loss.

Members of the Group

Aleurites fordii	Tung nut
Aleurites moluccana	Candlenut
Allamanda cathartica	Yellow allamanda
Poinciana gilliesii	Dwarf poinciana, Bird-of-Paradise*
Poinciana pulcherrima	Dwarf poinciana, Barbados-pride
Cassia fistula	Golden shower
Cassia nodosa	Pink shower
Chelidonium majus	Celandine
Clusia rosea	Clusia
Ilex aquifolium	English holly
Ligustrum ovalifolium	California privet
Ligustrum vulgare	Common privet
Lonicera periclymenum	Woodbine, honeysuckle
Lonicera tatarica	Tatarian honeysuckle, Garden-fly honeysuckle
Lonicera xylosteum	European fly honeysuckle
Pedilanthus tithymaloides	Christmas candle, Redbird cactus, Slipperflower
Rhamnus cathartica	Buckthorn
Rhamnus frangula	Alder buckthorn
Symphoricarpos albus (*S. racemosus*)	Snowberry, waxberry

* Bird-of-Paradise is also the common name for the non-toxic *Strelitzia reginae*.

Aleurites species

Toxicology

Several investigators have worked on the chemistry of the toxic principles in the tung-oil tree (*A. fordii*) but their exact nature is still unknown (39). The toxic effects have been ascribed to a toxalbumin, a saponin, and an unidentified, alcohol soluble substance. In any case, the toxic material is located solely in the kernels. The tree, nutshell and crude oil may produce simple contact dermatitis but are not otherwise considered toxic.

The kernels of the candlenut tree (*A. moluccana*) have a similar but milder effect than those from the tung-oil tree.

Poisonings have occurred after ingestion of one nut, however, the usual intoxicating dose is 3 or more nuts. Recovery has been observed after ingestion of 20 nuts.

Symptoms

The onset of symptoms is delayed for about 20 to 40 minutes after ingestion. After a brief period of nausea, the patient vomits and experiences violent abdominal cramps with diarrhea and tenesmus. Severe thirst and dryness of the mouth appear following emesis. The patient may become dizzy, lethargic or disoriented. In more severe poisonings, the patient becomes severely dehydrated and may show systemic involvement. This includes mydriasis, tachycardia, tachypnea, sometimes irregular respiration, and hyperthermia. Young children may become cyanotic.

Neurological signs have been reported in only a few cases. These include cramps in the legs and arms, paresthesias and formication. Headache usually does not appear until the primary symptoms have subsided. Hyporeflexia has been reported in one case.

The urine becomes quite concentrated as a result of dehydration and some evidence of slight renal damage may appear, such as casts, epithelial cells, and glycosuria.

Case History

This intoxication was seen in a 3 year old girl seven and one-half hours after ingestion of an unknown number of tung nuts. Prior to admission she suffered from nausea, vomiting and protracted diarrhea. She had also complained of headache, cramping abdominal pain and pain in the lumbar area.

"Cyanosis was present around the lips and ears. The heart beat was rapid, but regular. Respirations were irregular, but the lungs were clear. The pupils were dilated, but reactive. Reflexes were absent. The skin showed great extracellular fluid deficit. The urine possessed a high specific gravity (1.023); there was a 1 plus glycosuria, and white blood cells were present. The yellow mucous stool was negative for occult blood. Methemoglobinemia was ruled out as a possible cause of the cyanosis.

"She was treated with magnesium sulfate and mineral oil by mouth, Coramine and caffeine stimulation, oxygen and intravenous fluids (1,000 cc. of 5 per cent glucose in physiologic saline, and 1,000 cc. of 5 per cent glucose in water). She responded to treatment and was discharged the next morning asymptomatic." (8)

Prognosis

Fatalities have been reported but the prognosis is usually quite good. In most intoxications the patient becomes asymptomatic within 24 hours.

Treatment

The violent emesis usually removes the bulk of the ingested material from the stomach. Except in severe cases, the patient requires only mild symptomatic support and rest. Dehydration should be corrected with fluids and electrolytes as indicated. Magnesium sulfate by mouth seems to reduce the severity of the intoxication. Children may need respiratory assistance with oxygen. Although central nervous system stimulants, particularly caffeine, have been employed in tung nut poisoning, there seems to be no real indication for their use.

Botanical Descriptions

Aleurites fordii (figure 14). Tung nut, China wood-oil-tree. This is a small deciduous tree with a smooth bark, milky sap and thick twigs. The leaves are heart-shaped and 5 to 10 inches long. The flowers are produced in large clusters at the tips of the twigs in the springtime before the leaves appear. They are about 1 inch in diameter and have 5 to 7 pale pink or white blossoms streaked with deep brownish lines running lengthwise. The fruits are nearly globular, 2 to 3 inches in diameter and dark green turning brown. Each fruit contains 3 to 7 large, hard, rough coated seeds. It grows in Texas and along the Gulf states and eastern coast to North Carolina. Family: Euphorbiaceae.

Aleurites moluccana. Candlenut, Candle-berry-tree, Varnish-tree. This tree is similar to the previous species but grows to about twice the height. The flowers are white, the fruit 2 inches or more across. It is grown as an ornamental in Florida, to a limited extent elsewhere in the far south and Hawaii. Family: Euphorbiaceae.

Allamanda cathartica

The allamanda has an undeserved reputation as a "dangerously" poisonous plant and is included only because it is a frequent cause of inquiry.

The bark, leaves, seeds, fresh flowers, and juice have a cathartic effect. The intoxication is self-limiting and no treatment need be employed.

Botanical Description

Allamanda cathartica (figure 15). Yellow allamanda, Common allamanda. This is a sprawling shrub which will grow as a vine on a support. The leaves emerge from the stem usually in groups of four and are about 6 inches in length. It is one of the most common ornamentals in the southern tip of Florida, where it rarely fruits. The fruit is a spiny capsule. Family: Apocynaceae.

Poinciana gilliesii

Toxicology

The seed pods on this plant resemble that of the garden pea. The seeds contain an irritant substance of unknown structure. Intoxications have been reported after the ingestion of approximately 5 seed pods (4).

Within 30 minutes after consumption a severe gastroenteritis develops with nausea, emesis and profuse diarrhea. These effects persist for approximately 24 hours.

Treatment

The administration of demulcents, such as milk or egg white, prior to gastric lavage is recommended. This may be followed by the administration of additional demulcent. If vomiting or diarrhea is extended, particularly in young children, scrupulous care must be taken to prevent dehydration and electrolyte imbalance.

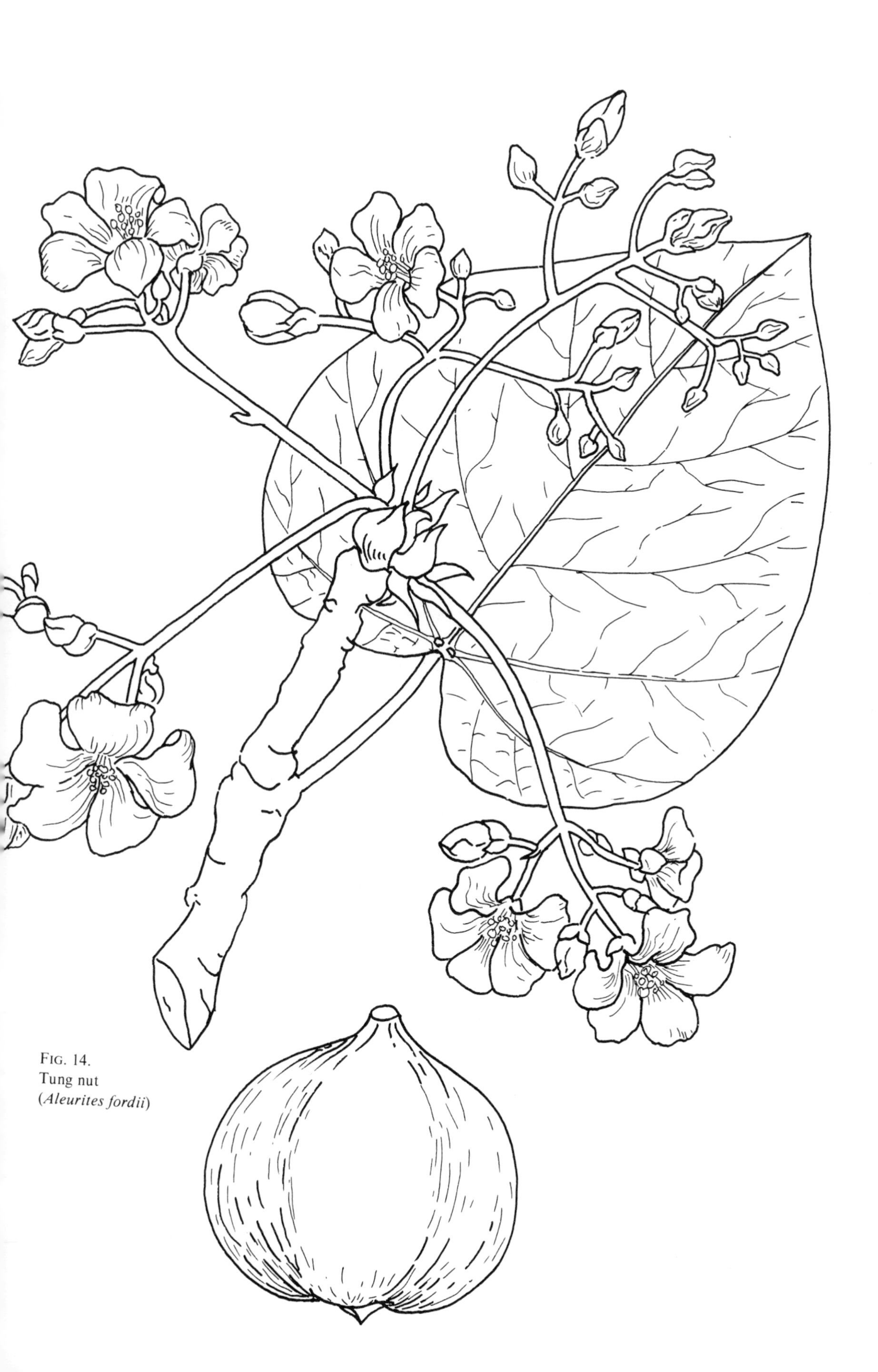

FIG. 14.
Tung nut
(*Aleurites fordii*)

Fig. 15.
Allamanda
(*Allamanda cathartica*)

Botanical Descriptions

Poinciana gilliesii (*Caesalpinia gilliesii*). Dwarf poinciana, Bird-of-Paradise. This is a shrub to small tree cultivated in the Gulf Coast states and westward to Arizona and elsewhere as a pot plant. The leaflets are numerous and very small. The flowers are light yellow with bright red stamens. The seed pods are similar to those of a pea, about $^{3}/_{4}$ inch wide and 4 inches long. Family: Leguminosae.

Poinciana pulcherrima (*Caesalpinia pulcherrima*). Barbados-pride, Barbados flower-fence, Dwarf poinciana. This is a prickly shrub about 10 feet high. The flowers are orange or yellow with bright red stamens. The pods are similar to those of the previous species. It is found in southern Florida. Family: Leguminosae.

Chelidonium majus

Toxicology

Although Celandine contains a large variety of alkaloids (10), most of the pharmacological studies have been concerned with chelidonin which exerts a papaverine-like action (32, 33). Celandine itself is an old medicinal plant which was used orally as a diaphoretic, diuretic, expectorant and purgative. Overdosage produced drastic catharsis and narcosis.

The fresh juice from the broken stem and leaves was used topically for corns and warts, however since the sap is extremely irritating, its use has been discontinued.

Symptoms

One would expect that the unpleasant odor as well as the persistent acrid, bitter taste would limit the quantity of material ingested. Intoxications in such a case would be limited to a burning sensation in the mouth and pharynx, abdominal pain, emesis and diarrhea.

In two fatal cases cited by Brugsch (16), these symptoms were accompanied by hemorrhagic gastritis, fever, somnolence and shock.

Treatment

See *Poinciana gilliesii*, page 48.

Botanical Description

Chelidonium majus (figure 16). Celandine. This is a perennial herb which grows to a height of about 4 feet and is characterized by its reddish-orange color juice. The flowers are yellow and about $^{2}/_{3}$ of an inch across. The seed capsule is a thin pod 1 to 2 inches in length. It is found in moist soil from Quebec westward to Iowa and south to Georgia and Missouri. Family: Papaveraceae.

FIG. 16.
Celandine
(*Chelidonium majus*)

Clusia rosea

When the stems, leaves or flowers of this plant are broken, an attractive, golden-yellow viscous sap is released. This sap can produce a violent and dangerous catharsis (2). The fruits also are reputed to be toxic.

Botanical Description

Clusia rosea. This is a small tree usually not greater than 20 feet in the United States with horizontal branches having thick, 8 inch long, leathery leaves. The leaves retain an impression made by a sharp point and were used as a paper substitute in Cuba during the Spanish-American War. The flower is about an inch in diameter with a white waxy appearance, mottled with red. The plant has a viscous yellow sap. The fruit is greenish-white, globose to 3 inches in diameter. It is cultivated in southern Florida. Family: Guttiferae.

Ilex aquifolium

As yet there is no reliable knowledge concerning the active substances of the English holly. It has been stated that the leaves contain a bitter principal Ilicin, a yellow coloring material Ilexanthin and Ilex acid (26). Contrary to earlier reports, caffein is not present. The fruit possesses an unknown active principal.

Eating the berry has produced vomiting and violent diarrhea. The fatal dose in children is about 20 to 30 berries.

Botanical Description

Ilex aquifolium. English holly. This is an evergreen tree which may reach heights of 40 feet. The leaves are a dark shiny green with coarse spiny teeth. The flowers are small but are replaced by bright scarlet berries. There are many horticultural varieties of this species which show differences in leaf, color, and toothing. It is cultivated primarily in the northeastern United States. Family: Aquifoliaceae.

Ligustrum spp

Toxicology

The berries, and possibly other parts of the privet, particularly the leaves, contain an unknown toxin (not Syringen). Reports of poisoning by this plant are infrequent. The only fatalities have involved children (16, 54).

Symptoms

A severe gastroenteritis with persistent emesis, diarrhea, and abdominal tenderness develop shortly after ingestion.

Prognosis

Death occurred in a 5-year-old boy within a few hours after chewing the berries. The persistence of gastroenteritis in non-fatal cases is remarkable; in one case colic continued for 37 days (16).

Treatment

See *Poinciana gilliesii*, page 48.

Botanical Descriptions

Ligustrum spp. Privet. This is a common hedge shrub. The *L. ovalifolium* is found in the southwest and the *L. vulgare* (figure 17) is now native in the eastern United States. These two species have a similar appearance, but both have many horticultural varieties which differ in leaf coloring and various degrees of white or yellow marking. The plants have small white funnel-shaped flowers growing on terminal clusters and form a black berry-like fruit with 1 to 4 seeds. Family: Oleaceae.

Lonicera spp

The nature of the toxins in the berry of the honeysuckles is unknown. Intoxications differ from the other members of this group in that non-shock related systemic reactions can be observed (16, 26).

Symptoms

Shortly after ingestion there is severe and persistent emesis, colic and diarrhea. There is a sensation of blood rushing to the head. The face, particularly the eyelids, becomes reddened. There is mydriasis and photophobia. Shock-like symptoms develop, including cold sweat, and tachycardia. Whether the cardiac rhythm disturbances are related to hypotension or are an intrinsic reaction to the toxins has not been investigated. There is a twitching of the limbs which may be followed by convulsions. Terminally there is respiratory depression and death in coma.

Prognosis

Lonicera poisoning is considered extremely serious. Recovery in non-fatal cases is prolonged, generally 3 days or more.

Treatment

See *Aleurites fordii*, page 47.

Botanical Descriptions

Lonicera periclymenum. Woodbine, Honeysuckle. This is a climbing woody vine with separate elliptic leaves to 3 inches long, bluish-green underneath. The flowers appear in groups of 1 to 4 on spikes. They are yellowish-white, two-lipped, to 2 inches long. The fruit is a red berry. It grows in New England. Family: Caprifoliaceae.

Lonicera tatarica. Tatarian honeysuckle, Garden-fly honeysuckle. This is a tall shrub. The older branches are hollow. The flowers are pink or white, double-lipped, to 1 inch long appearing in pairs. There are numerous cultivated varieties with white, rose, or yellow blossoms. This honeysuckle is

Fig. 17.
Privet
(*Ligustrum vulgare*)

cultivated throughout the northeastern United States and is generally escaped. Family: Caprifoliaceae.

Lonicera xylosteum (figure 18). European fly honeysuckle. This species grows as a shrub to 9 feet tall and has more rounded leaves than the two other varieties. The flower is yellowish, double-lipped, 1/2 inch long, hairy on the outside, appearing in pairs. The fruit is a dark red berry. Family: Caprifoliaceae.

Rhamnus spp *and Cassia* spp

Toxicology

The fruit and bark of the buckthorn trees (*Rhamnus*) contains a number of anthraquinone (emodin) glycosides which are collectively the basis of the cathartic cascara sagrada. The fresh plant material differs from commercial preparations of cascara sagrada in that it contains an emetic principle which is destroyed by drying and aging. Mild intoxications have occurred in children from ingestion of the berries, of which about 20 are required to induce a marked effect, or from chewing the fresh bark. Severe intoxications are mostly derived from the use of the bark as an abortifacient.

The pods of the golden shower (*Cassia fistula*) have compartments separating the seeds. The walls between the seeds in undried pods have a sticky substance which contains the emodin glycosides (43, 44) and is a commercial source of senna. The leaves and flowers, as well as some other species of *Cassia*, contain lesser quantities of this material.

Commercial preparations of either cascara sagrada or senna exhibit a latent period of approximately six hours since the action is restricted to the colon. This delay is usually not observed in intoxications from plant material due to the presence of other active ingredients.

Symptoms

The primary symptoms are nausea, dizziness, abdominal pain, emesis and a watery, bloody diarrhea. If sufficient material is absorbed kidney damage, oliguria and proteinuria, develops. The appearance of a red alkaline urine which turns yellow-brown when acidified (Bornträger's reaction) is due to the presence of the anthraquinone compounds and is of diagnostic value. The original color should be distinguished from hematuria.

Treatment

See *Poinciana gilliesii*, page 48.

Botanical Descriptions

Rhamnus cathartica. Common buckthorn. This small deciduous tree reaches a height of 12 feet. Some of it branches end in short thorns. The leaves are opposite, elliptic, about 3 inches long. They are marked with three prominent lateral veins curving upward on each side. It bears small greenish flowers in

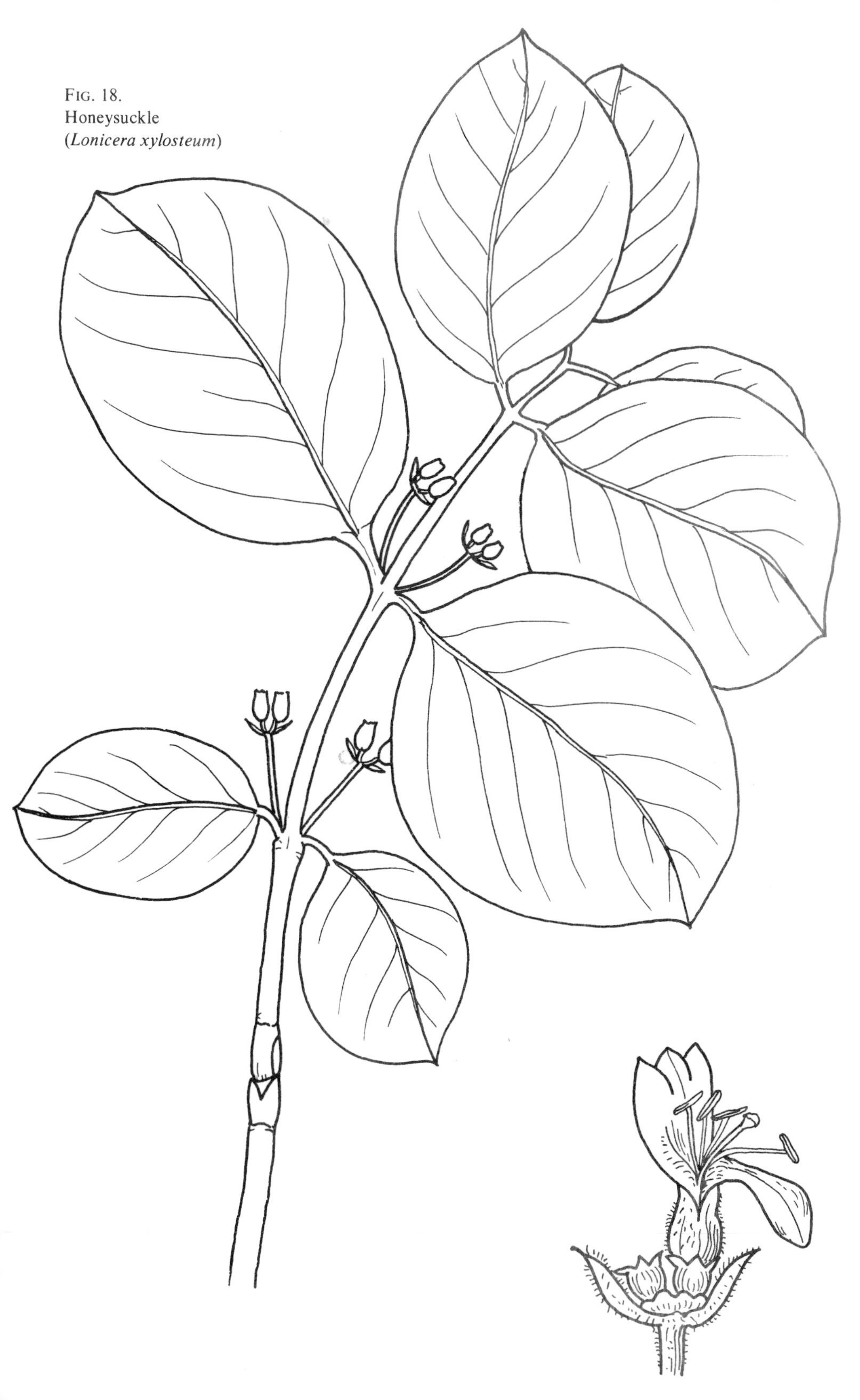

FIG. 18.
Honeysuckle
(*Lonicera xylosteum*)

clusters which are replaced by a black berry, commonly with 4 stones. It is both cultivated and escaped in northeastern United States. Family: Rhamnaceae.

Rhamnus frangula. Alder buckthorn. This is a deciduous tree which reaches a height of 12 feet. It is similar to the previous species except that the fruit is red turning black on maturity with 2 to 3 stones. It is generally escaped from cultivation especially in wet soil in Quebec and Nova Scotia to New Jersey and Indiana. Family: Rhamnaceae.

Cassia fistula. Golden shower, Pudding-pipe-tree. The golden shower grows to a height of 30 feet. It has large compound leaves, each leaflet being about 2 1/2 inches across. The flowers are pale yellow growing in 1 foot racemes. The blooms appear prior to leafing. The pods are cylindrical about 1 inch in diameter and 2 feet long turning a dark brownish-black at maturity. It is cultivated in southern Florida and Hawaii. Family: Leguminosae.

Cassia nodosa. Pink shower, Jointwood. This species is similar except that the flowers are bright pink.

Pedilanthus tithymaloides

All parts of the plant possess a caustic milky juice which may produce irritation and inflammation of the skin of susceptible persons. The latex is particularly injurious to the eye. Ingestion of either the seeds or the latex produces persistent emesis and drastic catharsis (14, 55). For treatment, see *Poinciana gilliesii*, page 48.

Botanical Descriptions

Pedilanthus tithymaloides. Christmas candle, Redbird cactus, Slipper-flower, Jew-bush. This is a stout-stemmed shrub, up to 9 feet with heavy elliptic leaves, from a 1/4 inch to 6 inches in length and 3/8 of an inch to 4 inches wide. The clusters of red flowers appear on the branch ends. The plant contains a milky latex. It is grown as a house plant except in the extreme southern part of Florida. Family: Euphorbiaceae.

Symphoricarpos albus

Snowberries are reported to produce emesis and drastic catharsis. One case involving four children was also characterized by the presence of delirium followed by a semi-comatose state (3). For treatment, see *Poinciana gilliesii*, page 48.

Botanical Description

Symphoricarpos albus (*S. racemosus*) (figure 19). Snowberry, Waxberry. The snowberry is a deciduous shrub which grows to a height of 3 feet with simple, opposite, oval leaves to 2 inches long. The flowers are 1/4 inch long, pinkish and bell-shaped occurring in little clusters from the main stem. The fruit is a snow-white berry. The plant is most often found in dry or rocky soil

FIG. 19.
Snowberry
(*Symphoricarpos albus*)

from Quebec to Alaska and along the northern border states. Family: Caprifoliaceae.

D. PLANTS PRODUCING DELAYED GASTROENTERITIS

The plants in this group exhibit a well defined latent period between ingestion and the appearance of gastroenteritis. This delay usually amounts to 1 or 2 hours but may, in the case of certain toxalbumins, be as much as 1 or 2 days.

The division of plants according to the symptomatology developing subsequent to the onset of gastroenteritis is made according to the following primary toxic components,

a. Toxalbumin group
b. Solanine group
c. Oxalate group
d. Colchicine group

With the exception of the oxalate group, in which intoxications are rarely severe because of the large quantity which must be ingested, intoxications from members of these groups must be considered serious.

The onset of symptoms after the ingestion of pokeweed (*Phytolacca americana*) is occasionally delayed up to one hour. This species is discussed in the previous section.

a. Toxalbumin Group

The plants in this category are all reputed to contain toxalbumins (phytotoxins). These toxic proteins are slowly absorbed from the gastroenteric tract so there is a prolonged latent period between ingestion and systemic effects.

Some species are known to contain additional non-nitrogenous toxins (saponins, glycosides, etc.). These substances sufficiently modify the symptomatology of intoxications to require separate descriptions for some species.

Members of the Group

Abrus precatorius	Crabs-eye, Precatory bean, Rosary pea, Jequirity bean, Prayer bead, Buddhist rosary bead, Mienie-mienie Indian bead, Seminole bead, Weather plant, Lucky bean
Ricinus communis	Castor bean, Palma Christi
Hura crepitans	Sandbox tree
Jatropha curcas	Barbados nut, Physic nut, Purge nut, Curcas bean
Jatropha gossypifolia	Bellyache bush
Jatropha hastata	Perregrina
Jatropha multifida	Coral plant, Physic nut
Robinia pseudoacacia	Black locust, Black acacia

Abrus precatorius

Toxicology

The seed coat and root of this plant contain a thermolabile toxalbumin, abrin. This extremely toxic substance with a lethal dose estimated to be 0.01 mg/kg., is stable in the gastroenteric tract from which it is slowly absorbed.

Abrin has a pronounced irritant effect on mucous membranes. The primary systemic toxic action is due to depression of the vasomotor center, accompanied by a less pronounced direct vasodilating action. Death is caused by cardiac failure secondary to circulatory collapse.

Pathological changes include acute gastroenteritis with multiple hemorrhages, swelling of the abdominal and retroperitoneal lymph nodes, and capillary damage with marked hemorrhages of the retina. Focal necrosis in the liver and lesions of the kidney have also been reported (5).

Deaths in children have occurred after ingestion of one well chewed seed. Severe though non-fatal intoxications have also been reported (35).

Because of the hard coating, the ripe seed is harmless if swallowed whole. The unripe seed, however, has a soft and easily broken shell and is thus more dangerous.

The jequirity bean is used extensively in beadwork and jewelry in the West Indies. Tourists have introduced them via these products to many areas. Because of the irritating action on the ocular conjunctiva, cold infusions were once used in medicine for the treatment of trachoma and also to brighten corneal opacities. Results of these practices were unpredictable, frequently leading to ocular damage and occasionally death. In the southern United States, the seeds are reported to be used as an abortifacient.

Symptoms

The symptoms may develop anywhere from a few hours to several days after ingestion. One should expect severe gastroenteritis with pronounced nausea, and vomiting. Most of the systemic reactions will be as a consequence of hypotension. These include muscular weakness, tachycardia, trembling of the hands, flushing of the skin, and convulsions. The only constant neurological findings are mydriasis and tetany. Hallucinations have been observed with children.

Prognosis

Survivals have been reported following severe systemic involvement, nevertheless, intoxications by abrin should be considered as very serious. The severity of the retinal hemorrhages produced has resulted in permanent visual defect.

Treatment

Since there is a long latent period associated with abrin poisoning little value may be anticipated from the induction of emesis or from gastric lavage. If a stomach tube is to be employed, care should be taken because of the pronounced necrotizing action of the toxic agent. Protectives such as bismuth subcarbonate or magnesium trisilicate may be administered to reduce the degree of gastroenteric erosion. Fluids and electrolytes will be needed to replace losses due to emesis and diarrhea. Treatment is essentially symptomatic in regard to vasomotor collapse and convulsions. Calcium gluconate is indicated for tetany and a high carbohydrate diet to minimize liver damage. Since an elevated environmental temperature markedly increases toxicity, it may be worthwhile to provide external cooling.

Botanical Description

Abrus precatorius (figure 20). Rosary pea, Crabs-eye, Precatory bean, Jequirity bean, Prayer bead, Buddhist rosary bead, Mienie-mienie Indian bead, Seminole bean, Weather plant, Lucky bean. This is a slender, twining, woody-like vine generally supported on other plants. The flowers are red to purple. The pea-shaped pods, about 1½ inches in length, contain hard, brilliantly scarlet seeds with a small jet-black spot at the base. The rosary pea is common in Florida and occasionally found in Hawaii. Family: Leguminosae.

Ricinus communis

Toxicology

The primary poisonous action of the seed of the castor bean is derived from the toxalbumin ricin but the plant also contains a number of allergens. The lethal dose of ricin is estimated to be 0.5 mg/kg. Intoxications occur after the ingestion of 2 or 3 seeds. Five or 6 seeds are considered fatal in a child and about 20 in the adult. However, there seems to be a wide variation in response since much smaller quantities have killed. The action of ricin on the digestive tract, liver, and kidney is similar to that of the other toxalbumins.

Allergic responses, such as bronchial asthma, dermatitis and conjunctivitis, to the castor bean and its products are well known. A severe case of pollinosis has also been reported (47, 49, 59).

Symptoms

The delay of appearance of symptoms is related to the quantity ingested and may vary from a few minutes to several hours and even days in some cases. The reaction may begin with a burning sensation in the mouth and throat, but the clinical picture is dominated by severe hemorrhagic gastroenteritis. Persistent nausea and emesis, colic, intense thirst, and profuse, sometimes bloody diarrhea are seen. These symptoms are followed by head-

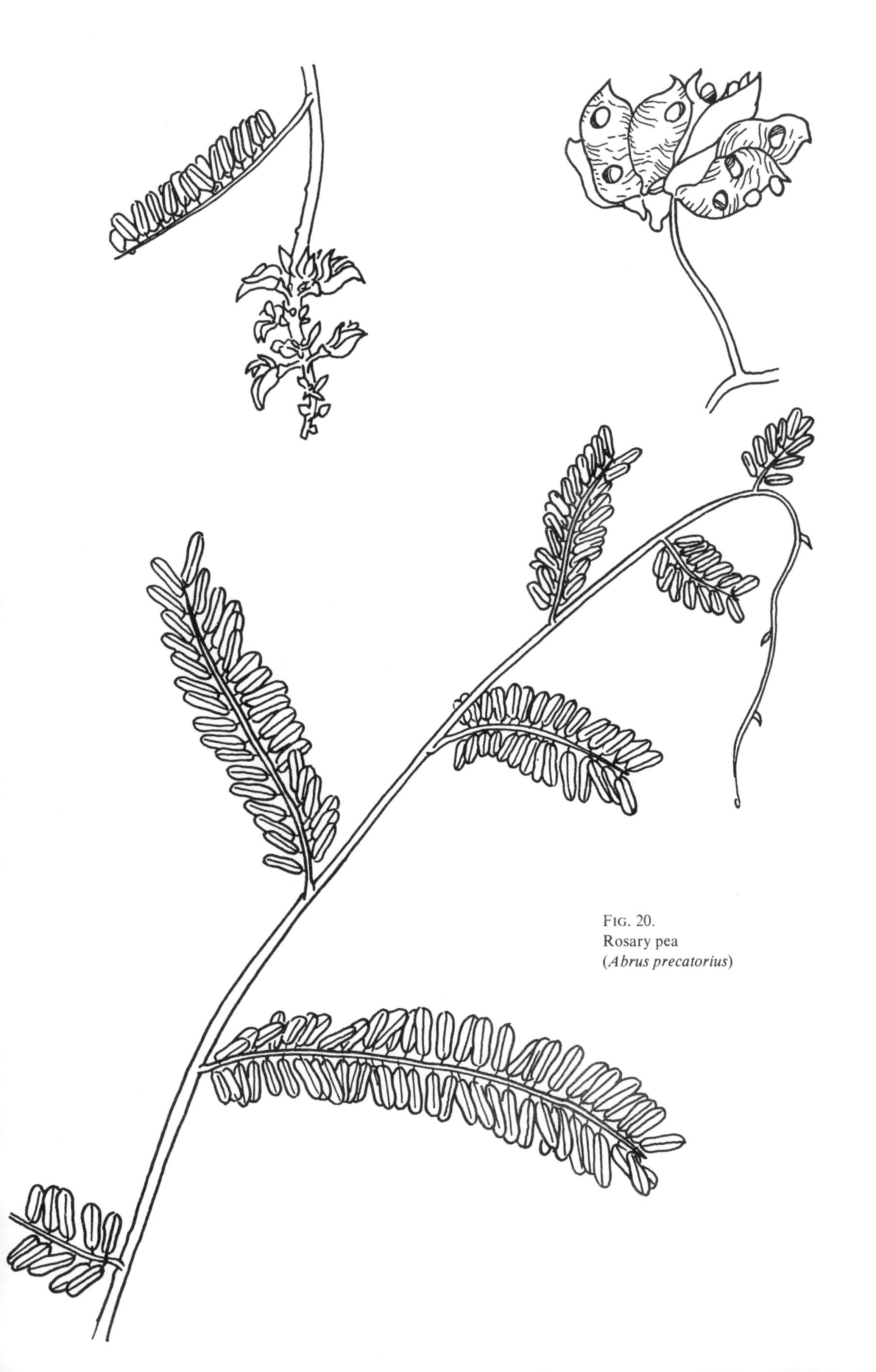

FIG. 20.
Rosary pea
(*Abrus precatorius*)

ache, dizziness and depression. Later signs of degeneration of the liver and damage to the kidney are evident.

In severe cases electrocardiographic changes, particularly prolongation of the Q-T interval, hypotension, and circulatory collapse are produced (45).

Prognosis

If the seeds are swallowed whole, intoxication will be milder since the hard coating impedes absorption. The mortality is usually given as 6%. This figure does not reflect the true toxicity of ricin since the amount of material absorbed is small compared to the amount destroyed in the gastroenteric tract or expelled by vomiting and diarrhea. Another factor which affects mortality is the individual's sensitivity to both the toxalbumin and allergens present.

Treatment

Gastric lavage should be conducted, after which gastroenteric protectives such as bismuth subcarbonate or magnesium trisilicate may be administered. If the diarrhea does not cause electrolytic depletion, it may be allowed to run its course to facilitate the elimination of toxic material. Appropriate care, however, must be taken to avoid dehydration.

In nonfatal cases, intoxication persists from three to ten days. During this time it may be useful to supply a high carbohydrate intake in an effort to minimize liver damage. Preparations should be made for the possible advent of renal failure and secondary shock, see Chapter I.

Botanical Description

Ricinus communis (figure 21). Castor bean, Palma Christi, Castor-oil-plant, Koli (Hawaii). The castor bean is a tree-like plant growing on stout stems to 15 feet. The leaves are large, sometimes to 3 feet across, and variably notched into 5 to 11 lobes. The greenish-white to rust colored flower clusters form at the end of the branches on upright stems 6 to 12 inches long. The seed pod is a spiny capsule about 1 inch long and contains 3 black seeds mottled with white or brown each about 1/2 inch long. It is widely escaped throughout the southern United States and Hawaii and is cultivated as an ornamental elsewhere. Family: Euphorbiaceae.

Hura crepitans

Toxicology

The seeds of *Hura crepitans* contain a toxalbumin, and the sap contains two toxic substances identified as hurin and crepitan (14). Crepitan produces intoxications resembling those from *Ricinus communis* or *Abrus precatorius.* Both the seeds and the sap are emetocathartic and dangerously toxic. The seeds have an agreeable taste; 2 or 3 are usually sufficient to induce emesis and drastic catharsis (2).

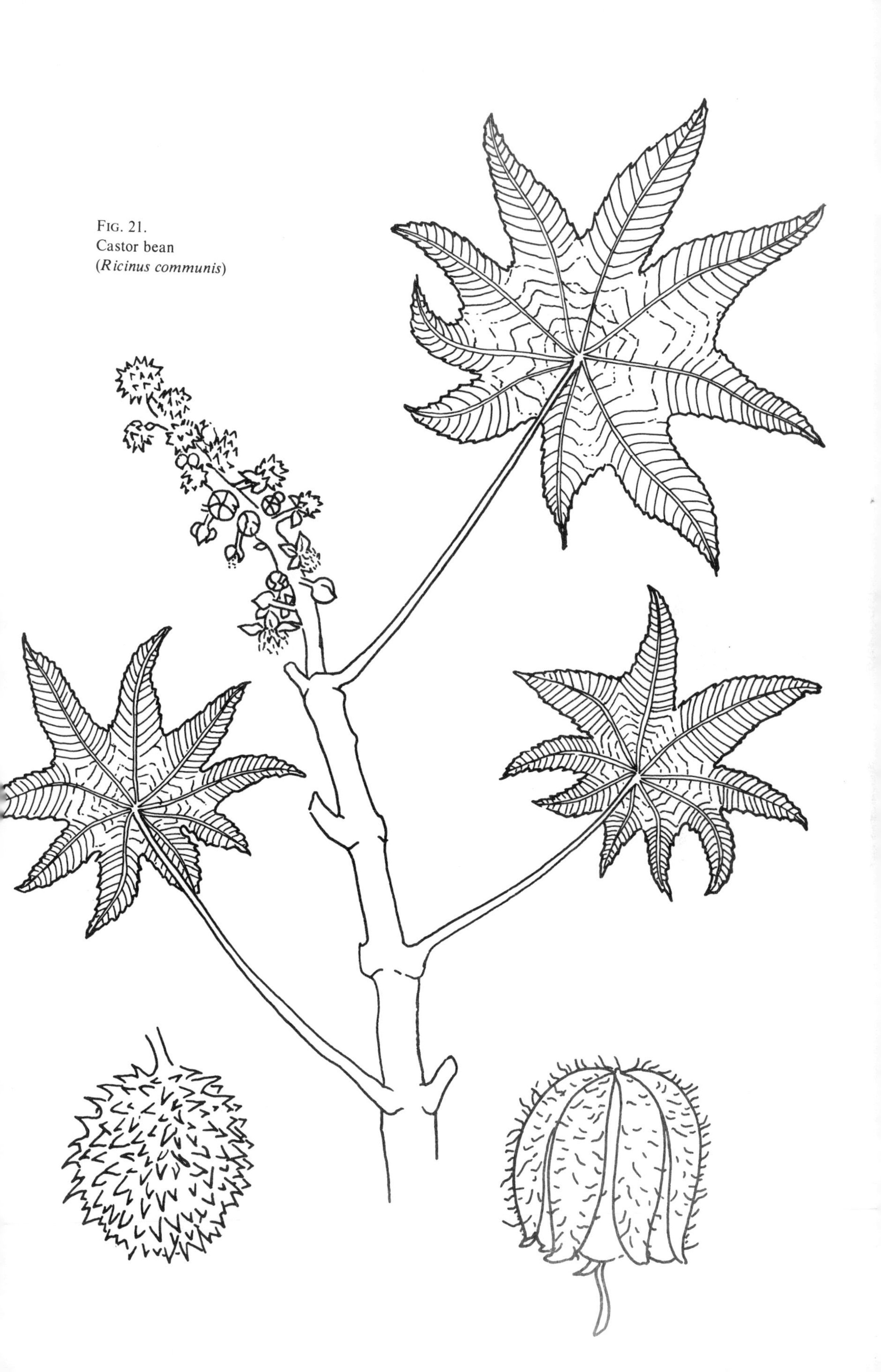

FIG. 21.
Castor bean
(*Ricinus communis*)

The juice from all parts of the tree causes inflammation, edema and blistering of the skin. Eye contact may result in temporary blindness.

Treatment of systemic poisoning should be directed along the same lines as for *Abrus precatorius*. For the management of the contact dermatitis and eye irritation, see Chapter XI.

Botanical Description

Hura crepitans (figure 22). Sandbox tree, Monkey pistol. This tree grows to heights of 60 feet or more with a trunk diameter of 3 feet at the base. Both the trunk and any exposed roots are covered with short spines. The leaves are oval, slightly serrate, approximately 7–8 inches wide. The green, inverted cone-shaped anthers (male flowers) are 1½ to 2 inches long. The flowers are deep red. The woody fruits are capsular, about 3 inches wide and 1½ inches thick, deeply ribbed and resemble a small pumpkin. These explode when ripe with considerable force throwing the flat round seeds. The pop made during the explosion is the source of the name monkey pistol. The tree is cultivated in southern Florida and Hawaii. Family: Euphorbiaceae.

Jatropha spp

Toxicology

Jatropha curcas most frequently figures in instances of human poisoning but the other members of this genera are presumed to contain the same or a similar toxalbumin. In addition to the toxalbumin, curcin, other poisonous substances of lesser importance have been found in the seed of *Jatropha curcas*. These include a dermatitis-producing resin, an alkaloid, and a glycoside which produces cardiovascular and respiratory depression (14, 15). Because the seeds have a pleasant taste, they are particularly attractive to children. The toxic dose is reportedly 3 seeds although, like other toxalbumin-containing plants, there is considerable variation in individual susceptibility.

Symptoms

The onset of action is about 1 hour after ingestion but may be even more prolonged. It is characterized by intense abdominal pain, nausea, vomiting and diarrhea (38).

In severe intoxications, the muscles of the extremities may be contracted by spasms. Intense polypnea or a quick panting respiration is seen together with hypotension and electrocardiographic abnormalities (14, 58, 63).

Case History

A 3 year old boy was admitted to the hospital with persistent vomiting and diarrhea which followed the ingestion of several seeds of *Jatropha curcas*. He was unable to retain food or water. Three and a half hours following the ingestion the patient appeared lethargic, cyanotic, and acutely ill. His skin

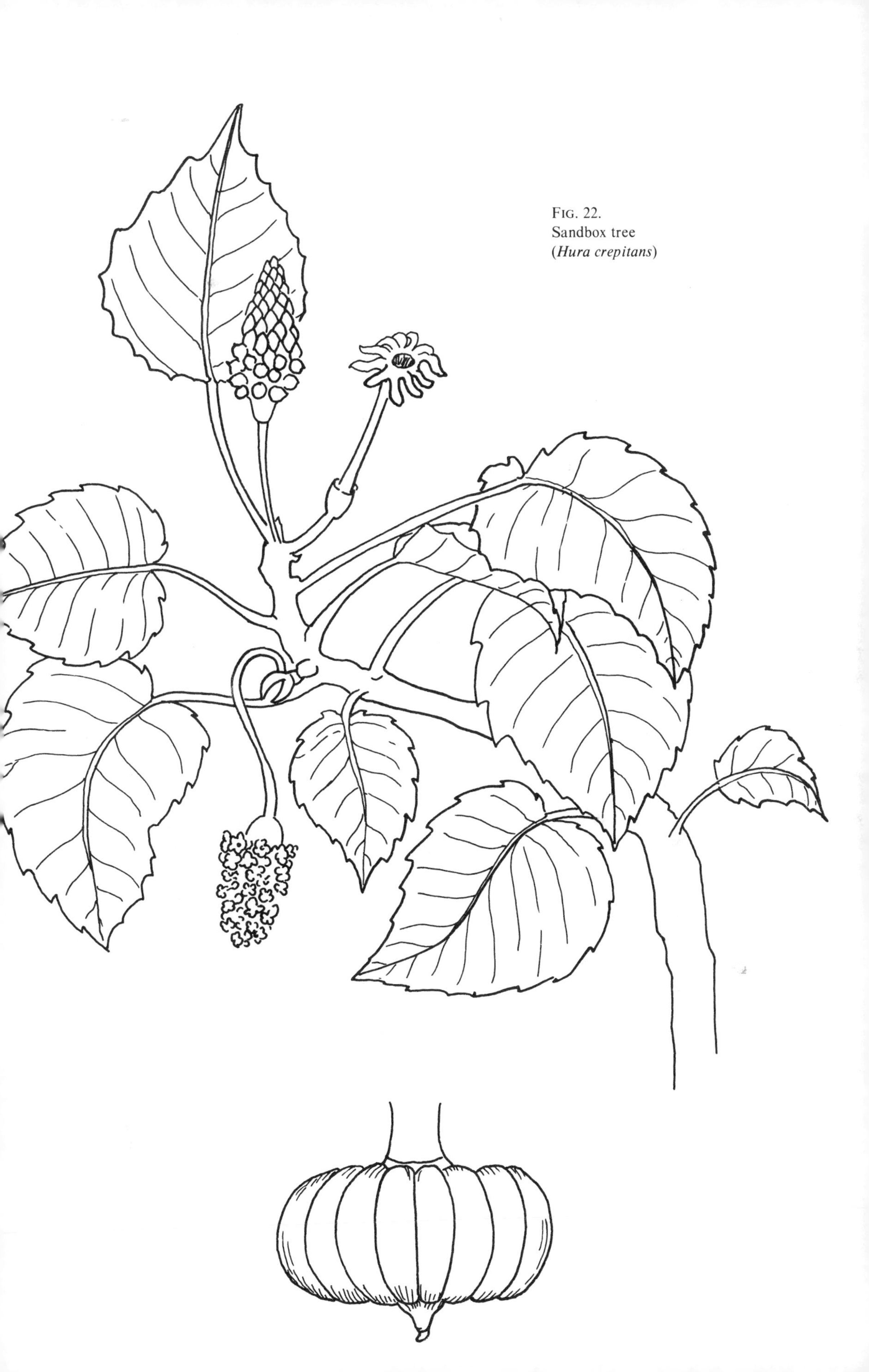

Fig. 22.
Sandbox tree
(*Hura crepitans*)

was cold and clammy. Severe dehydration was indicated by the poor skin turgor, sunken eyeballs, and deepening periorbital shadows.

The hemoglobin was 14.2 gm/100 ml, the red blood cell count, 5.4 million, and the platelets were normal. The white blood cell count was 27,000 per cu mm, and the differential was normal. The urine showed a trace of albumin, the elements consisting of 2 to 4 white blood cells per high power field and many granular and some hyaline casts. The carbon dioxide level was 17 mEq per liter or 38 volumes per cent; sodium 134 mEq per liter; chlorides, 101 mEq per liter; and potassium, 4.4 mEq per liter.

The child was given 1,000 cc of homeolytic electrolyte solution. The patient was oliguric for the first 24 hours. He responded to treatment, and 20 hours after admission he was able to tolerate oral feedings without any vomiting or diarrhea, and was voiding well. He was discharged from the hospital after 3 days without complication (38).

Prognosis and Treatment

The management of *Jatropha* poisoning is similar to that for the castor bean. Since the onset of symptoms is not unduly prolonged, gastric lavage should be conducted unless vomiting has been extensive. The course of intoxication is short; the patient may become asymptomatic within 24 hours. Poisonings in children living in tropical countries are frequent, some with fatal results.

Botanical Descriptions

Jatropha curcas (figure 23). Barbados nut, Physic nut, Purge nut, Curcas bean, Kukui haole (Hawaii). The barbados nut is a small spreading shade tree about 15 feet high. The spear-shaped slightly lobed leaves are up to 6 inches across. The inconspicuous greenish flowers grow on stems in small clusters. The tree bears a fleshy green fruit containing three seeds just under 1/2 inch in length. It is found in southern Florida and Hawaii. Family: Euphorbiaceae.

Jatropha gossypifolia. Bellyache bush. This herbaceous plant rarely grows more than 3 feet tall. The leaves are similar to the previous species except that they are covered with hairs. The flowers are purple. There is a small capsular fruit containing three tiny brown seeds. It is infrequently found in southern Flordia. Family: Euphorbiaceae.

Jatropha hastata. Perregrina. This is a shrub which grows to 5 feet. The flowers are scarlet. The leaves are an oblong ellipse with a sharp point at the tip, with either a plain margin or with 1 or 2 deeply cut lobes at the base. It grows in southern Florida particularly in the Lower Keys. Family: Euphorbiaceae.

Jatropha multifida (figure 24). Coral plant, Physic nut. The coral plant grows as a small tree to 20 feet. The leaves are deeply cut; sometimes being up to 1 foot across. The flower is scarlet and resembles a small piece of coral.

FIG. 23.
Barbados nut
(*Jatropha curcas*)

FIG. 24.
Coral plant
(*Jatropha multifida*)

The fruit is a small capsule slightly over 1 inch long. It is cultivated in southern Florida and Hawaii. Family: Euphorbiaceae.

Robinia pseudoacacia

Toxicology

Two toxalbumins, phasin and robin, have been isolated from the bark, seeds and leaves. The flowers are not poisonous.

Symptoms

After a delay of about 1 hour, the patient exhibits nausea, epigastric pain and emesis. The vomitus may contain blood and mucus. In moderate to severe poisoning there may be stupor, mydriasis and, less commonly, dyspnea. Various features of shock: tachycardia, cold extremities, a weak peripheral pulse, and parasthesias, may be seen. Convulsions are infrequent, but muscular fasiculations may appear (19, 26).

Prognosis

Fatalities are rare. The patient usually becomes asymptomatic within 2 days.

Treatment

The gastroenteritis and epigastric pain may be managed with protectives such as bismuth subcarbonate or magnesium trisilicate in conjunction with the conservative administration of meperidine (Demerol). Institution of intravenous fluids will reduce the tendency for the development of shock.

Constipation should be anticipated in *Robinia* poisoning so the usual diets ordered for patients with gastroenteritis will require the appropriate modification.

Botanical Description

Robinia pseudoacacia (figure 25). Black locust, Black acacia. The black locust is a tree to 80 feet distinguished by its stout, woody thorns along the trunk and branches. There are compound leaves each having 7 to 19 elliptic leaflets, 1 inch in length. The white, very fragrant flowers are formed in clusters. The pods are reddish brown, about 4 inches long, and reamin on the tree over winter. It is native from Pennsylvania to southern Indiana and Oklahoma, Georgia and Louisiana, and is occasionally planted farther north and westward to Iowa. A species variety is found in New York. Family: Leguminosae.

b. Solanine Group

Toxicology

The toxic principles in this group are the glycoalkaloids which are collectively termed solanine. Hydrolysis cleaves the solanine compounds into two components, a steroidal alkaloid (alkamine), of which at least six are

FIG. 25.
Black locust
(*Robinia pseudoacacia*)

known, and a sugar. The unhydrolyzed glycoalkaloid is poorly absorbed through the intestine. It has a saponin-liked character which is responsible for its pronounced irritant action. Thus in mild solanine intoxications gastroenteritis will be the predominant finding. The free alkamine is apparently more readily absorbed and is no doubt responsible for most of the systemic reactions.

The members of this group belong to the family *Solanaceae* which is composed of 75 genera. Not all of these genera contain toxic plants, but some which do, for example *Solanum*, contain over 1,000 individual species. Only a few are known to have produced solanine intoxications in man. Even a single species may show a widespread variation in toxicity due to such factors as genetic strain, climate, soil, exposure to light, the plant part ingested and its maturity. For example, the common Irish potato which is eaten with impunity by millions of people throughout the world has been associated with sporadic outbursts of serious and even fatal solanine poisoning (31, 72).

Certain berries, for example the ground cherry (46) and the black nightshade (51), are toxic when green and harmless when ripe, whereas others such as those of the jessamine produce solanine poisoning when green (24) and atropine poisoning when mature (53).

Since many of these plants, particularly the *Solandra* spp, contain variable amounts of the atropine alkaloids, signs of mixed intoxication may be seen. This probably explains certain inconstant findings, such as mydriasis, hyperpyrexia, delirium and salivary suppression, in the case reports of poisoning incidents.

One of the plants in this group, *Solanum pseudo-capsicum*, contains in its leaves the cardioactive substance solanocapsine (34) which may affect the signs of toxicity. In the single pharmacological study on this compound (69), the intravenous administration of the pure alkaloid into humans with normal cardiac rhythm produced bradycardia which became maximal in about 10 minutes and persisted for about half an hour. The slowing was not affected by prior treatment with atropine. In animal experiments, the compound produced sinus bradycardia, lengthening of the P-R and S-T segments and spreading of the QRS complex.

Members of the Group

Cestrum spp	Jessamine
Physalis spp	Ground-cherry
Solandra spp	Chalice vine
Solanum aculeatissimum	Devil's apple, Soda apple
Solanum dulcamara	European bittersweet, Climbing nightshade
Solanum gracile	Graceful nightshade
Solanum nigrum (*S. americanum*)	Black nightshade
Solanum pseudo-capsicum	Jerusalem cherry
Solanum sodomeum	Apple of Sodom, Popolo
Solanum tuberosum	Potato

Symptoms

Some hours after ingestion a harsh, scratchy feeling develops in the mouth and pharynx. This is followed by nausea and anorexia, emesis, colic and diarrhea. A rise of body temperature is common and therefore the intoxication may be confused with bacterial gastroenteritis.

Systemic involvement other than mild depression and headache is not common but, if present, is usually not dramatic. The patient can exhibit sweating, salivation, dyspnea and progressive apathy and muscular weakness. Headache is usually seen, possibly related to cerebral edema. Sensory loss may occur.

In the later stages of the intoxication there are bloody stools due to intestinal ulceration and hemorrhage as well as signs of renal damage with proteinuria and hemoglobinuria. Convulsions may occur but coma with a falling body temperature and respiratory paralysis is a more common terminal event (67). It should be recalled that additional symptoms due to concomitant atropine poisoning may be present.

Case History

Alexander, *et al.* (1), present a case report for a 9 year old girl who had eaten a number of berries of *Solanum dulcamara.* The following day she began vomiting 'coffee-ground' material four times during the five hours before admission.

"The child responded weakly to questioning and complained only of abdominal pain and thirst. She looked exhausted, the skin was pallid and dry, the expression anxious. There were slight restless movements of arms and head. She was not delirious. A feature which remained marked throughout was dyspnea. Inspiration was short and gasping; expiration was prolonged and active and accompanied by a sigh. The respiratory rate was 32 per minute.

"The pupils were of normal size and reacted to light. Although the child was dehydrated the tongue was moist. Examination of chest and abdomen revealed nothing of significance. The extremities were warm. There was neither paresthesia nor paralysis. Temperature 96.4°F. (35.8°C.), pulse rate 140 per minute, blood pressure 120/88."

Gastric lavage and enema were conducted and fluid was given by mouth and rectum. Oxygen and C.N.S. stimulants were administered.

"Some improvement in her general condition was maintained for 24 hours, but she later became weaker and more cyanosed and her respirations became very feeble." Death occurred in the morning, 5 days after eating the berries. Except for some moderate fatty infiltration and necrosis seen in the microscopic examination of the liver and acute inflammation of the mucosa of the stomach and intestine, the postmortem findings were negative.

Prognosis

Solanine has a relatively low toxicity for adults. Fatalities are rare. Generally symptoms are restricted to gastroenteric irritation, headache, and depression followed by uneventful recovery.

Treatment

Appropriate management for gastroenteritis is usually all that is required. The nursing staff should be alerted to immediately report changes indicating impending renal involvement.

Botanical Descriptions

Cestrum spp, see Chapter V.

Physalis spp. Ground cherry. This genus has about 17 species growing in the United States. A large number are grown for ornament for their attractive chinese lantern fruit pods. Inside the pod there is a globose berry which is edible when mature in some species. These ground plants and small bushes are both native and cultivated throughout the United States including Hawaii. Family: Solanaceae.

Solandra spp. Chalice-vine. These are woody plants, erect or climbing, frequently grown throughout the southeastern United States and California for their large, showy, tubular, creamy or yellow flowers. Family: Solanaceae.

Solanum aculeatissimum. Devil's apple, Soda apple, Cockroach berry, Kikania (Hawaii). This is a small shrub which grows to 2 feet with spiny stems and leaves. The latter are 4 inches long, oval and 5 to 7 lobed. The flowers are white and 7 inches across. The fruit is orange, globose, corrugated and 2 inches across. It grows wild in Hawaii, and along the coastal plain from Texas to North Carolina. Family: Solanaceae.

Solanum dulcamara (figure 26). European bittersweet, Climbing nightshade, Blue bindweed. This is a shrubby climber to 8 feet. The leaves are 4 inches long and frequently have 1 or 2 small lobes at the base. The flowers are $1/4$ to $1/2$ inch wide, blue, violet or white with bright yellow stamens. They grow in a loose cluster, later forming small berries turning red at maturity. The bittersweet is widespread in the northern United States. Family: Solanaceae.

Solanum gracile. Graceful nightshade. This species is nearly identical to *S. nigrum*. It occurs from Louisiana to North Carolina.

Solanum nigrum (*S. americanum*) (figure 27). Black nightshade. This weed is scattered throughout Canada and the United States including Hawaii. It is an annual standing about $2\frac{1}{2}$ feet high but sometimes found spreading along the ground. The notched leaves are 5 inches or more long. The white flowers form drooping clusters later to be replaced by a globose black berry, a quarter inch or more in diameter. There is a cultivated variety, which is nontoxic, known as the Garden huckleberry, Wonderberry and Sunberry. Family: Solanaceae.

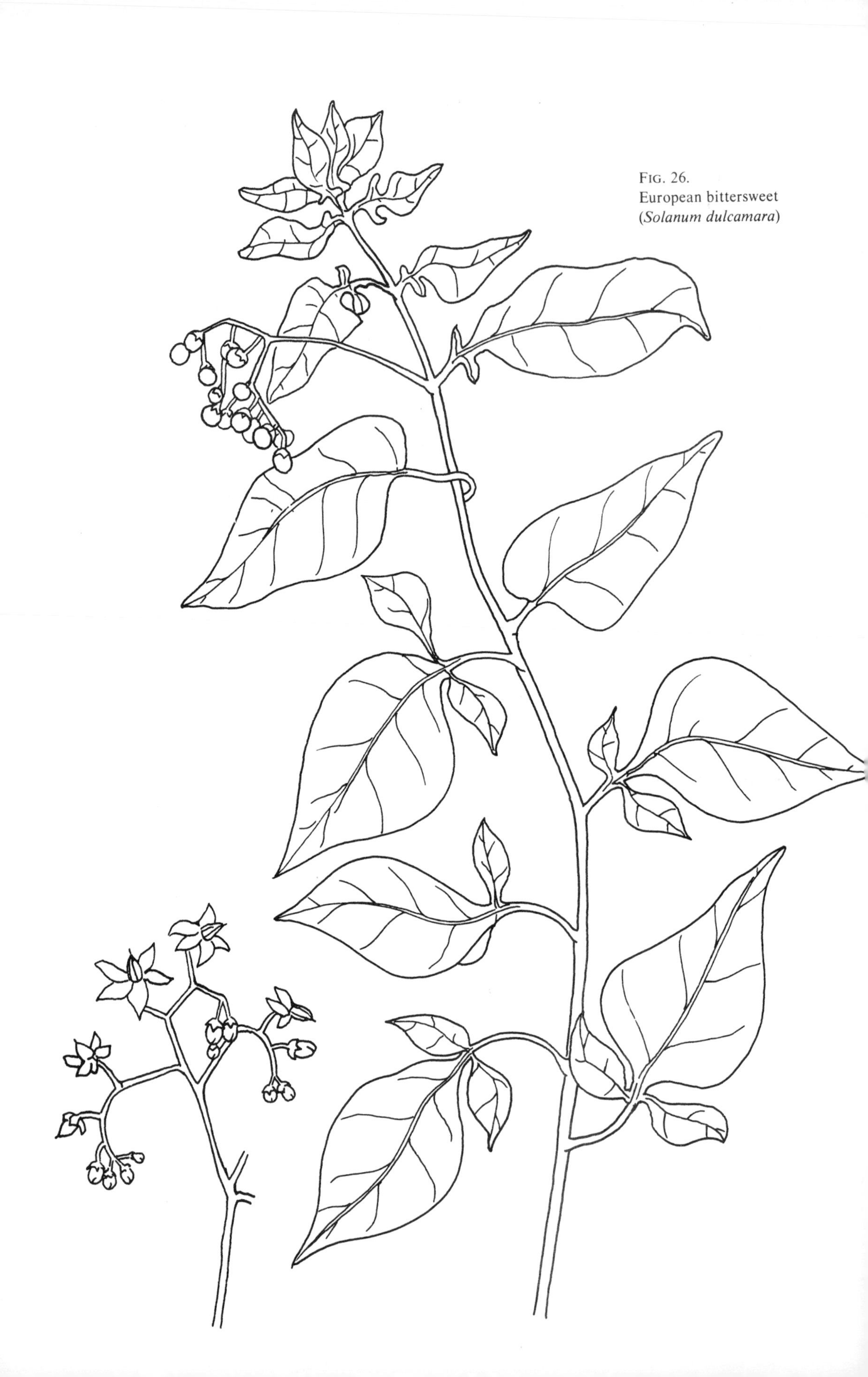

FIG. 26.
European bittersweet
(*Solanum dulcamara*)

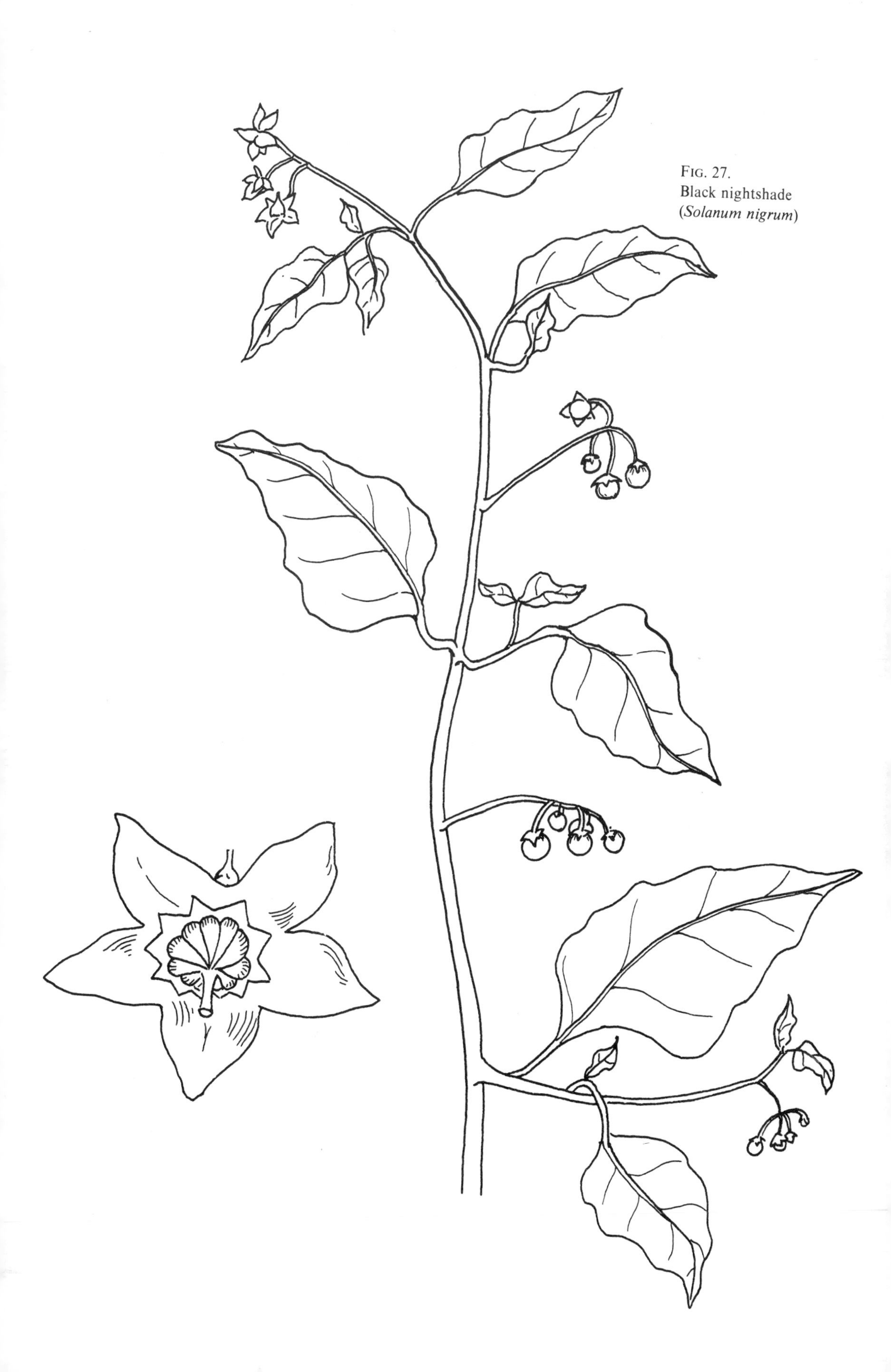

FIG. 27.
Black nightshade
(*Solanum nigrum*)

Solanum pseudo-capsicum. Jerusalem cherry. This shrub grows to a height of 4 feet but is frequently cultivated as a pot plant for its bright scarlet or yellow globular fruits which are $\frac{1}{2}$ inch in diameter. It has shining 4 inch oblong leaves. The flowers are white, $\frac{1}{2}$ inch across and may appear alone or in clusters. Family: Solanaceae.

Solanum sodomeum. Apple of Sodom, Popolo. This is a spiny shrub about 6 feet high with compound leaves. The flowers are about 1 inch across, and appear in clusters. It bears a globose, shining yellow fruit 1 inch in diameter. It is a common weed in Hawaii. Family: Solanaceae.

c. Oxalic Acid Group

Toxicology

Intoxication with plants containing oxalic acid is not common because of the large quantity of plant material which must be ingested in order to produce severe symptoms. The pronounced itching, which is characteristic of oxalic acid poisoning, does not occur because of the low concentrations present in these plants; in rhubarb leaves, for example, there is less than 1%.

Oxalic acid exerts a corrosive action on the entire gastroenteric tract. The systemic toxic manifestations mainly result from the formation of insoluble calcium oxalate causing a decrease in the concentration of ionizable calcium. Hypocalcemia affects the function of the heart, the neuromuscular and central nervous systems. Kidney damage, resulting from changes in tubular function due to the oxalate ion or mechanical injury from precipitated calcium magnesium oxalate, can often be detected but is seldom the cause of death.

Species of rhubarb cultivated in this country are devoid of the anthroquinones which are responsible for the cathartic properties of medicinal rhubarb (*R. officinalis* and *R. palmatum*).

Members of the Group

Rheum rhaponticum	Garden rhubarb, Pie plant, Wine-plant
Rumex acetosa	Garden sorrel
Psedera quinquefolia (*Parthenocissus quinquefolia*)	Virginia creeper, American ivy

Symptoms

The absorption of pure oxalic acid takes place rapidly but these plants are digested slowly and therefore intoxications sometimes have a prolonged course. Nausea and stupor are usually the earliest presenting symptoms. Generally 1 or 2 days pass after the ingestion of the plant before severe gastroenteritis develops. This is accompanied with vomiting and sometimes bloody diarrhea. The patient may have a swollen abdomen caused by a fermentation of undigested plant material. Headache and somnolence intensify but coma or convulsions are seen only in extremely severe poisoning.

Frank tetany rarely occurs. However, Chvostek's sign may be present and tetanic spasms, particularly in the facial muscle may be seen. Oliguria and oxaluria and, less commonly, albuminuria and hematuria occur as a sign of kidney damage (41, 64).

Prognosis

Fatal poisoning is rare; however, even in the absence of severe systemic reactions, permanent kidney damage may be produced.

Treatment

The stomach should be evacuated by induced emesis or gastric lavage with milk or lime water unless corrosion of the mucosa of the mouth or esophagus is already present. The specific therapy indicated if any signs of tetany are present, including convulsions, is the administration of calcium. This may be given orally as a 5% solution (1 to 2 g) of calcium chloride or as large quantities of milk.

If renal function is unimpaired, large quantities of fluids should be given to prevent precipitation of calcium oxalate in the renal tubules. Hemodialysis has been employed successfully for the treatment of rhubarb poisoning complicated by anuria (64).

Botanical Descriptions

Rheum rhaponticum. Garden rhubarb, Pie plant, Wine-plant. This common cultivated garden plant is easily recognized by its large 1 ½ foot long heart-shaped leaves and red colored stems. Family: Polygonaceae.

Rumex acetosa. Garden sorrel, Green sorrel. This perennial is occasionally cultivated for greens and is sparsely naturalized from Newfoundland to Alaska south to Connecticut and Pennsylvania. It is about 3 feet high. The leaves are 5 inches long, shaped like an elongated arrowhead. Family: Polygonaceae.

Psedera quinquefolia (*Parthenocissus quinquefolia*). Virginia creeper, American ivy. This is a high climbing vine with numerous, much branched tendrils. The leaf is typically divided into 5 coarsely toothed stalked leaflets to 6 inches long. It bears clusters of small, black berries resembling tiny grapes. It is found from Maine to Florida west to Kansas and Texas. A variety of this plant with fewer leaflets is found from Illinois to the west and southwest. Family: Vitaceae.

d. Colchicine Group

The alkaloid colchicine is contained in all parts of plants in this group. A number of related substances are also present but they are of minor toxicological significance.

Members of the Group

Colchicum autumnale	Autumn crocus
Colchicum speciosum	
Colchicum vernum (*Bulbocodium vernum*)	
Gloriosa superba	Glory lily or Climbing lily
Gloriosa rothschildiana	

Toxicology

Colchicine is a pronounced mitotic poison. The depression of the cell division reaches its maximum after about 10 hours, which explains the long, partially dose dependent, latent period between ingestion and the appearance of symptoms. Excretion of colchicine is slow; hence, sub-toxic daily doses may be cumulative (46).

Poisoning has occurred by mistaking these plants for edible foods such as the leaves of *Colchicum autumnale* for a salad green and the tuber of *Gloriosa superba* for sweet potato. Children using the dried seed pods of the autumn crocus as rattles have been poisoned from consuming the seeds.

A major pathway of excretion is in the milk, so human intoxications have resulted from the use of milk from poisoned livestock.

Acute or chronic intoxications associated with the ingestion of any of these plants is indistinguishable from the clinical characteristics of overdosage seen in the use of colchicine or its derivatives in the treatment of gout.

Symptoms

The symptoms of colchicine poisoning appear after a latent period of 2 to 6 hours, even with large doses. They begin with burning and rawness in the mouth and throat, a sensation of strangling, dysphagia, intense thirst, nausea and abdominal discomfort, followed by violent and uncontrollable vomiting and purging, colic and tenesmus. The extensive fluid loss may lead to shock and collapse. Kidney damage is evidenced by hematuria and oliguria.

Other symptoms are not marked except in fatal poisoning and then only as terminal events. Muscular spasms are rare but have been noted. Altered reflex activity and sensitivity disturbances may be seen in the lower extremities together with some ascending paralysis. In the later stages, leucopenia and thrombocytopenia have been observed, but agranulocytosis or aplastic anemia are generally associated with chronic ingestion. Depilation is also associated with chronic exposure although a striking case of near total alopecia has been recorded following the single ingestion of tubers from *Gloriosa superba* (see the case report which follows).

Four to 12 hours before death occurs, the body temperature begins to fall. Functional disturbances of the central nervous system become apparent and respiratory effort is diminished due to ascending paralysis of the central nervous system (26, 74).

Case History

The patient was a 21 year old woman who had mistakenly eaten the boiled tubers of *Gloriosa superba* as yams. It was estimated that the quantity of colchicine involved was in the order of 350 mg. "About two hours after this meal she had started vomiting, and about 8 hours later had profuse watery diarrhea, which continued throughout the night. She had vomited 25 times that night and had 20 watery stools.

"On admission she was unconscious, restless, dehydrated, and collapsed. Her pulse rate was 122/min., of moderate volume and in sinus rhythm; blood-pressure was 95/70 mm. Hg, and respiratory rate was 18 per minute. Apart from these findings, nothing abnormal was noted. She had no cyanosis or dyspnea. Her white-cell count was 8,800/c.mm., with a differential count of polymorphs 76 per cent, lymphocytes 21 per cent, eosinophils 3 per cent. Her blood urea was 37 mg/100 ml; serum potassium 3.7 mEq/liter; serum sodium 142 mEq/liter. She did not pass any urine on the day of admission. On the day of admission she was treated with a slow intravenous drip-infusion of 3 pints normal saline and 1 pint 5 per cent dextrose with added vitamins.

"Her condition improved on this regimen. Blood-pressure rose to 100/70 mm. Hg, and the pulse rate fell to 110/min. The following morning she collapsed again, the blood-pressure could not be recorded, and the pulse was imperceptible. Hydrocortisone hemisuccinate, methoxamine, and noradrenaline were then added to the drip.

"Two days after admission, the day after her collapse in the ward, her general condition improved, blood-pressure was 90/70 mm. Hg, pulse rate 104/min., of moderate volume, and in sinus rhythm. No other abnormalities were detected.

"Five days after admission the patient was found to have a subconjunctival hemorrhage in her left eye. Her menstrual period, which was ending the day she ate the tubers, continued for a further 20 days. A platelet count carried out at this state was 475,000/c.mm.; white-cell count was 5,000/c.mm., with polymorphs 50 per cent, lymphocytes 49 per cent, eosinophils 1 per cent, and packed cell volume 35 per cent. Hemoglobin was 11.3 g./100 ml., and mean corpuscular hemoglobin concentration 30 mg./100 ml.

"Twelve days after admission marked alopecia was noticed, especially affecting the scalp hair, and within 2 days most of the hair on her scalp had dropped out, as had her axillary hair and part of the pubic hair. She was seen in the clinic subsequently, and within a week after her discharge from hospital, 23 days after admission, she was completely bald. Two months later her scalp hair had regrown to half an inch (12.7 mm.). Pubic hair showed re-

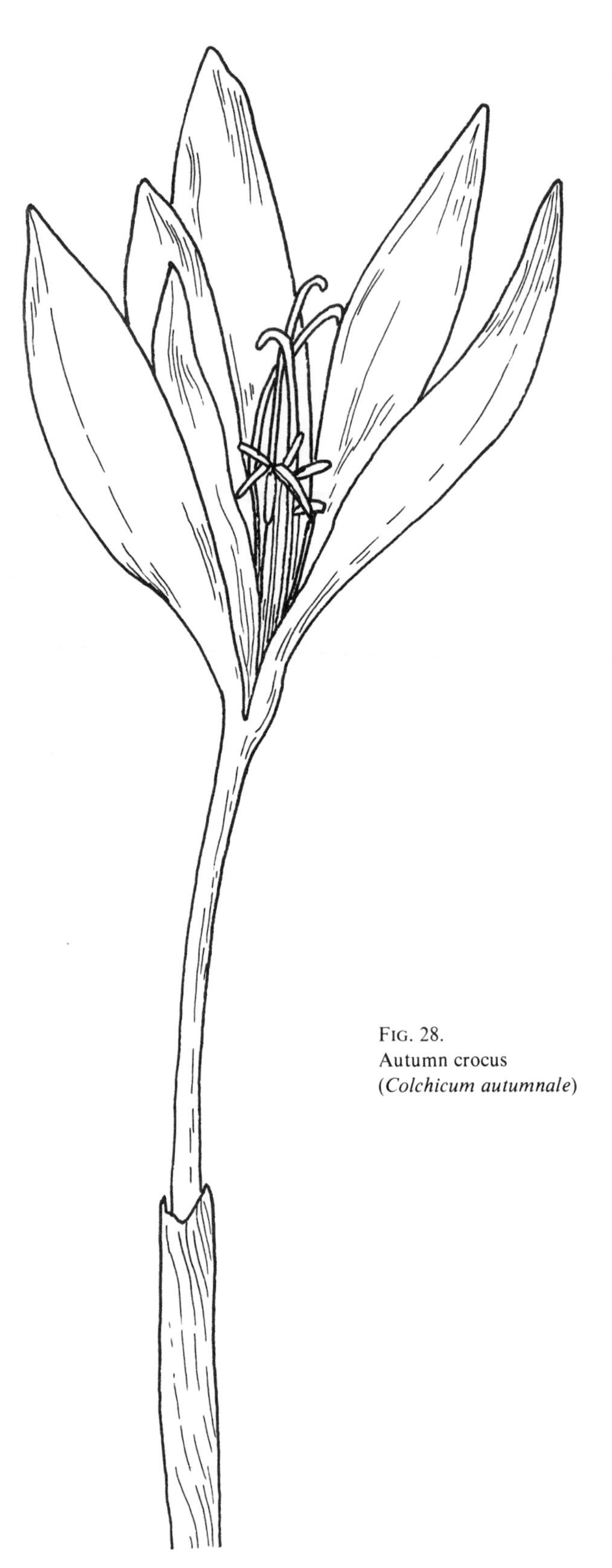

FIG. 28.
Autumn crocus
(*Colchicum autumnale*)

FIG. 29.
Glory lily
(*Gloriosa superba*)

growth. Her axillary hair remained very scanty. After 5 months her scalp hair was 2 to 3 in. (5.1 to 7.6 cm.) long" (27).

Prognosis

Since colchicine is very slowly excreted, the intoxication will have a prolonged course. The lethal dose varies considerably. Death is due to respiratory paralysis or circulatory collapse associated with fluid loss. Death sometimes occurs during a relapse after a symptom-free period.

Treatment

Gastric lavage should be instituted. It is imperative that the fluid and electrolyte balance be maintained in order to prevent the development of secondary shock. If necessary, meperedine (50 to 100 mg IM) alone or combined with atropine should be given to relieve the severe abdominal pain. Preparations should be made to assist the respiration in the event that muscular paralysis develops.

Botanical Descriptions

Colchicum spp. These plants are cultivated for their long tubed purple or white flowers which appear in the autumn. They are rarely escaped. Figure 28 is of the autumn crocus (*C. autumnale*), which illustrates the general characteristics of the other species. Family: Liliaceae.

Gloriosa superba (figure 29). Glory lily. This is a climbing lily with tuberous roots and lanced-shaped leaves prolonged into tendrils. The flower is yellow changing to red, about 3 inches long. Family: Liliaceae.

Gloriosa rothschildiana. This is similar to the *G. superba.* The flowers are crimson and yellow, whitish at the base, to 3 inches long. Family: Liliaceae.

REFERENCES

1. Alexander, R. F., Forbes, G. B. and Hawkins, E. S. A Fatal Case of Solanine Poisoning. Brit. Med. J. ii, 518 (1948).
2. Allen, P. H. Poisonous and Injurious Plants of Panama. Am. J. Trop. Med. Hyg. *23*, Suppl. 1 (1943).
3. Amyot, T. E. Poisoning by Snowberries. Brit. Med. J. *1:* 986 (1885).
4. Anon. Toxicity Studies of Arizona Ornamental Plants. Ariz. Med. 512 (1958).
5. Anon. Toxicity of Jequirity Beans. J. Am. Med. Assoc. *157:* 779 (1955).
6. Arnold, H. L. *Poisonous Plants of Hawaii.* Tongg Pub. Co., Hawaii, 1944.
7. Bacon, A. E. An Experiment with the Fruit of Red Baneberry. Rhodora *5:* 77 (1903).
8. Balthrop, E., Gallagher, W. B., McDonald, T. F. and Camariotes, S. Tung Nut Poisoning. J. Fla. Med. Assoc. *40:* 813 (1954).
9. Balucani, M. and Zellers, D. D. Podophyllum Resin Poisoning with Complete Recovery. J. Am. Med. Assoc. *189:* 639 (1964).
10. Bandelin, F. J. and Malesh, W. Alkaloids of *Cheledonium majus* L., Leaves and Stems. I. dl-Tetrahydrocaptisine. J. Am. Pharm. Assoc. Sci. Ed. *45:* 702 (1956).
11. Barnes, B. A. and Fox, L. E. Poisoning with Dieffenbachia. J. Hist. Med. Allied Sci. *10:* 173 (1955).
12. Baxter, J. N., Lythgoe, B., Scales, B., Trippett, S. and Blount, B. K. Taxine—I, The Major Alkaloid of the Yew, *Taxus baccata* L. Proc. Chem. Soc. (London) 9 (1958).
13. Black, O. F. Calcium Oxalate in the Dasheen. Am. J. Bot. *9:* 448 (1918).

14. Blohm, H. *Poisonous Plants of Venezuela*. Harvard Univ. Press, Cambridge, Mass., 1962. *Jatropha*, Pp. 53–7, *Pachyrhizus*, Pp. 40–1, *Pedilanthus*, P. 60, *Sapindus*, Pp. 67–8, *Hura*, Pp. 51–2.
15. Bose, B. C., Sepaha, G. C., Vijayvargiya, R. and Saifi, A. Q. Observations on the Pharmacological Actions of *Jatropha curcas*. Arch. Int. Pharmacodyn. *130:* 28 (1961).
16. Brugsch, H. *Vergiftungen im Kindesalter*. Ferdinand Enke, Stuttgart, 1956. *Chelidonium* p. 158, *Ilex* p. 174, *Ligustrum* Pp. 176–7, *Lonicera* p. 177.
17. Clark, A. N. G. and Parsonage, M. J. A Case of Podophyllum Poisoning with Involvement of the Nervous System. Brit. Med. J. *2:* 1155 (1957).
18. Dudley, W. H. Fatal Podophyllin Poisoning. Med. Rec. *37:* 409 (1890).
19. Emery, A. T. Report of Thirty-two Cases of Poisoning by Locust Bark. N. Y. Med. J. *45:* 92 (1887).
20. Ferguson, H. C. and Edwards, L. D. A Pharmacological Study of a Crystalline Glycoside of *Caulophyllum thalictroides*. J. Am. Pharm. Assoc. *43:* 16 (1954).
21. Forsyth, A. A. *British Poisonous Plants*, Bull. 161, Ministry of Agriculture, Fisheries and Food, London, 1954.
22. French, C. Pokeroot Poisoning. N. Y. Med. J. *72:* 653 (1900).
23. Frohne, D. and Pribilla, O. Tödliche Vergiftung mit *Taxus baccata*. Arch. Toxikol. *21:* 150 (1965).
24. Fruthaler, G. J. Solanine Poisoning. Ochsner Clin. Rep. *1:* 50 (1955).
25. Fyles, F. *Principal Poisonous Plants of Canada*. Canada Dept. Agr., Exp. Farms. Bull. 39 (2nd Series), 1920.
26. Gessner, O. *Die Gift- und Arzneipflanzen von mitteleuropa*. Carl Winter, Heidelberg, 1953. *Aesculus*, p. 253, *Arum*, p. 646, *Daphne*, p. 548, *Gloriosa*, p. 567, *Ilex*, p. 642, *Lonicera*, p. 636, Protoanemonin group, p. 531, *Robina*, p. 579, *Taxus*, p. 135, *Wisteria*, p. 318.
27. Gooneratne, B. W. M. Massive Generalized Alopecia after Poisoning by *Gloriosa superba*. Brit. Med. J. *1:* 1023 (1966).
28. Graf, E. Taxus Alkaloids IV. Taxin B, the Chief Constituent of *Taxus baccata* L. Arch. der Pharm. *291:* 443 (1958). C.A. *53*, 4335c (1959).
29. Gress, E. M. Poisonous Plants of Pennsylvania. Bull. Penn. Dept. Agr. *18*, No. 5 (1935); Reprinted 1953, Gen. Bull. 531.
30. Guthrie, A. Poisoning by Poke Root. J. Am. Med. Assoc. *9:* 125 (1887).
31. Hansen, A. A. Two Fatal Cases of Potato Poisoning. Science *61:* 340 (1925).
32. Hanzlik, P. J. The Effects of Chelidonin on Smooth Muscle. J. Pharm. & Expt. Therap. *7:* 99 (1915).
33. Hanzlik, P. J. The Pharmacology of Chelidonin. A Neglected Alkaloid of *Chelidonium*, or Tetterwort. J. Am. Med. Assoc. *75:* 1324 (1920).
34. Harris, S., managing ed. *Dictionary of Organic Compounds*. Oxford Univ. Press, N.Y., 1965. Pp. 2904–5.
35. Hart, M. Hazards to Health. Jequirity-Bean Poisoning. New Eng. J. Med. *268:* 885 (1963).
36. Hartwell, J. L. and Schrecker, A. W. The Chemistry of Podophyllum. Fortsch. Chem. Org. Natur. *15:* 83 (1958).
37. Hegnauer, R. The Distribution of Hydrocyanic Acid in Cormophytes II. Cyanogenesis in Taxus. Pharm. Weekblad. *94:* 241 (1959). C. A. *53*, 15229c (1959).
38. Ho, R. K. B. Acute Poisoning from the Ingestion of Seeds of *Jatropha curcas*, Report of Five Cases. Hawaii Med. J. *19:* 421 (1960).
39. Huang, C. L. Pharmacological Studies on Tung Toxins. Proc. 33rd. Ann. Tung. Ind. Conv., Biloxi, Miss., 1966. Pp. 18–19, 29–30.
40. Jacobziner, H. Briefs on Accidental Chemical Poisonings in New York City. N.Y. State J. Med. *61:* 2463 (1961).
41. Jacobziner, H. and Raybin, H. W. Rhubarb Poisoning. N.Y. State. J. Med. *62:* 1676 (1962).
42. Jacobziner, H. Accidental Chemical Poisonings (Jack-in-the-Pulpit). N.Y. State J. Med. *62:* 3130 (1962).
43. Kapadia, G. J. and Khorana, M. L. Studies on Active Constituents of *Cassia fistula* Pulp. I. Colorimetric Estimation of Free Rhein and Combined Sennidin-like Compounds. Lloydia *25:* 55 (1962).
44. . . . II. The Combined 1,8-Dihydroxyanthraquinone Derivatives. Lloydia *25:* 59 (1962).
45. Kaszas, T. and Papp, G. Ricinussamen-Vergiftung von Schulkindern. Arch. Toxikol. *18:* 145 (1960).

46. Kingsbury, J. M. *Poisonous Plants of the United States and Canada.* Prentice-Hall, Englewood Cliffs, N. J., 1964. *Aesculus*, p. 218, *Agrostemma*, Pp. 245–6, *Colchicine*, p. 450, *Daphne*, p. 386, *Physalis*, p. 287, Protoanemonin, p. 141, *Saponaria*, p. 250, *Taxus*, p. 121.
47. Layton, L. L., DeEds, F. and Moss, L. Fractionation of the Allergenic Proteins of Castor Seed. Fed. Proc. *19*, Suppl. 4–6: 195 (1960).
48. Leonard, B. E. and Sherratt, H. S. A. Pharmacology of the Alkaloidal Fraction from the bark of the Jamaican Shade Tree *Pithecolobium samath* Benth. Nature *191:* 287 (1961).
49. Lindenbaum, S. E. Case Report: Pollinosis Due to *Ricinus communis* or Castor Bean Plant. Ann. Allergy *24:* 23 (1966).
50. Manno, J. E., Fochtman, R. W., Winek, C. L. and Shanor, S. P. Toxicity of Plants of the Genus *Dieffenbachia.* Tox. Appl. Pharmacol. *10:* 55 (1967).
51. Martin, F. N. Jr. Poisonous Cultivated Plants. Bull. Tulane Med. Fac. *12:* 159 (1953).
52. Moore, B. The Chemical and Pharmacological Properties of Hederin, A Sapo-Glucoside Contained in the Leaves of Common Ivy (*Hedera helix*). J. Pharm. Exp. Therap. *4:* 263 (1913).
53. Morton, J. F. Ornamental Plants with Poisonous Properties. Proc. Fla. State Hort. Soc. *71:* 372 (1958).
54. Muenscher, W. C. *Poisonous Plants of the United States.* Macmillan, N.Y., 1964. P. 190.
55. Oakes, A. J. and Butcher, J. O. Poisonous and Injurious Plants of the U.S. Virgin Islands. Agr. Res. Serv., U.S. Dept. Agr., Misc. Publ. No. 882 (1962). Pp. 80–2.
56. Pohl, R. W. Poisoning by *Dieffenbachia.* J. Am. Med. Assoc. *117:* 812 (1961).
57. Poulsson, E. Untersuchungen-uber *Caltha palustris.* Arch. Exp. Path. Pharmakol. *80:* 173 (1916).
58. Randall, J. A. Twenty-two Cases of Poisoning by the Seed of *Jatropha curcas.* U.S. Naval Med. Bull. *8:* 290 (1914).
59. Saragea, M., Vladutiu, A., Negur, T. and Rotaru, N. Antibodies to *Ricinus communis* (Castor Bean) in a Rural Community. Ann. Allergy *24:* 179 (1966).
60. Schweitzer, H. Tödliche Saponinvergiftung durch Genuss von Rosskastanien. Med. Klin. *47:* 683 (1952).
61. Slinger, W. N. Ineffectiveness and Toxicity of Podophyllin in Treatment of Tinea Capitis. J. Am. Med. Assoc. *149:* 261 (1952).
62. Sollman, T. *A Manual of Pharmacology.* 8th ed. W. B. Saunders, Philadelphia, 1957. Pp. 667–9.
63. Standley, P. C. Flora of the Lancetilla Valley Honduras. Field Mus. Nat. Hist., Bot. Series 10. Publ. 283 (1931).
64. Streicher, E. Akutes Nierenversagen und Ikterus nach einer Vergiftung mit Rhabarberblättern. Dtsch. med. Wschr. *89:* 2379 (1964).
65. Tyler, V. E. Jr. Note on the Occurrence of Taxine in *Taxus brevifolia.* J. Am. Pharm. Assoc., Sci. ed. *49:* 683 (1960).
66. Verhulst, H. L. Wisteria. National Clearinghouse Poison Control Centers. July–August 1961.
67. von Oettingen, W. F. *Poisoning*, Sec. ed. Philadelphia, Saunders, 1958 *Daphne*, p. 322, *Podophyllum*, p. 505, *Solanum*, Pp. 539–40.
68. Ward, J. W., Clifford, W. S., Monaco, A. R. Fatal Systemic Poisoning Following Podophyllin Treatment of Condyloma Acuminatum. Southern Med. J. *47:* 1204 (1954).
69. Watt, J. M., Heimann, H. L., and Epstein, E. Solanocapsine—A New Alkaloid with a Cardiac Action. Quart. J. Pharm. Pharmacol. *5:* 649 (1932).
70. Wiesner, K. and Orr, D. E. The Structure of Pithecolobium. Tetrahedron Letters No. 16, 11 (1960).
71. Wildman, W. C. Alkaloids of the Amaryllidaceae in Manske, R. H. F. *The Alkaloids*, VI. Academic Press, New York, 1960. Pp. 295–312.
72. Wilson, G. S. A Small Outbreak of Solanine Poisoning. Monthly Bull. Ministry Health *18:* 207 (1959).
73. Wilson, T. The Common Daffodil (*Narcissus pseudo-narcissus*) as a Poison. Pharmaceutical J. (London) *112:* 141 (1924).
74. Woodbury, D. in Goodman, L. S. and Gilman, A. *The Pharmacological Basis of Therapeutics.* Third ed. Macmillan, New York, 1965. Pp. 339–341.

III PLANTS PRODUCING CARDIOVASCULAR DISTURBANCES

The plants in this chapter primarily affect conduction, rhythm or vasodepressor reflexes in the heart:

A. Digitalis Group
B. Aconitine Group
C. Veratrum Group
D. Veratrine and Andromedotoxin Group

The effects of poisoning from members of either the digitalis or veratrum group are essentially those of overdosage of these drugs as may be seen in clinical practice. Aconitine produces cardiac rhythm disturbances. The distinguishing feature of its intoxication is a tingling and formication which begins in the extremities and progresses to generalized paresthesias becoming most intense in the face. Veratrine and andromedotoxin exhibit effects mimicking both the paresthesias of aconitine and the bradycardia and extreme hypotension of veratrum.

Plants of the atropine and nicotine class also affect blood pressure and heart rate. These plants are each covered in a separate chapter.

Taxine intoxications with systemic involvement likewise exhibit cardiac conduction and rate disturbances. *Taxus* poisoning is discussed in Chapter II.

It should be remembered that intoxications from *any* plant which produces persistent emesis or diarrhea may exhibit hypotension, tachycardia and cardiac arrhythmias secondary to dehydration and electrolyte imbalance.

A. DIGITALIS GROUP

Toxicology

The plants in this group contain various cardiac glycosides related to digitalis which, from a toxicological point of view, do not exhibit differences in their overall action. Although quite a number of plant species contain cardioactive substances, only a few have been associated with human intoxications.* For the most part children have been affected from eating berries from these plants, chewing on the flowers or from drinking water from vases which have contained these flowers (10, 13).

* Other plants which must be categorized as potentially toxic in this group are the *Adenium* spp (Desert rose), *Asclepias currassavica* (Blood-flower), *Calotropis procera* (French jasmine, Crown flower), *Cryptostegia grandiflora* (Purple allamanda, India rubber vine), *Scilla* spp. (Squill), and *Urechites lutea* (Yellow nightshade).

Members of the Group

Convallaria majalis	Lily-of-the-valley
Digitalis purpurea	Foxglove
Nerium indicum	Sweet-scented oleander
Nerium oleander	Oleander
Thevetia peruviana (*T. nereifolia*)	Yellow oleander, Milk bush

Symptoms

After chewing or ingesting parts of the plant, there is local irritation to the mucous membranes of the mouth and stomach followed by emesis. Unlike the pure cardiac glycosides, diarrhea, persistent headache, and abdominal pain are common in plant poisoning because of the presence of saponins and other irritating substances. Otherwise the intoxication is similar to that which occurs after overdosage in digitalis therapy. Severe cardiac signs will be delayed in proportion to the latent period of the particular glycosides involved and to the quantity of glycosides absorbed through the intestine.

Prognosis

The prognosis will depend upon the promptness of recognition of a cardiac glycoside as the etiologic agent and on the presence of preexisting conduction or rhythm defects. It should be recalled that the cardiac actions of some glycosides may persist for 2 to 3 weeks.

Treatment

The desirability of instituting active therapy will depend upon an electrocardiograph analysis. If there is evidence of sufficient increase in ventricular irritability, such as frequent premature ventricular contractions, bigeminy or paroxysmal ventricular tachycardia, the patient may be given 5 to 10 g of potassium chloride orally or 80 mEq potassium per liter in 5 per cent dextrose and water intravenously as a slow infusion until improvement. A favorable response will usually occur within 40 minutes and last from 3 to 8 hours.

Severe ventricular involvement, or frequent multifocal contractions, long and frequent runs of ventricular tachycardia, or the appearance of paroxysmal ventricular fibrillation, may require therapy with disodium edetate (Endrate), dipotassium edetate (4), or trisodium edetate (sodium versenate). Surawicz (24) found that the average dose of disodium edetate required to be about 2.8 (0.5 to 4.0) g. It was infused as a 10 per cent solution in physiologic saline. The average period of the infusion was 17 (8 to 40) minutes, and in most instances was given at a rate of 0.2 g per minute. With trisodium edetate, Eliot (8) recommends that, in adults, a minimum of 3.0 g as a 16 per cent solution in 5 per cent dextrose and water should be given within 12 minutes, if possible, before a result is considered to be negative. Arm pain, circumoral paresthesia, and apprehension occurred in 40 per cent of his patients. The arm pain was readily relieved by massage and warm packs. The other symptoms could be relieved by slowing the rate of the infusion. Continuous EKG monitoring and care to avoid tetany must be exercised with a calcium chelating agent. After conversion, oral potassium chloride should be instituted to maintain the sinus rhythm. The edetates are unreliable, if effective at all, in the treatment of supraventricular arrhythmias produced by digitalis (7).

Digitalis glycosides may also produce a variety of conduction defects. If in complete heart block the idioventricular rhythm is inadequate to support life, isoproterenol may be administered. Animal experiments by Becker (2), however, suggest this approach be employed only as a last resort.

Botanical Descriptions

Convallaria majalis (figure 30). Lily-of-the-valley. This small perennial is grown around many homes in the north central and northeastern parts of the country. It has 2 oblong-oval leaves and a nodding flower stalk bearing several small bell-shaped, white fragrant flowers on one side. The lily-of-the-valley only rarely fruits. The berries are orange-red and fleshy. Family: Liliaceae.

Digitalis purpurea (figure 31). Foxglove, digitalis. The foxglove is cultivated in gardens and is frequently found wild in the north central and northeastern United States, along the Pacific coast and in Hawaii. It is an erect, biennial herb about 4 feet in height. The flowers develop the second year of growth on a short leafed central stalk. They are numerous, varying in color according to the variety from a whitish-lavender to purple. The interior of the tubular shaped flower may be spotted. The fruits are dry capsules containing many small seeds. Family: Scrophulariaceae.

Nerium indicum. Sweet-scented oleander. This plant is similar to the common oleander. Its height rarely exceeds 8 feet. The flowers are rose-pink to white, often double, fragrant and about 2 inches across. It is cultivated in Florida, Texas and California. Family: Apocynaceae.

Nerium oleander (figure 32). Oleander, 'Oliwa (Hawaii). The oleander is a full evergreen shrub which may grow to a height of 20 feet. The narrow leaves have a leathery texture and are about 8 inches long. The flowers form in terminal clusters at the end of the branches. They are about 3 inches across and may be white, yellowish to red or purple. The plant is cultivated in Florida, Texas, California and Hawaii, and is popular as a tub plant elsewhere. Family: Apocynaceae.

Thevetia peruviana (*T. nerifolia*) (figure 33). Yellow oleander, milk bush, Noho-Malie (Hawaii). This plant is most frequently seen as a shrub of between 7 to 17 feet but it may grow as a tree to 30 feet. The leaves are 6 inches long and 1/4 inch wide. The fragrant yellow flowers are funnel-formed growing in clusters at the ends of the branches. Yellow oleander forms an angular, plum-shaped, greenish-red fruit turning black at maturity. It is cultivated in Florida, southern California and Hawaii. Family: Apocynaceae.

FIG. 30.
Lily-of-the-valley
(*Convallaria majalis*)

Fig. 31.
Foxglove
(*Digitalis purpurea*)

Fig. 32.
Oleander
(*Nerium oleander*)

FIG. 33.
Yellow oleander
(*Thevetia peruviana*)

B. ACONITINE GROUP

Toxicology

Most of the aconitine-containing species are highly toxic. Parts of these plants have been used in folk medicine and intoxications have resulted from ingestion of the leaves (for parsley) and roots (for horseradish or celery). Poisoning is said to have been produced by absorption through the skin after prolonged contact with the leaves (3). The lethal dose of the pure aconitine alkaloid is estimated to be about 5 mg for an adult. Fatalities have occurred after ingestion of 2 to 4 grams of the root. Absorption is rapid after ingestion or on contact with mucous membranes. Death is produced by ventricular fibrillation or, more rarely, respiratory failure. The most distinguishing diagnostic feature of aconitine poisoning is skin paresthesias.

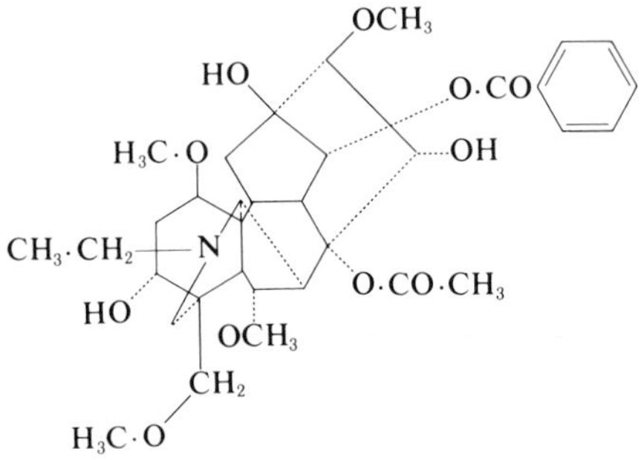

Aconitine

Members of the Group

Aconitum columbianum	Western monkshood
Aconitum napellus	Monkshood, Wolfbane, Aconite
Delphinium spp	Larkspur, Delphinium

Symptoms

Following ingestion there is a tingling and burning sensation of the lips, tongue and mouth followed by numbness. A similar effect is produced in the throat which develops into a feeling of constriction, accompanied by dysphagia and speech difficulty. Salivation, nausea and emesis usually occur during this phase of intoxication.

Distinctive symptoms of tingling and formication appear in the extremities, usually beginning in the fingers, which progress to generalized paresthesias, becoming most intense in the face (trigeminal nerve) and finally numbness. Associated with this is a transient feeling of warmth. Sweating may occur, however later the patient's skin becomes cold and clammy. There is a feeling of severe oppression in the chest.

The patient is apprehensive, restless, irritable, confused and suffers from intense headache. There is a blurring of vision and diplopia. The respiration becomes labored and pulmonary edema may develop. Miosis is present until the patient becomes asphyxial.

Muscular weakness is distinguished by general lethargy, vertigo and incoordination, progressive dyspnea and hyporeflexia. Muscular fasciculations and tonic or clonic convulsions are common. Ten to twenty per cent of a fatal dose of aconitine produces vagal slowing. Higher concentrations produce arrythmias of varying nature, primarily supraventricular tachycardia and conduction disturbances (9, 22, 23).

Prognosis

Poisoning from aconitine containing plants should be considered a medical emergency. Death usually occurs within 1 to 6 hours. Occasional fatalities have been reported a few minutes after ingestion as well as after a course of 4 days. Even after successful management the patient may exhibit exhaustion and sensory disturbances for a prolonged period.

Treatment

Since the progression of poisoning is rapid, it is necessary to evacuate the stomach contents as quickly as possible. Potassium permanganate (1:10,000) has been suggested as a procedure to inactivate aconitine which has entered the gastroenteric tract (11).

Atropine may be employed to abolish bradycardia due to vagal stimulation. The restoration of normal sinus rate may reduce the incidence of cardiac arrythmias. The arrythmias are relatively refractory to drug management. Numerous studies have been made in animals and isolated hearts employing various agents: quinidine (12), dichloroisoproterenol (15), digitalis (15), parasympathetic agents (15), and inorganic ions (15, 18). The combination of calcium and magnesium salts appears the most promising. In animals the intravenous administration of 10 ml/kg of a 3 per cent solution of calcium chloride followed by 3 ml/kg of a 12 per cent solution of magnesium sulfate was the most successful regimen (18). Success was reported in one case in which the patient exhibited paroxysmal supraventricular tachycardia with multiple multifocal ventricular extrasystoles by giving 40 ml of 10 per cent calcium gluconate followed by 5 ml 15 per cent magnesium sulfate intravenously (1).

Another case with ventricular fibrillation responded to intravenous administration of 0.1 per cent procaine (17). On the basis of the experimental work of Heistracher and Pillat (12) less consistent success should be anticipated with this therapy.

The respiratory failure seen in aconitine poisoning is probably secondary to circulatory failure associated with the cardiac arrythmias. Nevertheless one should be prepared to assist respiration as required. The employment of analeptics, though frequently recommended in the literature, is undoubtedly hazardous since aconitine itself may induce convulsions.

The patient should be kept warm and given other appropriate nursing care. There is no specific therapy indicated for the sensory disturbances.

Botanical Descriptions

Aconitum columbianum (figure 34). Western monkshood. This plant resembles the delphinium in foliage. It is a perennial about 3 feet in height. The flowers are blue or rarely white. This species is found from British Columbia to California and New Mexico. Family: Ranunculaceae.

Aconitum napellus (figure 35). Monkshood, Aconite, Wolfbane*, Helmet-flower, Friar's cap, Soldier's cap. The foliage of this plant resembles that of the delphinium. The characteristic helmet-shaped flower grows in a raceme at the top of the stalk. They are most commonly blue but many varieties exist in which the flowers are white, blue and white, pink and flesh colored. The dry seed pods contain many tiny seeds. This and other species of *Aconitum*, are in cultivation throughout all but the most southern parts of the United States. Family: Ranunculaceae.

Delphinium spp (figure 36). Larkspur, Delphinium. There are approximately 300 or more species of these popular garden flowers grown in the temperate zones. The flowers are mostly blue but may vary in garden varieties from white, pink or red. There is one cultivated species which has a yellow flower. The foliage is distinctive, the leaves being described as crow-foot shaped. The illustration is of *D. ajacis*, the rocket larkspur. Family: Ranunculaceae.

C. VERATRUM GROUP

Toxicology

Intoxications from the ingestion of the veratrum containing plants may produce alarming symptoms but are rarely serious. Aspects of poisoning by the plant sources do not differ in detail from the side effects seen with the therapeutic usage of the purified veratrum alkaloids. In the adult, intoxications may be confused with angina pectoris or acute coronary occlusion.

Members of the Group

Veratrum californicum	False hellebore, Corn-lily
Veratrum viride	Green hellebore, American white hellebore

Symptoms

Epigastric and substernal burning occur shortly after ingestion and are soon followed by salivation, nausea, and emesis. There may be sweating and flushing, blurring of vision, and confusion. Severe bradycardia and hypotension develop with occasional episodes of arrhythmias. High doses can produce transient respiratory depression and bronchiolar constriction.

* Correctly, the name Wolfsbane (or Wolfbane) applies to the species *Aconitum lycoctonum* which was transplanted to the United States from Europe. It is a much larger plant, growing to 6 feet, with yellow or cream colored flowers.

FIG. 34.
Western monkshood
(*Aconitum columbianum*)

FIG. 35.
Monkshood
(*Aconitum napellus*)

FIG. 36.
Larkspur
(*Delphinium ajacis*)

Case History

A case report of a mass poisoning in Korea from the ingestion of a soup containing *Veratrum nigrum* var. *japonicum* is given by Nelson (20). Although this variety is not found in the United States it exhibits the typical features of veratrum intoxication.

The soup was eaten at 12:00 by 14 men. At 1:00 p.m. 3 of these men began to vomit profusely, and 2 hours later they complained of seeing circles, yellow sheets of flame, and yellow and green spots before the eyes. At 3:00 p.m. 6 more men became ill. In addition to severe vomiting, prostration, weakness, and the visual disturbance described above, they complained of being unable to move the eye from a position of forward gaze. Over the next 7 hours the remaining 5 men reported similar symptoms.

Without exception, all the patients appeared extremely ill and had paroxysms of vomiting. The pulse rates were below 40 per minute; the most severely ill patient had a pulse of 4 to 5 per minute. All had injected conjunctivas, distended abdomens and difficulty in opening the eyes widely. No extraocular paralyses were noted. The average blood pressure was 80/60 mm; the highest before treatment being 105/60 and the lowest, 50/0 mm.

The patients were treated by infusion of isotonic sodium chloride solution and intravenous or subcutaneous epinephrine. Recoveries were essentially complete within 15 hours.

Prognosis

Poisonings from the veratrum containing plants is rarely fatal because of the rapid emesis and poor intestinal absorption of the alkaloids.

Treatment

The severe hypotension, bradycardia, and cardiac arrhythmias usually respond to the administration of atropine and positioning of the patient to facilitate venous return. Vasoconstrictors may be employed if the blood pressure response to the above measures is inadequate (21).

Botanical Descriptions

Veratrum californicum. False hellebore, Corn-lily. This is a stout perennial herb growing to 6 feet. The leaves are 20 inches long and 8 inches wide at the base of the plant, becoming narrower and smaller toward the top. Small white flowers marked with green grow in panicles along the top 18 inches of the stalk. This species is found along the Pacific coast from Washington to lower California. Family: Liliaceae.

Veratrum viride (figure 37). Green hellebore, American white hellebore. This hellebore is found in swampy areas in Canada, Alaska and as far south as North Carolina. It is similar to the previous species. The flowers are yellowish-green to greenish-white. The plant forms a small ovoid capsule about an inch in length containing large, flat-winged seeds. Family: Liliaceae.

FIG. 37.
American white hellebore
(*Veratrum viride*)

D. VERATRINE AND ANDROMEDOTOXIN CONTAINING PLANTS

Toxicology

The pharmacological properties of plants containing veratrine or andromedotoxin (19, 26) resembles, in some respects (14), that of the aconitine group, and, to a lesser extent, that of veratrum alkaloids. Fatal human poisoning has been recorded only for *Kalmia latifolia* (mountain laurel) and from the ingestion of honey (6, 27) derived from the nectar of the andromedotoxin containing plants.

The chemistry of the veratrine alkaloids is discussed in Manske (16) and of andromedotoxin (acetylandromedol) by Tallent (25).

Members of the Group

Veratrine-Containing Plants

Zygadenus venenosus	Death camas

Andromedotoxin-Containing Plants

Kalmia angustifolia	Lambkill, Sheep laurel
Kalmia latifolia	Mountain laurel, Calico bush, Sheep kill
Leucothoë spp	
Lyonia spp	
Pernettya spp	
Pieris spp	
Rhododendron spp	

Symptoms

Signs of systemic intoxication are usually delayed, sometimes for as much as 6 hours after ingestion, although there may be an immediate burning sensation in the mouth and pharynx. The symptoms include anorexia, salivation and sometimes emesis and diarrhea. The patient usually becomes drowsy and experiences an aconitine-like prickling sensation in the skin, headache, muscular weakness and dimness of vision. The effect on the circulation is similar to that of veratrum, beginning with bradycardia followed by severe hypotension. In lethal poisoning coma usually precedes death. Occasionally there are terminal convulsions (10, 13, 23).

Case History

Cameron (5) presents 2 cases of Death camas poisoning which illustrates the important differences that may occur in poisoning of similar etiology. The first was a 2 year old boy who ate the flowers. He vomited shortly after ingestion, became drowsy and comatose. On admission he presented a picture of shock. The skin was cool and pale. There was a rectal temperature of 97.4 F., a pulse rate of 88 and a blood pressure of 84/0. Respiration was slow and irregular. He was semi-conscious and cried out on movement or painful stimulus. There was a moderate spasticity of the arms and legs and the tendon reflexes were hyperactive. The pupils were unequally dilated.

The second case involved a 2 ½ year old boy who ate some bulbs which had been roasted on a bonfire. Within an hour he began to stagger and vomited several times before becoming unconscious. The findings were similar (temperature 98.0 F., pulse 62, blood pressure 52/30) but the muscle tone was less than normal and the deep tendon, abdominal and cremaster reflexes were absent.

Both children were given supportative care with oxygen, external application of heat and nikethamide. With the exception of a mild diarrhea, recovery was complete in 24 hours.

Prognosis

There is insufficient recorded data to predict an accurate prognosis. In livestock, andromedotoxin is known to produce acute parenchymatous nephritis with some necrosis in the tubules and some degree of hepatic degeneration.

Treatment

The cardiovascular effects respond to sympathomimetic amines. The bradycardia is usually refractory to atropine. Despite the delay in symptomatology, gastric lavage is recommended if spontaneous emesis did not occur. Considering the experience with respiratory depressants in general, the use of analeptic agents does not appear warranted.

Botanical Descriptions

Zygadenus venenosus (figure 38). Death camas. All species of *Zygadenus* have a general resemblance but exhibit considerable variation in toxicity. They are perennial herbs with grass-like leaves up to 1 ½ feet in length. The flowers form along the top of a central stalk and are mostly yellowish or whitish-green. Most species have an onion-like bulb but none have the characteristic onion odor. Species of *Zygadenus* may be found throughout the entire United States and Canada. Family: Liliaceae.

Kalmia angustifolia. Lambkill, Sheep laurel. This evergreen shrub is about 3 feet in height. The elliptic leaves are about 2 ½ inches long. The purple or crimson flowers are about ½ inch across and form in clusters at the end of the branches, later replaced by small capsules. The plant is distributed extensively in hilly areas in the northeastern United States and Canada. Family: Ericaceae.

Kalmia latifolia. Moutain laurel, Calico bush, Sheep kill. This species differs from the previous one in that it may reach a height of 10 feet. The leaves are about 5 inches long. The flowers are rose colored, marked inside with purple and about 1 inch across. It is also found in northeastern United States and Canada. Family: Ericaceae.

FIG. 38.
Death camas
(*Zygadenus venenosus*)

The remaining plants in this group all belong to the family Ericaceae. Since they act only as indirect sources of poisoning through contaminated honey, their description will be limited to their geographical distribution. *Leucothoë* spp, entire North America; *Lyonia* spp, east and southeastern United States westward to Ohio and Texas; *Pernettya* spp, chiefly pot plant but hardy north; *Pieris* spp, Virginia, West Virginia and Georgia; *Rhododendron* spp, southeastern Canada to Florida, westward to Texas and Illinois.

REFERENCES

1. Begemann, S. W. Genezing van aconitine-vergiftiging door intraveneuze toediening van calcii gluconas en magnesii sulfas. Ned. T. Geneesk. *105:* 321 (1961).
2. Becker, D. J., Nonkin, P. M., Bennett, L. D., Kimball, S. G., Sternberg, M. S., and Wasserman, F. Effect of isoproterenol in digitalis cardiotoxicity. Am. J. Cardiol. *10:* 242 (1962).
3. Brugsch, H. *Vergiftungen im Kindesalter.* Ferdinand Enke, Stuttgart, 1956. Pp. 144–6.
4. Burton, L. E., Picchioni, A. L. and Chin, L. Dipotassium Edetate as an Antidote in Poisoning from Oleander and its chief Glycoside, oleandrin. Arch. Int. Pharmacodyn. *158:* 202 (1965).
5. Cameron, K. Death Camas Poisoning. Northwest Med. *51:* 682 (1952).
6. Carey, F. M., Lewis, J. J., MacGregor, J. L. and Martin-Smith, M. Pharmacological and Chemical Observations on Some Toxic Nectars. J. Pharm. Pharmacol. *11:* 269 (1959).
7. Cohen, B. M., Spritz, N., Lubash, G. P., and Rubin, A. L. Use of calcium chelating agent (NaEDTA) in cardiac arrhythmias. Circulation *19:* 918 (1959).
8. Eliot, R. S., and Blount, S. G. Calcium, chelates, and digitalis: A clinical study. Am. Heart J. *62:* 7 (1961).
9. Ffrench, G. Aconitine-Induced Cardiac Arrhythmia. Brit. Heart J. *20:* 140 (1958).
10. Gessner, O. *Die Gift- und Arzneipflanzen von Mitteleuropa.* Carl Winter, Heidelberg, 1953. *Andromedotoxin* Pp. 500–2; *Digitalis* Pp. 183–215.
11. Hatcher, R. A. The Antidotal Action of Potassium Permanganate. J. Am. Med. Assoc. *105:* 502 (1935).
12. Heistracher, P. and Pillat, B. Electrophysiologische Untersuchungen über die Wirkung von Chinidin auf die Aconitinvergiftung von Herzmuskelfasern. Arch. Exp. Path. Pharm. *244:* 48 (1962).
13. Kingsbury, J. M. *Poisonous Plants of the United States and Canada.* Prentice-Hall, Englewood Cliffs, N. J., 1964. *Nerium* Pp. 264–6; *Zygadenus* Pp. 461–6.
14. Krayer, O., Rogers, B. H., Kupchan, S. M. and Deliwala, C. V. Pharmacological and Chemical Relation Between the Veratrum Alkaloids and the Zygadenus Alkaloids. Fed. Proc. *11:* 364 (1952).
15. Lucchesi, B. R. The Action of Dichloroisoproterenol (DCI) and Several Other Pharmacological Agents upon the Aconitine-Induced Ventricular Arrhythmia in the Isolated Rabbit Heart. J. Pharm. Exp. Therap. *137:* 291 (1962).
16. Manske, R. H. F. and Holmes, H. L. *The Alkaloids,* III. Academic Press, N. Y., 1953. Pp. 272–4; Manske, R. H. F. *ibid.* VII, 1960. Pp. 366–372.
17. Merchant, H. D., Choksi, N. D., Ramamoorthy, K., Parihar, L. M. and Shikaripurkar, N. K. Aconite Poisoning and Cardiac Arrhythmias, Report of 3 Cases. Indian J. Med. Sci. *17:* 857 (1963).
18. Mladoveanu, C., Vasilco, O., and Gheorghu, P. Le Sulfate de Magnesium et le chlorure de Calcium dans les Intoxications Expérimentales avec de l'Aconitine. Arch. int. Pharmacodyn. *53:* 494 (1939).
19. Moran, N. C., Dresel, P. E., Perkins, M. E. and Richardson, A. P. The Pharmacological Actions of Andromedotoxin, An Active Principle from *Rhododendron maximum.* J. Pharm. Exp. Therap. *110:* 415 (1954).
20. Nelson, D. A. Accidental Poisoning by *Veratrum japonicum.* J. Am. Med. Assoc. *156:* 33 (1954).
21. Nickerson, M. Veratrum Alkaloids in Goodman, L. S. and Gilman, A. *The Pharmacological Basis of Therapeutics.* Macmillan, New York, 1965. Pp. 716–820.

22. von Oettingen, W. F. *Poisoning, A Guide to Clinical Diagnosis and Treatment*, 2nd ed. W. B. Saunders, Philadelphia, 1958. P. 215
23. Sollman, T. *A Manual of Pharmacology*, 8th ed. W. B. Saunders, Philadelphia, 1957. *Aconitine*. Pp. 673–6, *Veratrine* Pp. 680–3.
24. Surawicz, B., MacDonald, M. G., Kaljot, V., and Bettinger, J. C. Treatment of Cardiac Arrhythmias with Salts of Ethylenediamine Tetracetic Acid (EDTA). Am. Heart J. *58:* 493 (1959).
25. Tallent, W. H. The Stereochemistry of Acetylandromedol. J. Org. Chem. *27:* 2968 (1962).
26. Waud, R. A. The Action of *Kalmia angustifolia* (Lambkill). J. Pharm. Exp. Therap. *103:* 69 (1940).
27. White, J. W. Jr. and Riethof, M. L. The Composition of Honey. III. Detection of Acetyl-andromedol in Toxic Honeys. Arch. Biochem. Biophys. *79:* 165 (1959).

IV PLANTS HAVING A NICOTINE-LIKE ACTION

Nicotine exerts a complex variety of effects in the body. Those of primary toxicological importance are the actions on the central nervous system, the autonomic ganglia, the smooth muscle of the intestine, and the striated muscle. Small concentrations of nicotine produce stimulation of the autonomic ganglia, medulla, and intestine. There is increased salivation, nausea, emesis, diarrhea, a sensation of (but not actual) sweating, dizziness, and occasionally tachypnea. Higher levels produce ganglionic blockade, sensory disturbances, fibrillary twitching of the striated muscle and clonic convulsion.

The plants in this division contain either nicotine, cytisine, coniine, or lobeline as the principal toxic constituent. The pharmacological differences between these alkaloids are of little significance from a toxicological viewpoint (7). Plants containing these alkaloids are treated in the order of the frequency with which they produce intoxications.

Cytisine

$CH_2 \cdot CH_2 \cdot CH_3$

Coniine

Nicotine

$C_6H_5 \cdot CO \cdot CH_2$ — $CH_2 \cdot CH(OH) \cdot C_6H_5$ — $N \cdot CH_3$

Lobeline

A. CYTISINE GROUP

Toxicology

Plants in this group contain lupine alkaloids principally cytisine. Minor alkaloids such as N-methyl-cytisine, laburnine and anagyrine may be present but their total concentration is less than that of cytisine. The concentration of the alkaloids varies in different plant parts, the highest concentration of cytisine being found in the mature seeds.

Cytisine is rapidly absorbed through the mucous membranes of the mouth and the gastroenteric tract and is excreted rapidly and mainly through the kidneys.

Cytisine resembles nicotine in its pharmacologic effects (7). Nausea and emesis are constant findings; pallor, drowsiness, tachycardia and incoordination are frequently present.

A number of cytisine-containing species grow in the United States which have not been associated with human intoxications in this country. These include the wild indigo (*Baptisia* spp), the dyers-greenweed (*Genista tinctoria*) and members of the genus *Ulex*.

Cytisine intoxications are most frequently associated with *Laburnum*. The *Sophora* spp have a reputation as dangerously toxic to humans, but this cannot be verified with actual case reports (5, 8).

Members of the Group

Gymnocladus dioica	Kentucky coffee-tree
Laburnum anagyroides (*Cytisus laburnum*)	Golden chain, Laburnum
Sophora secundiflora	Mescal bean sophora
Sophora tomentosa	Necklace-pod sophora

Symptoms

The symptoms usually develop within 1 hour, in most cases within 15 minutes after ingestion. Irritation of the mucous membranes of the mouth and increased salivation occur, followed by nausea, violent, persistent, sometimes bloody emesis. Abdominal pain is usually minimal. Diarrhea is rarely present and is not typical of cytisine poisoning.

The patient suffers from vertigo, excessive thirst, and cold sweat. A high rise in body temperature has been observed. The pupils are dilated. Oliguria or anuria may occur.

Headache is common. The patient may become confused or delirious and experience hallucinations. With lower doses, fasciculation and clonic-tonic convulsions are exhibited. With massive doses, usually only paralysis and coma may appear. Reflex action mediated through the spinal cord, e.g., crossed extensor and knee-jerk, are much reduced or abolished in even mild intoxications.

The action of cytisine on the autonomic ganglia results in hypertension until ganglionic blockade is established. During the hypertensive phase tachycardia is present but the pulse later becomes slow and irregular.

Relatively small doses of cytisine consistently produce hyperpnea but the respiration later becomes progressively weaker and may develop into a Cheyne-Stokes type. Death is due to respiratory failure. Respiratory embarrassment is accelerated if convulsions occur.

Mitchell (6) presents the symptoms recorded in 10 mild, non-fatal cases of *Laburnum* poisoning in children. Most of the children had been playing with the pods, shelling the seeds as they had seen green peas shelled, and had eaten either the seeds only or at most 1 or 2 whole pods. The symptoms, given in the table, usually came on about half an hour after ingestion, the longest interval being about 4 hours.

Case no.	Age (yr.)	Vomiting	Diarrhea	Drowsiness	Weakness	Incoordi-nation	Pallor	Mydriasis	Tachycardia
1	4	+	−	+	+	+	+	−	−
2	4	+	−	+	+	+	+	−	+
3	3 3/4	+	−	−	+	−	+	−	+
4	7	+	−	−	−	−	+	+	+
5	10	+	−	+	+	+	−	+	+
6	8	+	−	−	−	−	−	−	+
7	4 1/2	+	−	−	−	−	+	+	−
8	3	+	−	+	−	−	+	−	−
9	5	+	−	+	−	−	−	−	+
10	4 3/4	+	−	+	+	+	+	+	+

Prognosis

Usually the stomach is emptied rapidly by the violent emesis produced by cytisine-containing plants. In these instances the mortality is rather low, about 2 per cent. If vomiting is delayed, the prognosis is grave. Heavy smokers exhibit considerable resistance to cytisine. Death can occur from 4 to 9 hours after ingestion but may be delayed for several days.

Treatment

After ingestion, if emesis was not spontaneous, it either should be induced or gastric lavage, preferably with a dilute (1:10,000) solution of potassium permanganate, should be instituted as quickly as possible. Since charcoal is an effective absorbent for cytisine, this should be administrated orally in water or milk.

Preparations should be made to assist respiration with oxygen and to manage convulsions. Hypotension may be controlled with phenylephrine (Neosynephrine) 2 to 4 mg I.V. or like drugs.

Laxatives or pilocarpine nitrate (5 mg oral) may be required for the post-crisis management of atony of the gastroenteric tract. Urinary retention, though less common, may require catheterization or parasympathomimetic drugs, e.g. prostigmine (Neostigmine).

Botanical Descriptions

Gymnocladus dioica (figure 39). Kentucky coffee-tree. This tree may grow to heights of 100 feet. The leaves are compound. Greenish-white flowers grow on long terminal stems. The distinctive flat bulging pods are 3 to 6 inches long and 1 to 2 inches wide. The thick, very hard, nearly black seeds vary from 1/4 to 1/2 inch in diameter. The tree is found from the extreme southern

FIG. 39.
Kentucky coffee-tree
(*Gymnocladus dioica*)

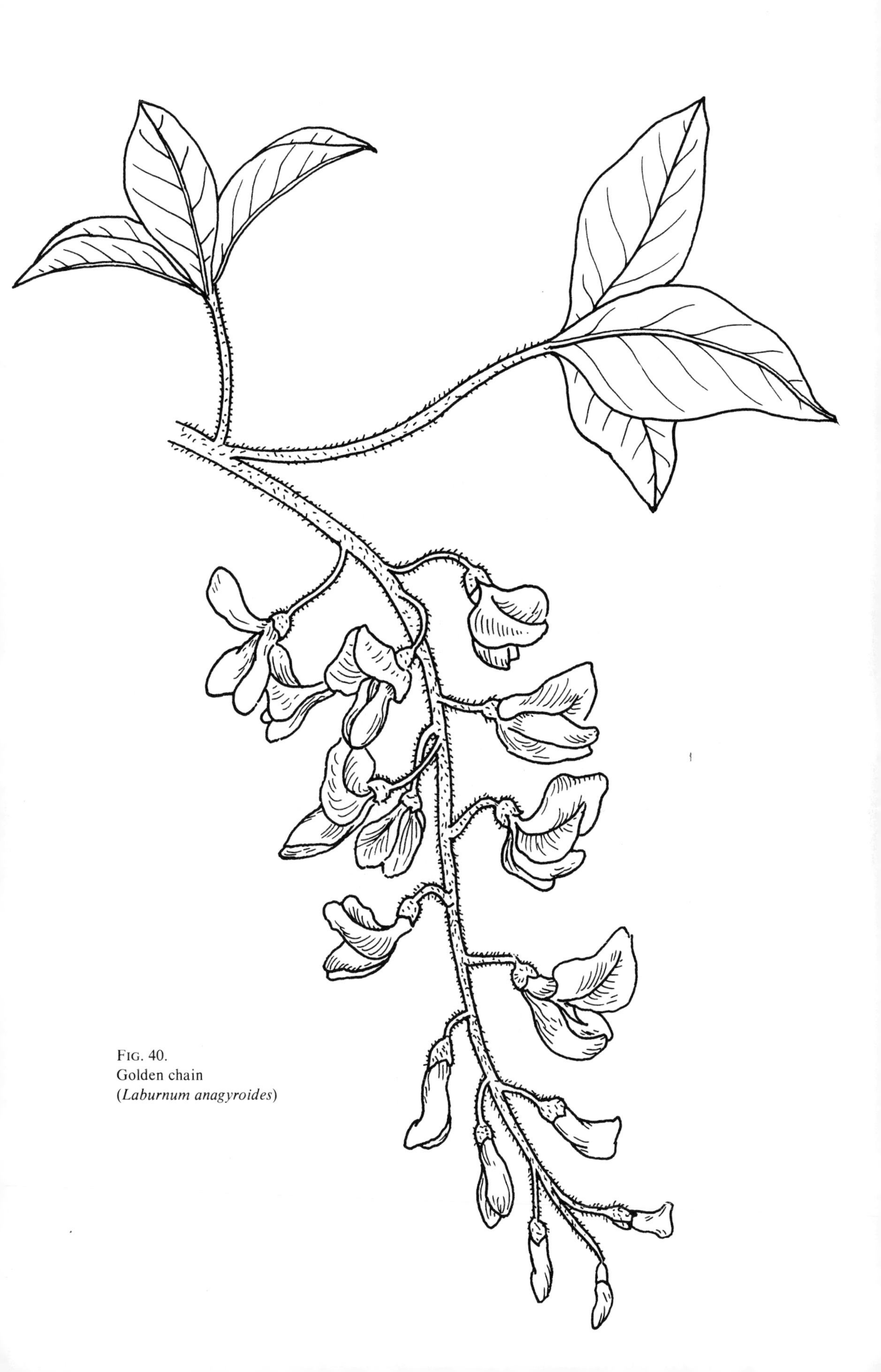

FIG. 40.
Golden chain
(*Laburnum anagyroides*)

FIG. 41.
Mescal bean sophora
(*Sophora secundiflora*)

edge of Ontario southward into New York and Virginia then west of the Appalachians through the midwestern states to eastern Nebraska. Family: Leguminosae.

Laburnum anagyroides (*Cytisus laburnum*) (figure 40). Golden chain, Laburnum, Bean tree. The golden chain is a small 30 foot tree which bears its golden yellow, sweet-pea shaped flowers in masses on terminal racemes. The seeds are contained in flattened, pea-shaped pods. The tree is widely cultivated in the southern states. Family: Leguminosae.

Sophora secundiflora (figure 41). Mescal bean sophora. This plant is seen as both a shrub and as a tree up to 35 feet. Compound leaves are about 4 to 6 inches in length, each having 5 to 15 leathery leaflets about 1 inch wide and 2 inches long. The bark of the tree is gray to black with shallow fissures and the twigs are velvety when young. The showy violet, fragrant flowers appear in clusters in March and April. The pod which forms in September is about 5 inches long, woody, and resembles a lumpy stringbean. It contains 3 to 4 hard red seeds. This plant is found only in western Texas, New Mexico and northern Mexico. Family: Leguminosae.

Sophora tomentosa. Necklace-pod sophora. This plant is an evergreen shrub of about 9 feet which bears yellowish-white flowers on erect racemes 4 to 16 inches long. The compound leaves have 13 to 21 leaflets, each about 2 inches long. The pod is similar to the previous species but the seeds are brown. This shrub may be found in Florida, southern Texas and on the coastal dunes of Baja California. Family: Leguminosae.

B. CONIINE GROUP

Toxic Principles

Conium maculatum contains the alkaloids: coniine, N-methyl coniine, conhydrine, γ-coniceine, and pseudoconhydrine. The quantitive ratios of these alkaloids varies as the plant matures (2, 4) but their overall pharmacological action is similar to nicotine (1, 3, 7). The alkaloids are distributed throughout the whole plant in dangerous quantities.

Aethusa cynapium contains only small concentrations of the coniine alkaloids and could probably not produce serious intoxications.

Members of the Group

Conium maculatum	Poison hemlock, etc.
Aethusa cynapium	Fool's parsley

Toxicology

Poisoning most frequently results from mistaking *Conium maculatum* for parsley or its seeds for anise. The symptoms and treatment are identical to that for cytisine.

Botanical Descriptions*

Conium maculatum (figure 42). Poison hemlock, Winter fern, Spotted hemlock. This plant resembles the carrot but the underground portion is white. The leaves may extend up to 4 feet from the ground, and the stems are usually spotted with purple. Crushing the leaves produces an unpleasant odor. Small white flowers are borne in umbrella-like clusters. The range of this plant is the northern United States and Canada. Family: Umbelliferae.

Aethusa cynapium (figure 43). Fool's parsley. This plant is nearly identical in appearance to *Conium maculatum* but the purple spotting is absent. It is found in the extreme northeastern part of the United States and eastern Canada. Family: Umbelliferae.

C. NICOTINE AND LOBELINE GROUP

Toxicology

All of the plants of the genus *Nicotiana* are presumed to contain the alkaloid nicotine as the principal, if not sole, toxic material.

Poisoning most frequently results from the use of nicotine-containing plants, particularly the seedlings, as salad greens. Fatalities have been reported only from the ingestion of *N. glauca* and *N. trigonophylla*, but probably all species of this genus are potentially toxic (5, 7).

Members of the *Lobelia* species contain over a dozen chemically and pharmacologically related alkaloids, of which lobeline is the principal prototype. These plants owe their reputation of high toxicity to fatal intoxications which occurred in the use of the plants or its extracts in home medicine (5). It is unlikely that anyone would casually ingest seriously toxic quantities.

Members of the Group

Nicotiana attenuata	Wild tobacco
Nicotiana glauca	Tree tobacco
Nicotiana trigonophylla	Wild tobacco; Desert tobacco
Nicotiana alata	
Lobelia berlandieri	
Lobelia cardinalis	Cardinal flower, Indian pink
Lobelia inflata	Indian tobacco
Lobelia siphilitica	Great lobelia; Blue cardinal flower

Prognosis and Treatment

See Cytisine, page 109.

Botanical Descriptions

Nicotiana attenuata. Wild tobacco, Coyote tobacco. The wild tobacco is an annual, 4 feet in height, with 4 inch broad ovate leaves. The flowers are white

* Care must be taken to distinguish these plants from *Cicuta maculata* which is botanically similar but toxicologically distinct. *Conium* has a single large root whereas the mature *Cicuta* plant exhibits a bundle of roots, see figure 49.

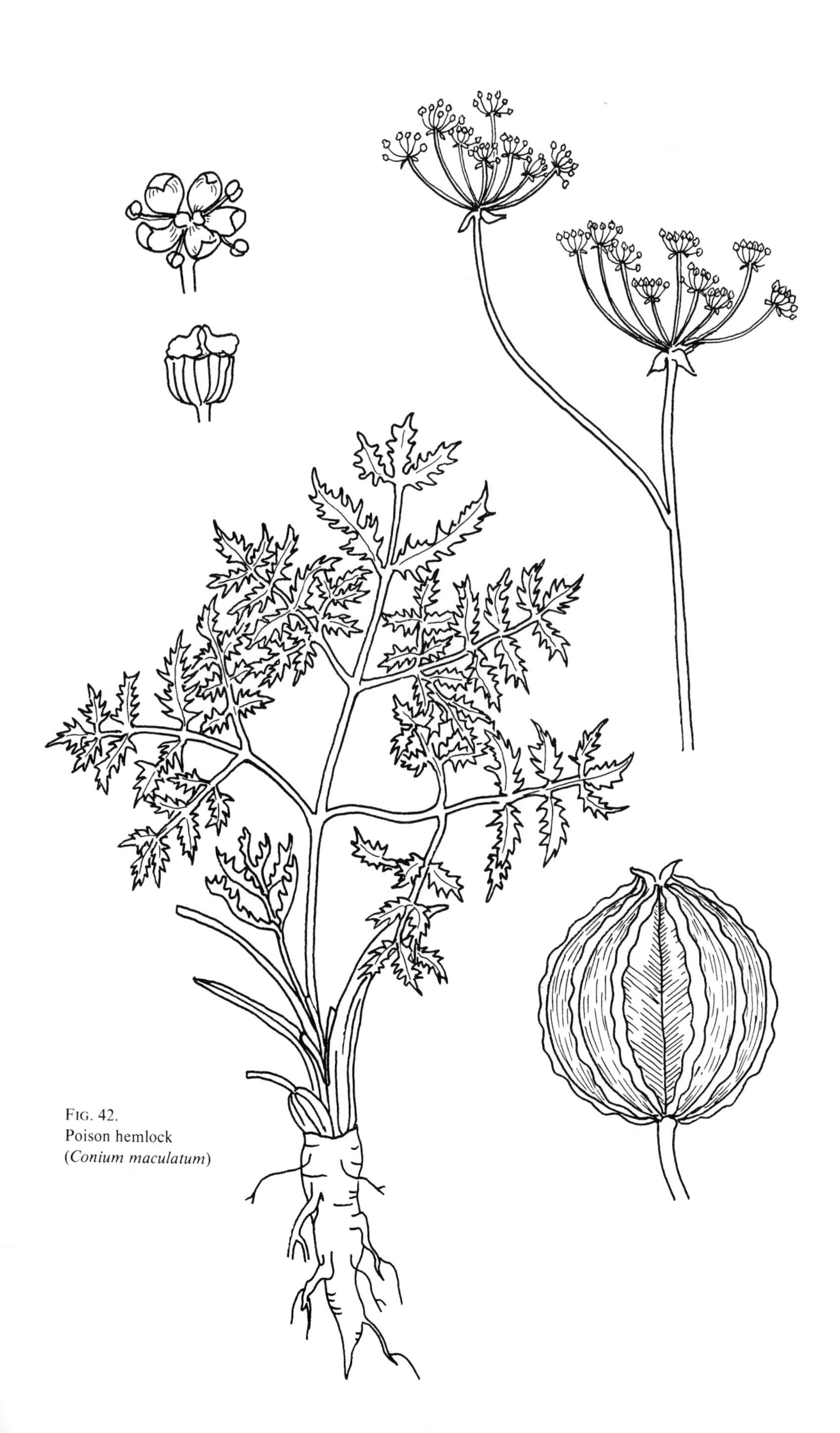

FIG. 42.
Poison hemlock
(*Conium maculatum*)

FIG. 43.
Fool's parsley
(*Aethusa cynapium*)

or greenish, opening at night. Its range extends from British Columbia, Washington to Montana, south to Arizona and New Mexico. Family: Solanaceae.

Nicotiana glauca. Tree tobacco. This is a shrub varying in height from 6 to 20 feet. The yellow flowers are tubular shaped, about 2 ½ inches long. It is common in waste areas in Texas, California and Hawaii. Family: Solanaceae.

Nicotiana trigonophylla. Wild tobacco, Desert tobacco. Wild tobacco is an annual which reaches a height of 3 feet with day-opening white or yellowish flowers 2 inches long and 1 inch across. It is found from California to Nevada and Arizona. Family: Solanaceae.

Nicotiana alata. This is a perennial which stands about 5 feet high. The flowers are pale white inside and pale violet beneath. They are fragrant at night and close in cloudy weather. Cultivated primarily as a pot plant. Family: Solanaceae.

Lobelia berlandieri. This annual is a range plant in western Texas. The leaves become papery when dry. The flowers form on a raceme. They are bluish-purple with white center. Family: Lobeliaceae.

Lobelia cardinalis. Cardinal flower. This is an erect, usually unbranched plant with a stout stem about 20 to 60 inches tall. The leaves are thin, elliptic shaped, 6 inches in length. The deep red flowers are borne in clusters at the top of the stems. The plant is both native and widely cultivated from eastern Canada south to Florida and west to Texas. Family: Lobeliaceae.

Lobelia inflata. Indian tobacco. The Indian tobacco is a weed in gardens and lawns ranging from eastern Canada south to Georgia and westward to Minnesota and Mississippi. It reaches a height of 40 inches and bears inconspicuous blue and white flowers and later forms an inflated ovoid pod. Family: Lobeliaceae.

Lobelia siphilitica. Great lobelia, Blue cardinal flower. This plant is similar to *Lobelia cardinalis* except that the flowers are blue or, more rarely, white. It is found in swamps from eastern Canada south to Texas. Family: Lobeliaceae.

REFERENCES

1. Bowman, W. C. and Sanghvi, I. S. Pharmacological Actions of Hemlock (*Conium maculatum*) Alkaloids. J. Pharm. Pharmacol. *15:* 1 (1963).
2. Cromwell, B. T. The Separation, Micro-Estimation and Distribution of the Alkaloids of Hemlock (*Conium maculatum* L.). Biochem. J. *64:* 259 (1956).
3. De Boer, J. The Death of Socrates. A Historical and Experimental Study on the Actions of Coniine and *Conium maculatum*. Arch. int. Pharmacodyn. *83:* 473 (1950).
4. Fairbairn, J. W. and Challen, S. B. The Alkaloids of Hemlock (*Conium maculatum* L.). Biochem. J. *72:* 556 (1959).
5. Kingsbury, J. M. *Poisonous Plants of the United States and Canada*. Prentice-Hall, Englewood Cliffs, N.J., 1964. *Lobelia* Pp. 390–2, *Nicotiana* Pp. 284–7, *Sophora* Pp. 357–8.
6. Mitchell, R. G. Laburnum Poisoning in Children. Lancet *261:* 57 (1951).
7. Sollmann, T. *A Manual of Pharmacology*, 8th ed. Saunders, Philadelphia, 1957. Pp. 451–467.
8. Vines, R. A. *Trees, Shrubs and Woody Vines of the Southwest*. Univ. Texas Press, Austin, 1960. Pp. 568–570.

V ATROPINE CONTAINING PLANTS

Toxicology

All parts of these plants contain the belladonna alkaloids, atropine, scopolamine, and hyoscyamine. Both in the United States (2, 5, 8, 11, 15, 20, 21, 22) and throughout the world (6, 13, 17, 19), the plant most frequently encountered as a source of atropine poisoning is the *Datura stramonium*. These cases generally involve children who have ingested the seeds. Both adults and children have been poisoned from the use of a decoction of the leaves as a home remedy, and less frequent incidents have been recorded from the misuse of the leaf as a pot herb or a salad green. Two cases given by Jacobziner (9, 10) involve its use as a psychedelic agent. A syndrome called Cornpicker's pupil may be produced by the dust (7, 18), in which mydriasis affecting one or both eyes is the only presenting sign.

Poisonings by other members of this group are less frequent. That from eating berries of *Atropa belladonna* is seen most often in England (1, 14); older reports involving poisoning from this plant in the United States have been challenged by Kingsbury (12) as due to faulty plant identification. The only recent report involving ingestion of *Cestrum* berries* is given by Morton (16). The roots of *Hyoscyamus niger* have been mistaken for horseradish and children have been poisoned from eating the seeds. Although *Lycium halimifolium* is found in the northern United States and Canada, records of human intoxications are found only in the European literature (6).

Bizarre cases have involved secondary poisoning from the ingestion of honey made from atropine-containing flowers (17) as well as the meat of animals which had recently consumed atropine-containing plants (4, 17).

Members of the Group

Atropa belladonna	Belladonna, Deadly nightshade
Cestrum diurnum	Day-blooming jessamine
Cestrum nocturnum	Night-blooming jessamine
Cestrum parqui	Green cestrum, Willow-leaved jessamine
Datura arborea	Angels trumpet

* The toxicity of the unripe berries of *Cestrum* is due to solanine, q.v., which presents an entirely different symptomatology. The atropine alkaloids are found only in the mature fruit.

Datura inoxia	
Datura metel	
Datura stramonium	Jimson Weed, Thorn apple
Datura suaveolens	
Hyoscyamus niger	Fetid nightshade, Insane root, Poison tobacco, Henbane
Lycium halimifolium	Matrimony vine, Box thorn

Differential Diagnosis

In some respects, symptoms of atropine intoxications are mimicked by the plants *Lantana camara* and *Conium maculatum* and by pathologic states such as encephalitis, meningitis, post-epileptic delirium, concussion, uremia and, particularly in the case of the elderly comatose patient, cerebral vascular accident. The delirium or maniacal state produced by atropine has been confused with overt psychosis.

Exclusion can be made on the basis of the following consistent signs of atropine poisoning: pupils equally dilated bilaterally; a hot, dry, sometimes flushed skin; and an increased heart rate. The diagnosis can be confirmed by isolation and identification of seeds obtained by gastric lavage or by the production of mydriasis following the instillation of a few drops of the patient's urine into the eye of a cat.

Since Cornpicker's pupil may result in only unilateral mydriasis, care in history taking will eliminate needless neurological examination.

Symptoms

Intoxications may vary to some degree depending upon the relative concentration of atropine to scopolamine in the plant, since scopolamine is not associated with peripheral vasodilation or a temperature increase, and rarely with excitement. The rate of onset also varies according to the mode of ingestion. Intoxications produced by drinking a decoction prepared from plant leaves usually is rapid and a comatose state may be precipitated prior to admission of the patient, whereas the onset of symptoms following the swallowing of unchewed seeds may be delayed for several hours.

The signs and symptoms of poisoning also depend upon the quantity of toxic material ingested. Usually there is an orderly progression in their appearance and intensification to full-blown, typical atropine intoxication classically described as "hot as a hare, blind as a bat, dry as a bone, red as a beet, and mad as a wet hen" (2, 3, 17). The early symptoms are visual disturbances, dryness of the mouth and intense thirst. Thus, increasing mydriasis and loss of accommodation result in photophobia and the salivary suppression progresses to dysphagia and speech difficulty. Although *Datura stramonium* seeds are mildly irritating, emesis is infrequent, possibly due to relaxation of the pyloric sphincter.

The skin becomes hot, dry and flushed. A diffuse nonpunctate erythematous rash may appear, especially on the face, neck and chest. Fever develops with temperatures of 101–104°F. common and as high as 109°F. reported. This is accompanied by headache, marked confusion, and muscular incoordination. Mania, delirium, auditory and visual hallucinations, and psychotic behavior may appear. Convulsions, particularly in young children, should be anticipated.

The pulse is rapid and weak with a tendency toward dicrotism. Other prominent signs of peripheral parasympathetic nervous system blockade include urinary retention and constipation.

In severe intoxications, the patient progress to stupor then coma with subnormal temperature, slow stertorous respiration and cyanosis.

Case History

The following typical case of *Datura stramonium* poisoning is given by Meiring (13). A 7 year old child with a history that she had eaten, 2 hours previously, some seeds from a weed growing in a vacant lot adjacent to her home and had subsequently became drowsy and extremely restless.

"The referring doctor indicated that he found her to have tachycardia, widely dilated pupils, and that she was delirious, weak and unable to stand.

"On arrival the child was extremely excited, almost to the point of acute mania, with rapid continuous purposeless limb movements, at times muttering and at times exhibiting screaming delirium.

"The pupils were widely dilated and did not react to light and the pulse rate was 190 per minute. The mouth was dry and the face extremely flushed.

"Examination of the heart, chest and abdomen in as far as it was possible in such a restless patient, revealed no other abnormalities.

"Gastric lavage with a solution of sodium bicarbonate was immediately performed and neostigmine, 0.5 mg., was given intramuscularly. Forty-five minutes later the pulse rate was 162 per minute, the blood pressure 100/60 mm. Hg. the pupils were still widely dilated and, though she was still excited and delirious, she had lost the continuous maniacal excitement.

"The neostigmine was repeated in the same dosage and an hour later her pulse was 132 per minute and she was fairly quiet, though still in a confused state with apparent hallucinations.

"Every now and then she would exhibit outbursts of wild excitement during which she would lash out against the cot sides with her arms and legs; it appeared likely that a convulsion might occur at any moment. She was therefore given 15 mg. phenobarbital intramuscularly which, though it may well have prevented a convulsion, had a rather disappointing effect on her maniacal outbursts.

"She was given 25 mg. promazine (Sparine) intramuscularly and gradually settled into a fitful sleep; this was undoubtedly partly due to the action of the phenobarbital. She was detained in hospital for a further 36 hours, and apart from a transient mild pyrexia and a desire to sleep for most of the next day she suffered no further ill-effects."

The child was discharged 2 days after the ingestion. The pupils were still somewhat dilated and very sluggishly reactive to light. Forty-eight hours later the eyes were still dilated but exhibited a normal light reaction. There were no other after effects.

Prognosis

Children tend to be more sensitive to belladonna poisoning, probably because of their greater sensitivity to hyperpyrexia. With prompt removal of the toxic material from the stomach, recovery, with the exception of pupillary dilation, is usually complete in 24 to 48 hours. If therapy is delayed, recovery will require several days. Amnesia of the period of intoxication is common in either case.

Fatalities are relatively uncommon. Psychic sequelae are reported only in the older literature.

Treatment

The stomach should be emptied and thoroughly washed as quickly as practicable since the belladonna alkaloids are absorbed rapidly. The tube has to be well lubricated because of the dryness of the pharynx. In intoxications from those plants which have berries (*Atropa belladonna* and *Cestrum* spp) the use of an emetic may be required.

No specific antidotes are available. Cholinergic drugs reduce the degree of parasympathetic blockade thereby relieving the dry mouth and tachycardia but they are of little value against the central nervous system effects. Barbiturates may be indicated for the control of severe or persistent convulsions and to reduce manic excitement. For the latter, phenothiazines have also been employed (13).

External cooling should be provided in an attempt to reduce the body temperature. Placing the patient in a darkened room and, if necessary, the direct instillation of pilocarpine will reduce eye discomfort. The nursing staff should be alerted to the possibility of urinary retention.

Botanical Descriptions

Atropa belladonna (figure 44). Belladonna, Deadly nightshade. Belladonna is a cultivated perennial about 3 feet high. The stems are much branched with ovate leaves about 6 inches long. Solitary flowers emerge from leaf joints and are blue-purple or a dull red about 1 inch long. The berry is nearly globular, about ½ inch in diameter and is purple to shiny black when mature. Family: Solanaceae.

Cestrum diurnum. Day blooming jessamine. This evergreen shrub grows to heights of 15 feet. The leaves are elliptic and 3 ½ inches long. The white flowers are thin and tubular. They are open and fragrant by day. The flowers are arranged in short clusters on separate stems. The berry is greenish-white to a bright purplish blue when immature and black when mature. It

FIG. 44.
Deadly nightshade
(*Atropa belladonna*)

is about $^{3}/_{8}$ inch in diameter, fleshy with purple juice, containing many seeds. The day jessamine is planted in the extreme south and is now naturalized in Hawaii. Family: Solanaceae.

Cestrum nocturnum. Night blooming jessamine. This is an evergreen shrub to 12 feet high with long, glossy, leathery leaves. The flowers are similar to those of the above species but fragrant and open at night. The fruit is a small greenish berry turning black at maturity. It is extensively planted in southern Florida and is found as a greenhouse plant in the north. Family: Solanaceae.

Cestrum parqui. Willow-leaved jessamine. This *Cestrum*, unlike the previous two species, is deciduous. It is a shrub usually to about 6 feet. The flowers are open and fragrant at night. It is possibly the hardiest jessamine. Family: Solanaceae.

Datura arborea. Angels trumpet. This plant forms a small tree. The soft hairy leaves emerge in pairs; within the pair one leaf will be about 6 inches long and the other about 8 inches. The trumpet shaped flowers occur singly with the flare part downward. They are white nerved with green, approximately 8 inches long, and have a distinctive musk-like odor. The seed capsule is smooth and about 2 $^{1}/_{2}$ inches long. It is cultivated in Florida to California and may be found as a tub plant elsewhere. Family: Solanaceae.

Datura metel (figure 45). This species is an annual bush about 5 feet high, the leaves appear singly and are about 8 inches in length. The 7 inch flowers grow with the flare upward. They exhibit shades ranging from white to purple, usually being more whitish on the inside. The seed capsule is about 2 inches long and is covered with small spikes. It grows on waste plains along the coast from Florida to Texas and in Hawaii. Family: Solanaceae.

Datura stramonium (figure 46). Jimson weed, Jamestown-weed, Thorn apple. The Jimson weed is found throughout the United States and Canada. It is an annual herb with a stout hollow stem growing to a height of 3 to 4 feet. The erect white flowers, about 4 inches in length, emerge at the branching of the stems. The capsules are 2 inches long, very prickly and filled with small brownish-black, kidney-shaped seeds. There are other varieties of *Datura stramonium;* var. *inerimis* has no thorns on the seed pod, var. *tatula* has purple flowers. In Hawaii the plant is known as Kikania and as La'au-Hano. Family: Solanaceae.

Datura suaveolens. This plant is similar to *Datura arborea.* It reaches a height of about 15 feet, with leaves and flowers each about a foot long. It does not form a seed pod in the United States. It is a common ornamental in the southeastern part of the country. Family: Solanaceae.

The genus *Datura* is currently undergoing revision. A number of other species are known to be cultivated in this country, most have the characteristic trumpet-like flower. They are toxicologically indistinguishable.

Hyoscyamus niger (figure 47). Henbane, Fetid nightshade, Insane root,

Fig. 45.
Angels trumpet
(*Datura metel*)

Fig. 46.
Jimson weed
(*Datura stramonium*)

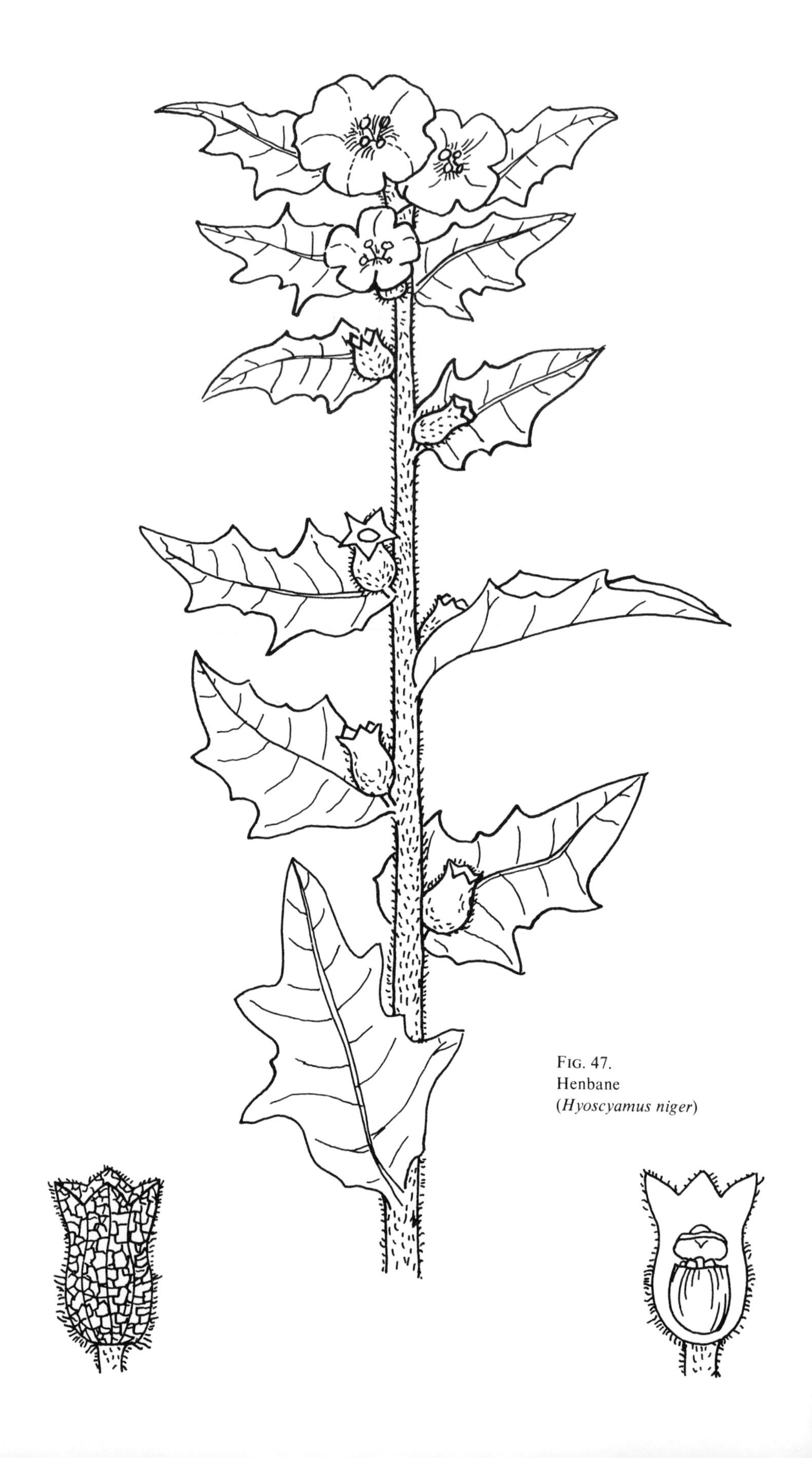

FIG. 47.
Henbane
(*Hyoscyamus niger*)

FIG. 48.
Matrimony vine
(*Lycium halimifolium*)

Poison tobacco. The henbane is a hairy, erect biennial herb about 2 ½ feet high with spindle-shaped roots. The 8 inch leaves are coarsely and somewhat irregularly toothed. The single flowers emerge from the main stem just above the leaves and are greenish-yellow to yellowish-white with purple veins and a purple throat. The seed pod forms inside the persistent calyx after the flower has dropped. It is found in Quebec and New England to Michigan and in scattered areas westward to the Pacific. Family: Solanaceae.

Lycium halimifolium (figure 48). Matrimony vine, Box thorn, False jessamine. The matrimony vine is an upright or spreading shrub to 10 feet tall. The branches are numerous and sometimes have long woody thorns. The leaves are between 1 to 1 ½ inches long. The flowers appear in clusters of 1 to 4 and are a dull pinkish violet. The fruit is an elliptical scarlet or orange-red berry about ¾ inch in length. It is cultivated and escaped along the northern border of the United States and the southern edge of Canada. Family: Solanaceae.

REFERENCES

1. Anon. Nightshade Poisoning. Lancet ii, 438, 513 (1948).
2. Arena, J. M. Atropine Poisoning: A Report of Two Cases from Jimson Weed. Clin. Ped. *2:* 182 (1963).
3. Blattner, R. J. Jimson Weed Poisoning: Stramonium Intoxication. J. Ped. *61:* 941 (1962).
4. Firth, D. and Bentley, J. R. Belladonna Poisoning From Eating Rabbit. Lancet ii, 901 (1921).
5. Garvin, J. A. and Ruh, H. O. Acute Poisoning Due to Eating the Seeds of the Jimson Weed (*Datura stramonium*). Arch. Ped. *40:* 827 (1923).
6. Gessner, O. *Die Gift- und Arzneipflanzen von Mitteleuropa.* Carl Winter, Heidelberg, 1953. p. 53.
7. Goldey, J. A., Dick, D. A. and Porter, W. L. Cornpicker's Pupil. Ohio State M. J. *62:* 921 (1966).
8. Hughes, J. D. and Clark, J. A. Stramonium Poisoning. A Report of Two Cases. J. Am. Med. Assoc. *112:* 2500 (1939).
9. Jacobziner, H. and Raybin, H. W. Internal Drug Poisonings Including Three Fatalities. Incident 3. N.Y. State J. Med. *60:* 3139 (1960).
10. Jacobziner, H. and Raybin, H. W. Fatal Salicylate Intoxication and Stramonium Poisoning. Incident 4. N.Y. State J. Med. *61:* 301 (1961).
11. Jennings, R. E. Stramonium Poisoning, A Review of the Literature and Report of Two Cases. J. Ped. *6:* 657 (1935).
12. Kingsbury, J. M. *Poisonous Plants of the United States and Canada.* Prentice-Hall, Englewood Cliffs, N. J., 1964. Pp. 275–284.
13. Meiring, P. de V. Poisoning by *Datura stramonium.* S. Afr. Med. J. *40:* 311 (1966).
14. Minors, E. H. Five Cases of Belladonna Poisoning. Brit. Med. J. *2:* 518 (1948).
15. Mitchell, J. E. and Mitchell, F. N. Jimson Weed (*Datura stramonium*) Poisoning in Childhood. J. Pediat. *47:* 227 (1955).
16. Morton, J. F. Ornamental Plants with Poisonous Properties. Proc. Fla. State Hort. Soc. *71:* 372 (1958).
17. Polson, C. J. and Tattersall, R. N. *Clinical Toxicology.* J. B. Lippincott, Philadelphia, 1951. Pp. 425–442.
18. Simmons, F. H. Jimson Weed Mydriasis in Farmers. Am. J. Ophth. *44:* 109 (1957).
19. Schumacher, N. A Case of Atropine Alkaloid Poisoning. Med. J. Aust. i, 547 (1965).
20. Rosen, C. S. and Lechner, M. Jimson-Weed Intoxication. New Eng. J. Med. *267:* 448 (1962).
21. Stiles, F. C. Stramonium Poisoning. J. Ped. *39:* 354 (1951).
22. Weintraub, S. Stramonium Poisoning. Postgrad. Med. *28:* 364 (1960).

VI PLANTS ACTING PRIMARILY ON THE CENTRAL NERVOUS SYSTEM

A. DEPRESSANTS

There is no plant in the United States which acts solely as a simple central nervous system depressant. However, certain plants discussed elsewhere in the text may produce somnolence as a consistent, non-terminal symptomatic feature. The more important of these are the andromedotoxin, veratrine, taxine, solanine and the soluble oxalate containing plants. All members of the nicotine group, certain hallucinogens, such as nutmeg and *Amanita muscaria* mushrooms, and many of the resin-containing gastroenteric irritants, e.g., pokeweed, are also capable of eliciting this response.

Serious depression and coma secondary to liver destruction may be anticipated in intoxications from the *Amanita phalloides* group of mushrooms and from the immature fruit of the akee (*Blighia sapida*). Inhalation of fumes during the field processing of turpentine (from *Pinus palustris*) may produce unconsciousness of long duration (38).

B. CONVULSANTS

The primary effect produced by plants of this group is convulsions, systemic effects outside the central nervous system usually being negligible. Most convulsive episodes are followed by a depressive phase which may be the condition in which the patient is presented to the physician. For this reason, a history should be obtained since these patients must not be treated, under any circumstances, with an analeptic agent.

Plants producing central nervous stimulation may be divided into three sub-groups for convenience of discussion. First is the *Cicuta* spp; this genus is one of the three major sources of fatal intoxications from plants in the United States. The second group can be labeled "Convulsants Occasionally Producing Human Poisoning." Although the toxic principles are distributed throughout the entire plant, it is invariably the seed capsule or fruit which is attractive to children and serves as the source of poisoning. Even though in most cases this part of the plant seems to contain relatively small concentrations of the convulsant (requiring fairly large ingestions to produce significant effect), each of these plants has been reported to have produced fatalities. The last category is termed the "Extractable Convulsants." These plants contain thujone, or related substances, which were once employed as anthelmintics. At present, crude decoctions of the needles or leaves are occasionally encountered as sources of intoxication when employed for their supposed abortifacient activity.

Cicuta Species (Water hemlock)

The various members of this genera are similar in appearance and need not be differentiated since their toxicological effect is similar. The convulsant, cicutoxin, is an unsaturated aliphatic alcohol which occurs throughout the whole plant. The highest concentration of cicutoxin is found in the stem and in the carrot-shaped rootstalk (rhizome). Different parts of the plant are eaten as the result of misidentification with edible species, particularly for wild parsnips, artichokes or sweet potatoes. The lethal dose for an adult is probably contained in one rhizome. The flowers are only slightly toxic and usually produce only mild gastroenteritis.

$$HOCH_2-(CH_2)_2-(C{\equiv}C)_2-(CH{=}CH)_3-\underset{\displaystyle OH}{\underset{|}{CH}}-(CH_2)_2CH_3$$

Cicutoxin

Symptoms

Within 15 minutes to 1 hour the patient experiences nausea, salivation, emesis and tremors. This is quickly followed by severe intermittent seizures resembling status epilepticus. Death occurs due to respiratory failure and exhaustion (38).

Prognosis

If the patient survives the acute intoxication, he is usually asymptomatic except for injury sustained during the convulsive episodes. Retrograde amnesia of the intoxication is common.

Treatment

The basis for the management is to reduce or abolish the convulsive activity (see Chapter I) and to prevent anoxia. If seizures have occurred, or appear imminent, gastric lavage should not be attempted without the aid of an anesthesiologist.

Botanical Description

Cicuta spp (figure 49). Water hemlock, Musquash root, Spotted cowbane. Species of *Cicuta* are distributed throughout the United States and Canada. The one pictured is *C. maculata*, which is in the eastern United States south to Missouri and west to Texas. They exhibit a similar appearance and are found only in wet or swampy areas. Their close resemblance to the *Conium* spp, which have a different toxicological action, should be noted. The *Cicuta* may be differentiated by its bundle of tuberous roots which appear chambered

FIG. 49.
Water hemlock
(*Cicuta maculata*)

on vertical section, and by the yellow, oily sap which emerges from a cut stem which has the odor of a raw parsnip. Family: Umbelliferae.

Convulsants Occasionally Producing Human Poisoning

Calycanthus spp	Carolina allspice, Sweet shrub, Strawberry shrub
Coriaria spp	
Melia azedarach	Chinaberry, Indian lilac
Menispermum canadense	Moonseed
Spigelia marilandica	Pink root
Strychnos nux-vomica	Nux vomica

Comments on Individual Species

The seeds of the *Calycanthus* spp contain the alkaloids calycanthidine and calycanthine, which exert an action similar to strychnine. Animal experimentation suggests that they also exhibit a direct myocardial depressant action (24).

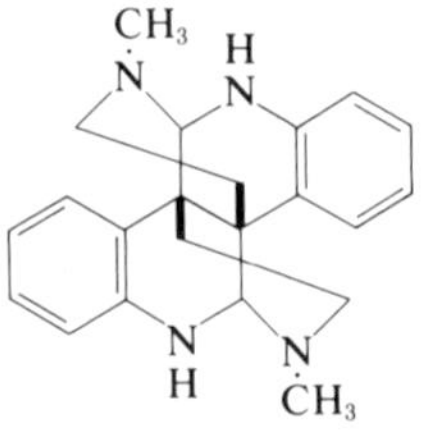

Calycanthine

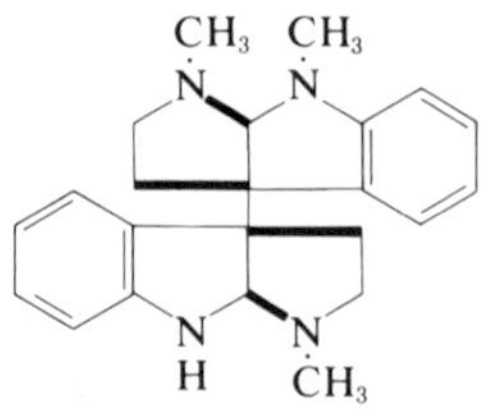

Calycanthidine

The juicy, red-purple to black pea-sized fruits of the *Coriaria* spp contain coriamyrtin. This substance resembles picrotoxin in that it produces tachycardia, tachypnea and a similar convulsive pattern. It has undergone rather intensive pharmacological investigation as it was once thought to be a possible barbiturate antagonist (2, 22, 33). The most common American species is *Coriaria myrtifolia*, which has produced fatal intoxications in children. Sublethal doses, if the experience with the New Zealand species *C. ruscifolia* is transferable, produce giddiness, stupor and coma, with or without delirium or convulsions. The delirium may approach acute mania. Amnesia is common. The pharmacology of the New Zealand species has been studied by Swanson (34).

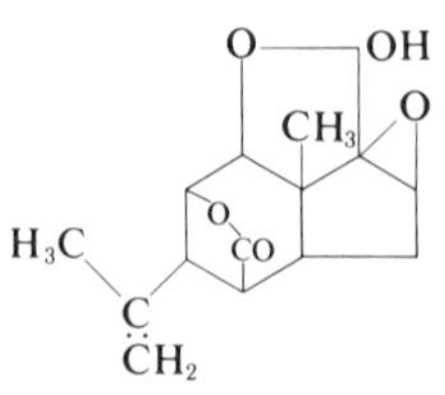

Coriamyrtin

Melia azedarach may exhibit various genetic strains since in some areas the fruit has been eaten with impunity and elsewhere it has produced fatalities (19). The symptoms, too, are highly variable. Their onset may be less than an hour after ingestion or delayed for several hours. They begin with faintness, ataxia, mental confusion and stupor. Some patients suffer from intense gastritis, emesis and diarrhea. Later effects suggest, at least in part, the onset of shock from fluid loss and electrolyte imbalance. This includes mydriasis, cold sweat, labored respiration, convulsions and partial to complete paralysis (3, 6, 38). In animals, fatty degeneration of the liver and kidney is produced if a day or two elapses before death (19). The nature of the toxic principles is unknown.

Unlike the other convulsants, the clinical management of *Melia azedarach* poisoning requires individualized care. Possibly prompt gastric lavage followed by the administration of demulcents such as egg white or milk may be sufficient to prevent an intensification of the intoxication. If emesis and diarrhea have been severe and persistent, particularly in young children, due attention should be given to avoid shock.

The fruit of *Menispermum canadense* resembles grapes and is alleged to have produced picrotoxin-like convulsions and death. No instances of poisoning have been found in the recent literature.

The concentration of alkaloid in *Spigelia marilandica* is probably inadequate to produce serious reactions unless a decoction of the plant or the root is ingested. The symptoms are vertigo, dimness of vision and mydriasis, spasms of the facial muscle and eyelids and general convulsions.

All parts, but particularly the flowers and seeds, of *Strychnos nux-vomica* contain strychnine and brucine. After a short prodromal period characterized by increased perceptual acuity, the patient exhibits muscular rigidity, dysphagia, muscle twitching, then intermittent, progressively intensifying tetanic contractions. In non-fatal cases, a sub-febrile temperature, paresthesias in the extremities, muscular rigidity, tachycardia and hyperhidrosis may persist for several days (38).

Treatment

With the exception of *Melia azedarach*, q.v., the basis for the management of all members in this sub-group is to reduce or abolish the convulsive activity (see Chapter I) and to prevent anoxia. For those plants containing toxins which are strychnine-like, isolation of the patient from external stimuli is essential. Regardless of etiology, if seizures have occurred, or appear imminent, gastric lavage should not be attempted without the aid of an anesthesiologist.

Botanical Descriptions

Calycanthus spp. These are aromatic deciduous shrubs from 3 to 10 feet tall with large, fragrant, brownish flowers borne at the tips of short branches.

They bear a 2 inch fruit. There are 2 species (*C. fertilis* and *C. floridus*) found on the eastern seaboard from Pennsylvania south to Alabama; a third species (*C. occidentalis*) of similar appearance is found in California. Family: Calycanthaceae.

Coriaria spp. These are large shrubs with racemes of small, greenish flowers and purple-black berry-like fruit. They are cultivated in the southern United States and California. Family: Coriariaceae.

Melia azedarach (figure 50). Chinaberry, Indian lilac, Pride-of-India, China tree. This is a tree to 50 feet with a rounded umbrella-like crown. It has compound leaves. The leaflets are about 2 inches long and serrated. The flowers grow in clusters on separate stems. They are purplish and fragrant. The fruit is globose, yellow to $^3/_4$ inch across and is persistent after the leaves fall. There are 3 to 5 smooth, black ellipsoid seeds in each fruit. It is commonly planted in the southern states as far north as Virginia, west to Texas and in Hawaii. Family: Meliaceae.

Menispermum canadense (figure 51). Moonseed. This is a woody, twining vine climbing to 12 feet high. Its leaves are about 8 inches long and slightly lobed. The fruit resembles that of the wild grape. It is found in moist woods and thickets and often cultivated as a trellis vine from western Quebec to Manitoba south to Georgia and Oklahoma. Family: Menispermaceae.

Spigelia marilandica. Pink root, Worm grass. This is a perennial herb growing to 2 feet with 4 inch ovate opposite leaves. The flowers grow all pointing in the same direction at the top of the stem. They are tubular, red on the outside, yellow on the inside, to 2 inches long. The pink root grows in moist woods from Florida to Texas northward to southern Indiana and North Carolina. Family: Loganiaceae.

Strychnos nux-vomica. This tree has a limited planting in Hawaii. The leaves are ovate $3^1/_2$ by 2 inches. The flowers are tubular, yellowish-white growing in terminal clusters. The berry is $1^1/_2$ inches across, hard-shelled, varying in color from yellow to orange. It contains several seeds which resemble gray velvet covered buttons about the size of a nickel. Family: Loganiaceae.

Extractable Convulsants

Intoxication from members of this group is almost always the result of the employment of aqueous decoctions for their supposed abortifacient action. Various evergreens, such as the arbor vitae (*Thuja* spp), white cedar (*Chamaecyparis thyoides*), cypress (*Cupressus* spp) and juniper (*Juniperus sabina*) as well as the tansy (*Tanacetum vulgare*) contain volatile oils in which thujone, or related substances, constitutes the primary toxic principle. An important feature of thujone poisoning from plant decoctions is that a single, large dose usually evokes only catharsis, whereas repeated smaller doses produce personality change and renal damage. Since these substances are cumulative, any dose in a series may precipitate convulsions. The following case reported by Brauch (4) is illustrative of the second type.

Fig. 50.
Chinaberry
(*Melia azedarach*)

Fig. 51.
Moonseed
(*Menispermum canadense*)

A 24 year old female, about 3 months pregnant, was admitted to the hospital in a dazed condition. During the previous 2 to 3 weeks she had been drinking, and perhaps using as a douche, a tea prepared from *Thuja occidentalis*. A marked personality change had been noted during this time; she had become inattentive, forgetful, negligent in appearance, and sensitive to criticism.

The patient became deeply stuporous. The pupils were fixed, slightly widened, but reactive to light. Respiration was normal and regular. The blood pressure was 110/80, the pulse was 90/minute and regular. The extremities were rigid. The upper arm reflexes were hyperactive; abdominal reflexes in all segments evoked; patellar and achilles reflexes active. The Babinski, Oppenheim, Rosolimo, and Chvostek's signs were not elicited. Except for a trace of albumin, the urine was negative.

During the night the patient had persistent emesis and diarrhea. By morning her temperature had risen to 101.8°F. Beginning pulmonary edema was evident. The pulse rate was 144/minute. This was followed by repeated tonic-clonic convulsions. These took the following form. "The deeply stuporous patient lies on her back, the left extremities limp, the paralyzed right hand held in a fist enclosing the thumb. A twitching begins in the right hand, then suddenly the entire arm springs up. Simultaneously there is a slight flexing of the left arm, and a sudden violent clonic twitching of the right half of the face, right arm and right leg. The head is shook with jerky shivers." The duration of each seizure ranged from 40 to 70 seconds, with no cessation of respiration but accompanied with some cyanosis. These attacks continued, at the rate of about 15 an hour, until death the next day.

By the final evening, the temperature had continued to rise to 102.5°F. The pulse was 150/minute. The spinal pressure was elevated. The terminal urine was turbid; it contained hyaline casts, erythrocytes and albumin.

Treatment

The production of neurological damage by the chronic consumption of sub-convulsive concentrations of thujone and its relatives has not been unequivocally demonstrated. Nevertheless, supportive care similar to that for meningitis seems indicated: adequate fluid intake and urine output, electrolyte support, and control of emesis and convulsions. Whether specific anticonvulsants are useful has never been tested.

Botanical Descriptions

The evergreens belonging in this group are shrubs to small trees. The leaves of most are flat and scale-like. The plants are cone-bearing. They are found throughout North America to the Arctic. Except for the juniper most are found in wet soil. Family: Cupressaceae.

Tanacetum vulgare. Tansy. This is a coarse, aromatic perennial, growing to 3 feet. The leaves are numerous and fern-like. The yellow flowers are borne in clusters of 20 to 200. It is a well established weed throughout most of the United States and adjacent Canada. Family: Compositae.

C. HALLUCINOGEN PRODUCING PLANTS

Like the hallucinogenic mushrooms of Groups II and IV (Chapter IX), ingestion of plants which produce delirium or hallucinations as their principal effects is usually deliberate. A number of the plants in this category are not native but are locally cultivated or illicitly brought into this country to provide a supply of the psychosis-producing material. Numerous other plants having similar properties are known and may be introduced within the next few years. An extensive list of these potential sources has been prepared by Schultes (31).

Certain plants may produce a delirium as only a secondary symptom of an acute intoxication and have been discussed elsewhere. The most important of these are the atropine-containing plants.

Members of the Group

Botanical Name	*Common Name*	*Constituent*	*Selected References*
Cannabis sativa	Hemp, Marijuana, Pot, Weed, Mary Jane, Reefer, Grass	Tetrahydrocannabinols	42
Lophophora williamsii	Peyote, Mescal, The Button, Moon, Tops, Cactus, The Bad Seed, P, Big Chief	Mescaline	15, 20, 28, 29, 37
Ipomoea violacea	The Heavenly Blue Morning Glory	Lysergic acid monoethylamide	8, 13, 16
var. *alba*	Pearly Gates Morning Glory	Lysergic acid monoethylamide	
*Rivea corymbosa**	Ololiuqui	Lysergic acid monoethylamide	16, 30, 39
Myristica fragrans†	Nutmeg	Myristicin and related compounds	5, 10, 11, 14, 23, 26, 32, 35, 36, 40, 41
Vinca rosea (*Catharanthus roseus*)	Periwinkle	See text	

* Occasionally confused in literature with Ipomoea.

† The outer husk of the nutmeg (which is mace) is also active but seldom encountered as a psycho-active material.

Pattern of Usage

Ludwig and Levine (21) recognize three categories of hallucinogenic drug users: "First, there are the people who are primarily and preferentially narcotic drug addicts who have used the hallucinogenic agents on one or several occasions mainly for kicks or curiosity. They seldom seek these drugs and tend to use them infrequently, as for example when these agents come their way through a friend or at a party. Rarely do they take the hallucinogenic agent alone but tend to take it after a fix with heroin, hydromorphone hydrochloride, morphine, or some other narcotic drug to which they are addicted at the time.

"Second, there are the group of people, aptly described as the professional potheads, who have had extensive experience with various drugs. The most commonly used drug by this group is marijuana but amphetamines and barbiturates are also popular. Many have had some experience with the narcotic drugs, but on the whole they tend to avoid the opiates. Hallucinogenic agents are used by these people mainly on special occasions, such as parties. It is rare for users to take drugs alone. They are mainly taken with friends or at intimate gatherings of people.

"Third, there are a small number of people who take the hallucinogenic agents repeatedly over a sustained period of time to the exclusion of all other drugs. The frequency of drug use during these periods of time is variable. Generally, these patients seemed different from those in the second group, who primarily smoke marijuana. They did not take these drugs in a group for social purposes but used them mainly as a means of attaining some personal, esoteric goal."

With the exception of marijuana, which is smoked, the crude plant material is usually ingested as such. Certain cult-like variations may be encountered in different parts of the country. Thus nutmeg may be suspended in tea, milk, coke or whatever the local practice dictates. Morning glory seeds are simply crushed between the teeth and swallowed. Mescal buttons, like nutmeg, are usually chopped up and then chewed at the same time the individual sips tea, coffee, wine or milk to help disguise the taste. The ground buttons may also be put in gelatin capsules and swallowed. Although marijuana is active orally it is almost invariably smoked. Aqueous preparations of these plants for parenteral use have been encountered. See, for example, Fink (13).

Psychic Effects

The subjective effects produced by all of these plants are grossly similar. The intensity and nature of the response are as much dependent upon the personality of the subject and his environment as it is upon the potency and quantity of the hallucinogenic agent.

The most typical effect is the development of a dreamlike state described by Jaffe (17) as a "period of altered consciousness in which ideas seem disconnected, uncontrollable and freely flowing, coming in disrupted sequences." Perception is disturbed. With low doses temporal and spatial distortion is predominant. Larger doses induce vivid visual hallucinations and, more rarely, auditory hallucinations. Delusions and depersonalization are common.

Physiological Effects

Marijuana and nutmeg produce nausea, dryness of the mouth and throat, thirst, increased appetite, ataxia, and sometimes tremor. Marijuana has no effect on pupillary size but nutmeg sometimes produces mydriasis. Both substances produce a more pronounced drowsiness than the other hallucinogens. Marijuana potentiates the action of barbiturates and amphetamine.

The lysergic acid monoethylamide containing plants (*Ipomoea* and *Rivea*) elicit nausea, mydriasis, tremor, hyper-reflexia and sympathomimetic effects. Tolerance and cross tolerance develops for mescaline, the ergot hallucinogens and psilocybin (contained in certain hallucinogenic mushrooms).

There is a recent report (25) concerning the smoking of dried leaves of the periwinkle (*Vinca rosea*) to produce a hallucinogenic response. The alkaloids contained in this plant are well characterized (18) but what products might be transmitted in smoke are not known. The physiological reactions which have been described, hallucinations, ataxia, alopecia, and paresthesias, are consistent with those seen in the therapeutic application of vincristine and vinblastine. If these cytotoxic agents are indeed responsible for the evoked response, serious renal and hepatic damage, leukopenia, and persistent neuropathies may be anticipated (1).

Prognosis

Toxicity is minimal and recovery is usually uneventful (7, 9, 12, 27). Prolonged psychotic reactions are rarely produced unless there is a severe underlying hysterical or paranoid personality pattern associated with the subject. Occasional severe reactions have appeared in normal individuals who have been given hallucinogenic material without their prior knowledge nor subsequent explanation. The greatest danger is derived from injury inflicted by the subject to himself or others during the psychotic episode which result from intensification of pre-existing personality defects, particularly paranoid persecution or from delusions of grandeur ("I can fly!"). The inherent danger of operating a motor vehicle while affected by a hallucinogen is apparent.

Treatment

A person under the influence of hallucinogenic substances should not be left alone. An understanding attendant provides orientation and can direct the course of psychotic experience to some extent, thus limiting panic reactions.

Although rarely needed, chlorpromazine, 25–50 mg orally, will terminate severe psychotic reactions from mescaline, psilocybin and the ergot containing plants. Barbiturates may also be used to reduce simple agitation except in intoxications produced by marijuana, possibly nutmeg, and in mixed intoxications involving narcotics.

An attempt should be made to refer these patients for psychiatric evaluation.

Botanical Descriptions

With the exception of the periwinkle, the plant products employed as hallucinogenic agents are usually seen in a semi-processed form. Although *Cannabis sativa* is now found wild in most of the United States, it is not usually the source of marijuana for cigarettes because the concentration of tetrahydrocannabinols is too low.

Vinca rosea (*Catharanthus roseus*). Periwinkle. This perennial rarely exceeds 2 feet. It is erect and rarely branched bearing flat, petaled, white, pink or reddish-purple flowers at the tops of the stems. It is widely escaped in southern Florida and Hawaii and cultivated as an annual in the north. Family: Apocynaceae.

REFERENCES

1. A.M.A. Council on Drugs. *New Drugs*. Am. Med. Assoc., Chicago, Ill., 1966. Pp. 484–8.
2. Bleckwenn, W. J., Hodgson, E. R., Herwick, R. P. A Clinical Comparison of Picrotoxin, Metrazol, and Coriamyrtin Used as Analeptics and as Convulsants. J. Pharm. Exp. Therap. *69:* 81 (1940).
3. Blohm, H. *Poisonous Plants of Venezuela*. Harvard Univ. Press, Cambridge, Mass., 1962. Pp. 45–6.
4. Brauch, F. Das klinische Bild der Thujavergiftung. Zeit. Klin. Med. *119:* 86 (1932).
5. Calloway, E. III. Personal Experiences with Nutmeg. Ethnopharmacologic Search for Psycho-Active Drugs, Symposium, San Francisco, Calif., January 28–30, Editor-in-Chief, Daniel H. Efron, Co-Editors, Bo Holmstedt and Nathan S. Kline. U.S. Dept. Health, Education and Welfare; U.S. Government, Printing Office.
6. Carratala, R. E. Fatal Intoxication by Fruit from *Melia azedarach*. Revista Asoc. Med. Argentina *53:* 338 (1939). C.A. *33:* 6951 (1939).
7. Cohen, S. Lysergic Acid Diethylamide: Side Effects and Complications. J. Nervous and Mental Disease *130:* 30–40 (1960).
8. Cohen, S. Suicide Following Morning Glory Seed Ingestion. Am. J. Psych. *120:* 1024 (1964).
9. Cohen, S. and Ditman, K. S. Complications Associated with Lysergic Acid Diethylamide (LSD-25). J. Am. Med. Assoc. *181:* 161 (1962).
10. Cushny, A. R. Nutmeg Poisoning. Proc. Roy. Soc. of Med. *1*, Part 1: No. 4, 39 (1908) (Therap. and Pharma. Sect.).
11. Dale, H. H. Note on Nutmeg-Poisoning. Proc. Roy. Soc. of Med. *2*, Part 1: No. 4, 69 (1909) (Therap. and Pharma. Sect.).
12. Elkes, J. The Dysleptics: Note on a No Man's Land. Comprehensive Psychiatry *4:* 195 (1963).
13. Fink, P. J. Morning Glory Seed Psychosis. Arch. Gen. Psychiat. *15:* 209 (1966).
14. Green, R. C. Jr. Nutmeg Poisoning. J. Am. Med. Assoc. *171:* 166 (1959).
15. Hoch, P. H., Cattel, J. P. and Pennes, H. H. Effects of Mescaline and Lysergic Acid (d-LSD-25). Am. J. Psych. *108:* 579 (1952).
16. Hofmann, A. The Active Principles of the Seeds of *Rivea corymbosa* and *Impomoea violacea.* Bot. Museum Leafl. Harvard Univ. *20*, No. 6: 194 (1963).
17. Jaffe, J. H. Drug Addiction and Drug Abuse, in Goodman, L. and Gilman, A. *The Pharmacological Basis of Therapeutics*, 3rd ed., New York, 1965. Pp. 204–8.
18. Johnson, I. S., Armstrong, J. G., Gorman, M., and Burnett, J. P. The Vinca Alkaloids: A New Class of Oncolytic Agents. Cancer Res. *23:* 1390 (1963).
19. Kingsbury, J. M. *Poisonous Plants of the United States and Canada*. Prentice-Hall, Englewood Cliffs, N.J., 1964. Pp. 206–8.
20. Klüver, H. *Mescal. The Divine Plant and Its Psychological Effects*. Kegan Paul, Trench, Trubner & Co. Ltd., London, 1928.
21. Ludwig, A. M., Levine, J. Patterns of Hallucinogenic Drug Abuse. J. Am. Med. Assoc. *191:* 92 (1965).
22. Maloney, A. H. Studies on the Pharmacological Action of Coriamyrtin. J. Pharm. Exp. Therap. *57:* 361 (1936).
23. McCord, J. A. and Jervey, L. P. Nutmeg (myristicin) Poisoning: Case Report. S. Carolina Med. J. *58:* 436 (1962).
24. McGuigan, H. and von Hess, C. L. Isocalycanthine and Its Quaternary Base. J. Pharm. Exp. Therap. *3:* 441 (1912). See also, Chen, A. L., Powell, C. E. and Chen, K. K. The Action of Calycanthine. J. Am. Pharm. Assoc. *31:* 513 (1942).
25. *Miami Herald* (Florida) June 2, 1967.
26. Payne, R. B. Nutmeg Intoxication. New Eng. J. Med. *269:* 36 (1963).
27. Savage, C., Stolaroff, M. J. Clarifying the Confusion Regarding LSD-25. J. Nerv. and Mental Dis. *140:* 218 (1965).
28. Schultes, R. E. Peyote (*Lophora Williamsii*) and Plants Confused With It. Bot. Museum Leafl. Harvard Univ. *5:* 61 (1937).

29. Schultes, R. E. Peyote and Plants Used in the Peyote Ceremony. Bot. Museum Leafl. Harvard Univ. *4:* 129 (1937).
30. Schultes, R. E. A Contribution to our Knowledge of *Rivea corymbosa*: The Narcotic Ololiuqui. Bot. Museum of Harvard Univ. (1941).
31. Schultes, R. E. The Search for New Natural Hallucinogens. Lloydia *29:* 293 (1966).
32. Shulgin, A. T., Sargent, T. and Naranjo, C. The Chemistry and Psychopharmacology of Nutmeg and of Several Related Phenylisopropyl Amines. Ethnopharmacologic Search for Psycho-Active Drugs, Symposium, San Francisco, Calif., January 28–30, 1967, Editor-in-Chief, Daniel H. Efron, Education and Welfare; U.S. Government Printing Office.
33. Swanson, E. E. and Chen, K. K. The Pharmacological Action of Coriamyrtin. J. Pharm. Exp. Therap. *57:* 410 (1936).
34. Swanson, E. E. Tutin: Its Pharmacological Action and Its Antagonism with Sodium Amytal. J. Am. Pharm. Assoc. *20:* 2 (1940).
35. Truitt, E. G. Jr., Calloway, E. III, Braude, M. C. and Krantz, J. C. Jr. The Pharmacology of Myristicin, A Contribution to the Pharmacology of Nutmeg. J. Neuropschy. *2:* 205 (1960).
36. Truitt, E. G. Jr. The Pharmacology of Myristicin and Nutmeg. Ethnopharmacologic Search for Psycho-Active Drugs, Symposium, San Francisco, Calif., January 28–30, 1967, Editor-in-Chief, Daniel H. Efron, Education and Welfare, U.S. Government Printing Office.
37. Unger, S. M. Mescaline, LSD, Psilocybin, and Personality Change. Psychiatry *26:* 111 (1963).
38. von Oettingen, W. F. *Poisoning, A Guide to Clinical Diagnosis and Treatment.* 2nd ed. W. B. Saunders, Philadelphia, 1958. *Cicuta* p. 304, *Pinus* p. 586, strychnine p. 543.
39. Wasson, R. G. Notes on the Present Status of Ololiuqui and the Other Hallucinogens of Mexico. Bot. Museum Leafl. Harvard Univ. *20:* 161 (1963).
40. Weil, A. T. Nutmeg as a Psychoactive Drug. Ethnopharmacologic Search for Psycho-Active Drugs, Sympsium, San Francisco, Calif., January 29–30, 1967, Editor-in-Chief, Daniel H. Efron, Co-Editors, Bo Holmstedt and Nathan S. Kline. U.S. Dept. Health, Education and Welfare; U.S. Government Printing Office.
41. Weiss, G. Hallucinogenic and Narcotic-like Effects of Powdered Myristica (Nutmeg). Psychiatric Quarterly *34:* 346 (1960).
42. Wolstenholme, G. E. W. and Knight, J. *Hashish: its chemistry and pharmacology.* Ciba Foundation Study Group No. 21. Little, Brown and Company, Boston, 1965.

VII CYANOGENETIC PLANTS

Toxicology

A vast number of plants contain glycosides which will release hydrocyanic acid upon ingestion. The nature of these plants falls generally into the category of invaders in forage crops and thus do not present a human poisoning problem. Human intoxications in nearly all cases have resulted from the ingestion of seed kernels (the unbroken seeds are harmless) of the fruit plants listed below or from the ingestion of the tubers of the *Manihot* plant. One case of poisoning is on record from *Hydrangea* buds eaten in a salad.

Members of the Group

Eriobotrya japonica	Japanese plum, Loquat
Hydrangea macrophylla	Hydrangea
Manihot spp	Tapioca plant
Prunus spp	Almond, Apricot, Cherry, Choke cherry, Wild cherry, and Peach

Symptoms

Vomiting, ataxia, dyspnea, muscular weakness, fibrillary twitchings, stupor, coma, and convulsions prior to or after losing consciousness is the usual sequence following ingestion of toxic quantities of cyanogenetic glycosides. Cyanohemoglobin is easily demonstrated if there is any question concerning the etiology of the intoxication.

A detailed description of 5 cases of poisoning from ingestion of choke cherry seeds is given by Pijoan (5). Numerous cases involving other plants are cited by Polson and Tattersall (6) and by Sayre (7). Cyanide is not a cumulative poison. However, chronic intoxication from the daily ingestion of plants containing cyanogenetic glycosides is seen in certain tropical areas (4).

Treatment

The treatment does not vary from the procedure established for cyanide poisoning from any source. In severe cases, the inhalation of amyl nitrite followed by immediate vomiting or gastric lavage, and the subsequent intravenous injection of sodium nitrite (3 per cent sol. at a rate of 2.5 to 5 ml per minute), plus sodium thiosulfate (approx. 50 ml of a 25 per cent sol. I.V.), or sodium tetrathionate is indicated. Repeat injections if signs of toxicity persist, using similar or smaller doses.

Supportive treatment may include artificial respiration, as well as oxygen, warmth, vascular supportive drugs (e.g., ephedrine), and other symptomatic measures. The stomach may be washed with 5 per cent aqueous sodium thiosulfate leaving 200 ml of this solution in the stomach at completion of lavage (1, 2).

Done (3) makes the following precautionary statements concerning therapy of acute cyanide poisoning. Administration of the antidotes may *per se* produce alarming symptoms: vomiting, syncope, headache, and unconsciousness frequently occur early during the administration of nitrite. Nitrites are hypotensive agents, and severe hypotension may accompany their administration. For this reason it is desirable that an assistant obtain frequent blood pressure measurements throughout the period that sodium nitrite is being injected; the injection should be interrupted or slowed if a sharp fall in blood pressure occurs. When practicable, it is helpful to have an intravenous infusion of physiologic saline or dextrose solution running during the treatment so that the rate of flow can be increased when necessary to maintain circulatory adequacy. The hypotension produced by nitrite may be partly overcome by placing the patient in the Trendelenburg position. Hypotension may occur also during the administration of thiosulfate.

Continuous inhalation of amyl nitrite may prevent adequate oxygenation; therefore, there is good reason to utilize the interrupted schedule of administration suggested above.

Botanical Descriptions

Eriobotrya japonica. Loquat, Japanese plum. This tree is a symmetrical evergreen attaining a height of about 20 feet. Its large, stiff leaves are rough to the touch. The leaves are from 8 to 12 inches in length. The fragrant dingy white flowers grow in terminal clusters. The fruit is pear-shaped, yellow and up to 3 inches in length. It is grown in California, the Gulf states and in Florida, and may be found as a pot plant in other locations. Family: Rosaceae.

Hydrangea macrophylla (figure 52). The hydrangea is a large bush, growing to 15 feet. The stems and twigs are usually reddish-brown. The leaves are 6 inches or more long, dark green above, grayish and fuzzy underneath, and scalloped around the margin. The tiny white flowers are borne in huge clusters. There are many cultivated varieties with white, rose, deep blue or greenish-white flowers which are persistent, turning brown as they dry. It is grown throughout the United States and Canada. Family: Saxifragaceae.

Manihot spp. Tapioca plant. These are shrubs or trees cultivated in Texas, Lower California and Hawaii. They have fleshy roots, the leaves are alternate and deeply lobed. One or 2 species are used to make edible products. Family: Euphorbiaceae.

Fig. 52.
Hydrangea
(*Hydrangea macrophylla*)

REFERENCES

1. Chen, K. K. and Rose, C. L. Nitrite and Thiosulfate in Cyanide Poisoning. J. Am. Med. Assoc. *149:* 113 (1952).
2. Chen, K. K. and Rose, C. L. Treatment of Acute Cyanide Poisoning. J. Am. Med. Assoc. *162:* 1154 (1956).
3. Done, A. K. Clinical Pharmacology of Systemic Antidotes. Clin. Pharmacol. Therap. *2:* 750 (1961).
4. Montgomery, R. D. The Medical Significance of Cyanogen in Plant Foodstuffs. Am. J. Nutr. *17:* 103 (1965).
5. Pijoan, M. Cyanide Poisoning from Choke Cherry Seed. Am. J. Med. Sci. *204:* 550 (1942).
6. Polson, C. J. and Tattersall, R. N. *Clinical Toxicology*. J. B. Lippincott, Philadelphia, 1959. Pp. 114–5.
7. Sayre, J. W. and Kaymakcalan, S. Cyanide Poisoning from Apricot Seeds among Children in Central Turkey. New Eng. J. Med. *270:* 1113 (1964).

LIVER DAMAGING PLANTS

Certain species of *Senecio* and *Crotalaria* produce thromboses in the medium size and small hepatic veins with the subsequent development of cirrhosis (Chiari's syndrome). The condition is common in the West Indies among drinkers of "Bush Tea" prepared from these plants. For further details on clinical and chemical aspects of these and other hepatotoxic plants (e.g., *Heliotropium* and *Cycas*) the reviews of Bras and McLean (2), Hill, *et al.* (10), and Schoental (15) and the note by Altschule (1) should be consulted. See also Cycads, Chapter X. Species of *Senecio* commonly used in "herbal teas" in the United States have not been reported to exhibit this effect on the liver.

Other than that from fungus contamination of food and certain mushrooms (Chapter IX), human hepatotoxicity from plant sources is rare in the United States. The only other known, potentially dangerous hepatotoxin is contained in the seeds and unripe fruit of the Ackee tree.

Member of the Group

Blighia sapida — Ackee (Akee)

Toxic Principles

Hypoglycin A, β-methylene-cyclopropyl-L-α-amino-propionic acid, and hypoglycin B, a dipeptide formed from hypoglycin A and glutamic acid, have been isolated from the ackee fruit by Hassal and Reyle (5, 6, 7) and identified by von Holt, *et al.* (13). Both are present in the seeds but the fleshy aril contains only hypoglycin A. The immature aril contains more than 12 times the hypoglycin A than the ripe aril. The pharmacology of the whole ackee has been studied by Doughty and Larson (4) and that of the pure hypoglycin by Chen, *et al.* (3) and von Holt (11, 12).

$$H_2N\cdot\underset{\displaystyle COOH}{\underset{|}{CH}}\cdot CH_2\cdot CH_2\cdot CO\cdot NH\cdot\underset{\displaystyle COOH}{\underset{|}{CH}}\cdot CH_2\cdot\triangle{:}CH_2$$

Hypoglycin B

Toxicology

Ackee poisoning has been associated almost entirely with the island of Jamaica where it has attained epidemic proportions during certain years under the name "Vomiting Sickness". Children between the ages of 2 to 5 years and, to a lesser extent 5 to 10 years are affected primarily.

Some attempt has been made to relate predisposition to ackee-induced vomiting sickness with pre-existing nutritional deficiencies, but such a relationship has not been conclusively established. However, those affected by ackee are often underweight and frequently show indications of deficiencies in vitamin B complex as well as protein lack, such as angular stomatitis, glossitis, mosaic skin, and hypochromotrichia. A sore mouth is reported to be the invariable precursor of vomiting sickness. It remains to be shown whether these signs of nutritional deficiencies are not, in themselves, produced by the ackee.

Symptoms

Hill (8) recognizes two clinical forms of ackee intoxication. In the first there is vomiting followed by a period of remission of 8 to 10 hours, then secondary vomiting with convulsions and coma. The second type is characterized by convulsions and coma at the onset.

A latent period of 6 hours to more than a day usually occurs between ingestion and the sudden onset of symptoms. Vomiting takes place in 60 to 90 per cent of the cases. This may be preceded by general epigastric discomfort in about a fourth of these.

Convulsions occur in about 85 per cent of fatal cases. Kernig's sign is generally absent. Body temperature is usually normal or slightly depressed. Systemic acidosis is a consistent finding. Coma varies from unconsciousness with restlessness and irritation to very deep depression with the absence of conjunctival reflexes. Hill observed in an epidemic in 1951 that patients suddenly became deeply comatose but after a few minutes recovered consciousness without any apparent loss of orientation.

Pathology

Immediate liver biopsy shows an almost complete absence of liver glycogen. Except for some degree of lymphoid hyperplasia in the mesentery and ileum together with fatty changes in the liver, post-mortem examinations are otherwise generally negative (9).

The low blood sugar and altered pH are readily demonstrated. The other clinical laboratory findings are unremarkable (8, 9).

Case History

A 6 year old boy had appeared well until 4 p.m. on the day before admission, when he had vomited once, bringing up a small quantity of undigested food. There was no abdominal pain or diarrhea. Following this the child seemed satisfactory and went to bed normally. He passed urine during the night at 1 a.m. and 6 a.m., and on each occasion he was seen by his father who thought he seemed well. At 7 a.m. the father called him but could not wake him. "The father thought the boy was in a deep sleep, but on trying to rouse him 15 minutes later the child was found to be unconscious, with his legs in rigid extension, arms tightly flexed on his chest, hands clenched, and jaw locked. This stiffness seemed to wax and wane, lasting about 10 minutes with longer intervals between.

"The patient arrived in the ward at 2 p.m., when he was found to be deeply comatose with stertorous respiration. He was afebrile, with a pulse of 120 and a blood pressure of 110/60. There were no signs of meningeal irritation. The eyes tended to rove about, with a transient squint. The fundi and pupils were normal. The limbs were flaccid at the first examination and all tendon reflexes were diminished. Painful stimuli produced no response, while the abdominal and plantar reflexes were absent. The child was well hydrated and moderately nourished; with only minor stigmata of malnutrition, in particular slight angular stomatitis and cheilosis. The liver was just palpable.

"During the first three-quarters of an hour after admission there were repeated attacks of stiffening of the limbs, each lasting about 1 to 2 minutes, accompanied by a rigor-like shaking. During these bouts the limbs became hypertonic with greatly increased reflexes.

"Investigations carried out immediately on admission showed: (1) Blood count: haemoglobin, 11.6 g. per 100 ml.; red cells, 3,500,000 per c.mm.; white cells, 17,000 per c.mm. (metamyelocytes 0.5 per cent, neutrophils 85 per cent, lymphocytes 14.5 per cent); E.S.R., 6 mm. per hour; haematocrit, 32 per cent; M.C.V., 91.4 μ^3; M.C.H.E., 36.3 per cent; M.C.H., 33.1 $\mu\mu$g (2) Liver-function tests: bilirubin (total), 0.6 mg. per 100 ml.; cephalin-cholesterol flocculation test, negative; gamma-globulin (Kunkel), 5.8 units; thymol flocculation, negative; thymol turbidity, 1.2 units; serum proteins, total 7.4 g. per cent (albumin 4.9 g., globulin 2.5 g.); cholinesterase (Michel), 0.7 unit. (3) Blood urea, 45 mg. per 100 ml. (4) Serum calcium, 11 mg. per 100 ml. (5) Carbon dioxide combining power, 40 volumes per 100 ml. (6) E.C.G., normal. (7) Blood sugar, 19 mg. per 100 ml. (8) Liver biopsy (immediate): almost complete absence of liver glycogen (0.7 per cent).

"Adrenaline, 5 minims (0.3 ml.), was given subcutaneously on admission and the blood sugar was estimated after 15 minutes. This showed no real change (18 mg. per 100 ml.). Treatment was then begun with an injection of 40 g. of glucose intravenously, in a 50 per cent solution, followed by a continuous intravenous drip of 9.5 per cent glucose solution. By 4:25 p.m. the blood sugar had risen to 700 mg. per 100 ml. and was associated with a marked glycosuria. No dramatic clinical effect was produced, although the coma appeared to be definitely lighter during the afternoon and evening. The blood sugar had fallen to 84 mg. per 100 ml. by 8:30 p.m., and thereafter remained between 80 and 100 mg. The child continued in a stuporose condition, and during the night he had two generalized tonic-clonic convulsions. Next day a further fit occurred at 5 a.m., following which the child died, the respiration stopping while the heart continued to beat for 15 minutes afterwards."

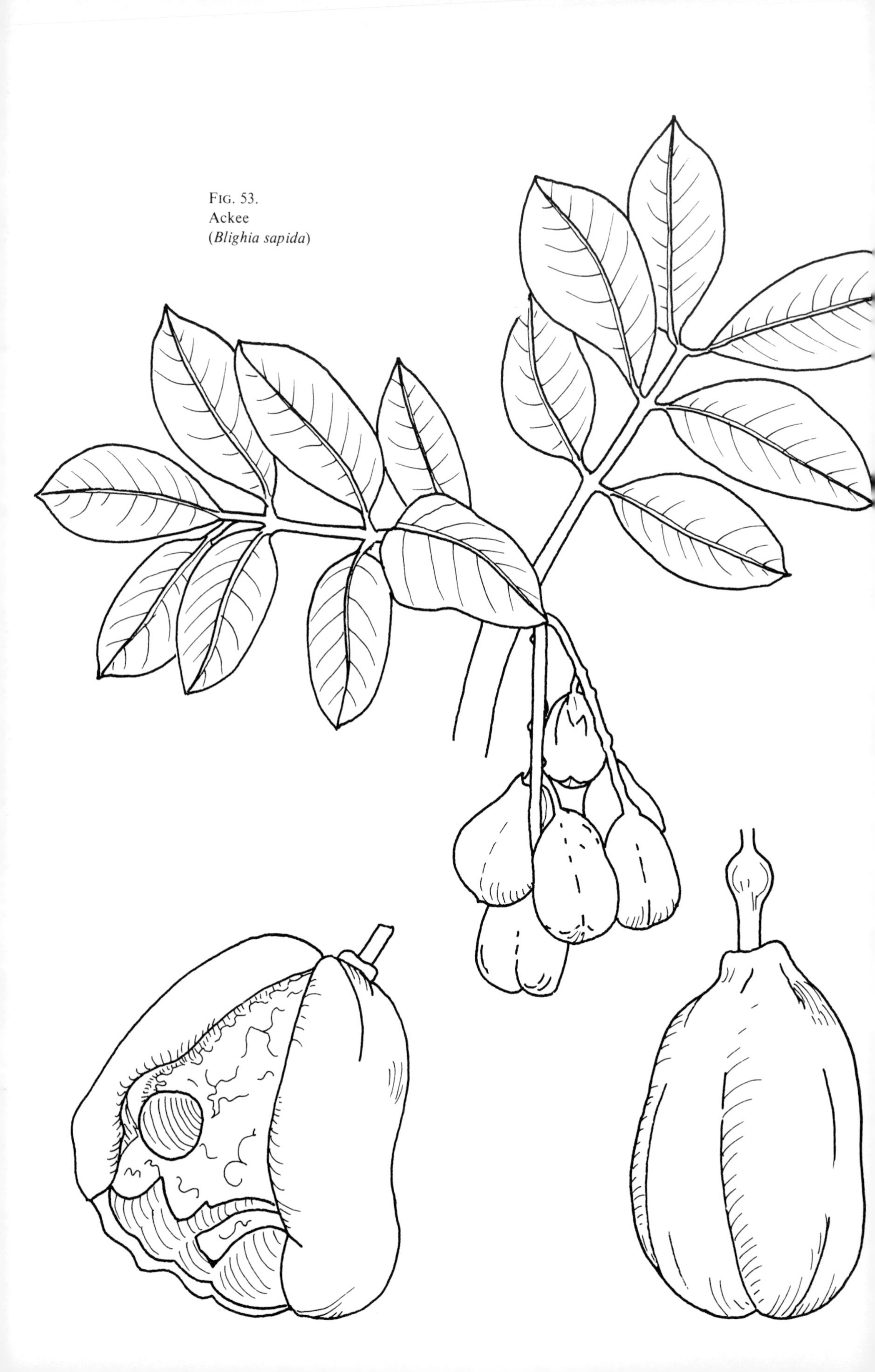

Fig. 53.
Ackee
(*Blighia sapida*)

Post-mortem examination was mainly negative save for lymphoid hyperplasia in the mesentery and ileum, together with fatty change in the liver (14).

Prognosis

The mortality rate is probably between 40 to 80 per cent (8). The average duration between the onset of vomiting and death is about 12½ hours, with an overall range from 1 hour to 4 days.

Treatment

There is no established treatment for ackee intoxications. Careful management of electrolyte balance and the immediate intravenous administration of glucose are suggested. In cases associated with frank vitamin B deficiency, the administration of thiamine and riboflavin may be helpful. (The subcutaneous administration of 2 mg/1 g/day of Riboflavin phosphate was shown by von Holt (11) to reduce the mortality in mice given hypoglycin A and to prevent the fatty infiltration in the liver.) It should be recalled that acidosis is a consistent finding in all cases of ackee poisoning.

Botanical Description

Blighia sapida (figure 53). Ackee, Akee. This south Florida tree reaches a height of 40 feet with a trunk up to 24 inches in diameter. The bark is gray and smooth. The compound leaves each have 6 to 10 oblong-shaped thin leaflets about 3 to 6 inches long. There is a prominent midvein. The flowers are small and greenish white. They form in racemes from the leaf stems. The fruit is a blunt, 3-sided capsule about 2½ inches long and 1½ inches in diameter. It is bright red at maturity, splitting open on the tree to reveal a bright yellow inner coating in which large black seeds are imbedded surrounded by a fleshy white coating (aril). Family: Sapindaceae.

REFERENCES

1. Altschule, M. D. Cirrhosis Due to Plant Toxins. Med. Sci. *14:* 38 (1963).
2. Bras, G. and McLean, E. Toxic Factors in Veno-Occlusive Disease. Annals N.Y. Acad. Sci. *111*, Art. 1: 392 (1963).
3. Chen, K. K., Anderson, R. C., McCowen, M. C. and Harris, P. N. Pharmacologic Action of Hypoglycin A and B. J. Pharmacol. Exp. Therap. *121:* 272 (1957).
4. Doughty, D. D. and Larson, E. Tissue Changes in Experimental Ackee Poisoning Pathological Changes Produced in Rabbits. Trop. Georgr. Med. *12:* 243 (1960).
5. Hassall, C. H., Reyle, K. and Feng, P. Hypoglycin A, B: Biologically Active Polypeptides from *Blighia sapida.* Nature *173:* 356 (1954).
6. Hassall, C. H. and Reyle, K. The Toxicity of the Ackee (*Blighia sapida*) and its Relationship to the Vomiting Sickness of Jamaica. West Indian Med. J. *4:* 83 (1955).
7. Hassall, C. H. and Reyle, K. Hypoglycin A and B, two Biologically Active Polypeptides from *Blighia sapida.* Biochem. J. *60:* 334 (1955).
8. Hill, K. R. The Vomiting Sickness of Jamaica. West Indian Med. J. *1:* 243 (1952).
9. Hill, K. R., Bras, G. and Clearkin, K. P. Acute Toxic Hypoglycaemia Occurring in the Vomiting Sickness of Jamaica. West Indian Med. J. *4:* 91 (1955).
10. Hill, K. R. Discussion on Seneciosis in Man and Animals. Proc. Roy. Soc. Med. *53:* 281 (1960).

11. von Holt, L. and von Holt, C. Biochemie des Hypoglycins A. I. Die Wirkung des Riboflavins auf den Hypoglycineffekt. Biochem. Z. *331:* 422 (1956).
12. von Holt, C. and Benedict, I. Biochemie des Hypoglycins A. II. Die Einfluss des Hypoglycins auf die Oxydation von Glucose und Fettsäuren. Biochem. Z. *331:* 430 (1959).
13. von Holt, C. and Leppla, W. Die Konstitution von Hypoglycin A und B. Hoppe-Seyler's Z. Physiol. Chemie *313:* 276 (1958); See also Carbon, J. A., Martin, W. B. and Swett, L. R. Synthesis of α-Amino-methylenecyclopropanepropionic Acid (Hypoglycin A). J. Am. Chem. Soc. *80:* 1002 (1958).
14. Jelliffe, D. B., Stuart, K. L. Acute Toxic Hypoglycaemia in the Vomiting Sickness of Jamaica. Brit. Med. J. *1:* 75 (1954).
15. Schoental, R. Liver Disease and "Natural" Hepatotoxins. Bull. Wld. Health Org. *29:* 823 (1963).

IX POISONING BY MUSHROOMS

It must be stressed that there is a tremendous variation in response among individuals to mushrooms (15, 50). Species eaten safely in quantity by some cause severe reactions in others. There is also considerable variation in the toxicity of mushrooms, normally regarded as poisonous, depending upon their maturity and growing conditions. The existence of different "chemical races" of mushrooms which cannot be recognized visually but which contain different concentrations of constituents may also be an important factor. In general, simple cooking does not affect toxicity except in the case of some of the mushrooms producing simple gastroenteritis. Finally, certain varieties of edible mushrooms may elicit toxic responses if the patient ingests alcohol or if the patient is undergoing drug therapy. An interesting case illustrating this latter action is given by Yaffee (75) of a patient who, while undergoing treatment with hydroxychloroquine, became seriously sensitized to mushrooms he had previously enjoyed.

An attempt has been made to restrict the selection of mushrooms in this section to those most likely to be encountered in intoxications. On this basis mushrooms categorized as "suspected" or which have not been reported to have produced intoxications in this country have been omitted. For more extensive listings the reader should consult Buck (12), Tyler (61), and the somewhat outdated work by Ford (22).

A review of the chemical constituents in mushrooms has been given by Tyler (60) and a specific study on the active principles more recently identified in *Amanita muscaria* by Eugster (20, 21).

Poisoning by mushroom ingestion presents a diagnostic burden to the physician because the identification of species requires the expert assistance of a trained mycologist. To overcome this, a classification system has been established based entirely on the rate of onset and nature of the presenting symptoms.

Rapid Onset

Group I. Mushrooms producing nausea, vomiting and diarrhea within 2 hours of ingestion. Paresthesias and tetany have been reported for some members.

Group II. Mushrooms producing gastroenteritis shortly after ingestion, with perspiration, salivation and visual disturbances.

Group III. Mushrooms producing immediate gastroenteritis and emesis, then lassitude, drowsiness, perceptual disturbances and euphoria.

Group IV. Mushrooms producing transient excitement, hallucinations and hilarity; mydriasis and occasional cardiac depression. Gastrointestinal symptoms are absent.

Delayed Onset

Group V. Mushrooms producing gastroenteritis with emesis and diarrhea 6 to 12 hours after ingestion, then somnolence, jaundice, anuria, and coma.

Group VI. Mushrooms producing emesis (but not diarrhea) 6 to 12 hours after ingestion, and jaundice.

Secondary Intoxication

Group VII. Mushrooms having a disulfiram (Antabuse) action. This effect is immediate following the ingestion of alcohol but a prolonged period is required after consumption of the mushrooms to produce a maximal sensitization to alcohol.

Poisonous Mushrooms of Group I

Mushrooms in this group, particularly when eaten raw, may produce severe but usually transient nausea and diarrhea within 2 hours of ingestion. Fatalities are rare but, based on foreign reports, are usually associated with the *Rhodophyllus* species. The therapeutic management consists of gastric lavage and supportive measures for simple gastroenteritis.

Members of the Group

Agaricus arvensis var. *palustris* A. H. Smith
Agaricus hondensis Murr.
Agaricus placomyces Peck
Boletus miniato-olivaceus Frost var. *sensibilis* Peck — Sensitive Boletus
Boletus luridus Fr. — Lurid Boletus
Boletus satanas Lenz — Satan's Boletus
Cantharellus floccosus Schw.
Chlorophyllum molybdites (Fr.) Mass. (= *Lepiota molybdites* (Fr.) Sacc.; *Lepiota morgani* (Peck) Sacc.)
Lactarius glaucescens Crossland
Lactarius rufus (Fr.) Fr.
Lactarius torminosus (Fr.) S. F. Gray
Naematoloma fasciculare (Fr.) Karst. (= *Hypholoma fasciculare* (Fr.) Kummer)

Paxillus involutus (Fr.)
Phaeolepiota aurea (Fr.) Konrad & Maubl. (= *Togaria aurea* (Fr.) W. G. Smith)
Rhodophyllus sinuatus (Fr.) Sing. (= *Entoloma sinuatum* (Fr.) Kummer; *Entoloma lividum* (St. Amans) Quél.)
Russula emetica (Fr.) S. F. Gray
Scleroderma cepa Pers.
Scleroderma aurantium Pers.
Tricholoma pardinum Quél.
Tricholoma venenatum Atk.

Comments on Individual Species

Agaricus species. It is extremely difficult to separate fact from fiction with respect to the toxicity of certain *Agaricus* species. Nevertheless some mention should be made of the fact that certain *Agaricus* species which smell of phenol, especially on cooking, or which stain yellow when cut, bruised, or cooked, are liable to cause mild to severe gastrointestinal disturbances in some individuals. Nothing is known about the active constituents of these species.

Boletus species. Intoxications are usually limited to gastroenteritis. *B. luridus*, which is quite rare in the United States, has been reported to produce "unpleasant paralytic symptoms."

Cantharellus floccosus. Produces gastroenteric disturbances in some individuals. Its toxicity is ascribed to nor-caperatic acid. A limited pharmacological study on this compound was conducted by Miyata (42).

Chlorophyllum molybdites. This mushroom is a frequent cause of gastroenteritis and has been responsible for fatalities. Its toxicity is probably not abolished by cooking (47).

Lactarius species. The purgative action of these species is usually abolished by parboiling; however, the ingestion of "cooked" *L. glaucescens* was fatal to a child (13). The ingestion of raw *L. glaucescens* and *L. torminosus* has been associated with fatalities.

Naematoloma fasciculare. A number of reports indicate that this is a very toxic species, having produced fatalities (68). A preliminary study of its toxic constituents has appeared (45).

Paxillus involutus. Is toxic when raw, producing gastroenteric disturbances (10, 51). Cooking renders the species edible.

Phaeolepiota aurea. A single report from Alaska states that this species produces a mild gastroenteritis (71). It is considered an edible delicacy within the mainland of the United States.

Rhodophyllus sinuatus. Produces severe gastroenteritis very shortly after ingestion. This may be accompanied by headache, vertigo, intense thirst, and occasionally changes in pupillary size. The intoxication may persist for several days. Both hepatotoxicity and death have been reported (61).

Russula emetica. Intoxications are usually limited to severe gastroenteritis.

Scleroderma species. A peculiar type of poisoning has been described by Stevenson (55) for the puffball *Scleroderma cepa.* In the case report, stomach pain developed within 30 minutes of ingestion followed rapidly by a general feeling of weakness and nausea. There was a tingling sensation over the entire body. The muscles became rigid in the extremities. Within 45 minutes tetany was far advanced and accompanied by stomach cramps, profuse sweating, and distinct facial pallor. After emesis there was prompt relief and the patient was asymptomatic in 24 hours. *Scleroderma aurantium* has been reported to produce emesis, apprehension, profuse sweating, and unconsciousness.

Tricholoma species. Members of this group, of which the 2 listed are most commonly encountered in intoxications, produce severe gastroenteritis similar to *Rhodophyllus sinuatus.*

Poisonous Mushrooms of Group II

Toxic Principle

These mushrooms contain pharmacologically active concentrations of muscarine (8, 9, 20, 21, 30, 39). Their ingestion produces effects identical to an overdose of any parasympathetic stimulant. Muscarine does not elicit central nervous system effects.

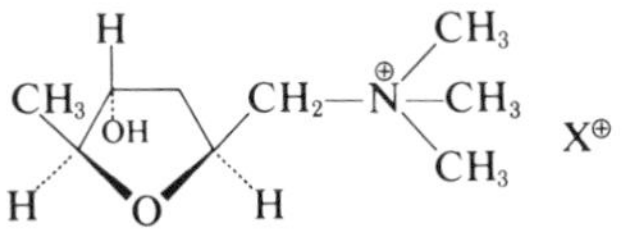

Muscarine

Members of the Group

Clitocybe dealbata (Fr.) Gillet (= *Clitocybe morbifera* Peck)	Sweat producing clitocybe
Inocybe napipes Lang	
Inocybe mixtilis (Britz.) Sacc.	
Inocybe griseolilacina Lange	
Inocybe lacera (Fr.) Quél.	
Inocybe decipientoides Peck	
Omphalotus olearius (Fr.) Sing. (= *Clitocybe illudens* (Schwein) Sacc.)	Deceiving clitocybe Jack-o-lantern

Symptoms

The onset of symptoms is usually rapid and may be within 15 minutes following ingestion. The intoxication usually begins with visual disturbances and heavy perspiration. Salivation, lacrimation, colicky pains, and muscular weakness are also exhibited. Emesis and diarrhea are not consistently found.

Increased vagal tone is reflected by bradycardia and occasional arrhythmias. The blood pressure may be depressed. Bronchiolar constriction and moist rales leading to acute asthmatic respiration should be anticipated (32).

Treatment

Gastric lavage should be administered unless spontaneous emesis has occurred. Atropine is a specific antidote for this type of intoxication and may be administered either orally or hypodermically in quantities sufficient, 0.5–1.0 mg, repeated in ½ hour intervals if required, to abolish the symptoms.

Prognosis

For *Clitocybe dealbata*, Alder (2) records a fatality rate of 7.9 per cent. Death, in most instances, may be presumed to result from sinus arrest.

Poisonous Mushrooms of Group III

Amanita muscaria and *Amanita pantherina* contain (in addition to pharmacologically inactive traces of muscarine) ibotenic acid and muscimol (pantherine) which have marked central nervous system effects (20, 21, 64). The other *Amanita* species listed have not been investigated chemically but are presumed to belong to this group. The substances responsible for the gastroenteric disturbances have not been identified.

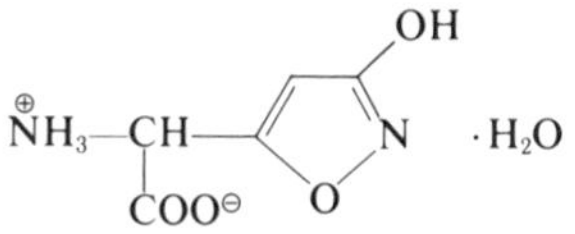

Ibotenic Acid ($\cdot H_2O$)

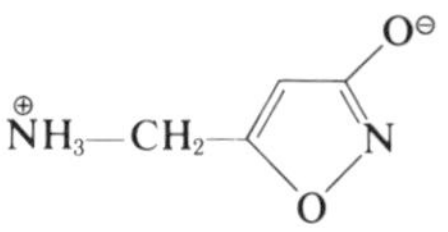

Muscimol (Pantherine)

Members of the Group

Amanita muscaria (Fr.) Hook	Fly Amanita; Fly Agaric (fig. 54)
Amanita pantherina (Fr.) Secr.	Panther Amanita
Amanita flavivolva Murr.	
Amanita cothurnata Atk.	Booted Amanita

Symptoms

Usually within 15 minutes the patient experiences drowsiness and gastroenteritis which may be accompanied by emesis. Frequently the patient will experience a light sleep for about 2 hours. This is followed by elation, hyperkinesis, frequently compulsive speaking and shouting, and visual hallucinations. The phase of central excitement may persist for 3 or 4 hours (29, 69) but cases lasting up to 18 hours have been described (49).

Neither ibotenic acid or pantherine produce gastroenteritis. In human experiments (67) employing the pure substances, 20 mg of ibotenic acid produced facial flushing, lassitude, and a severe occipital headache lasting for

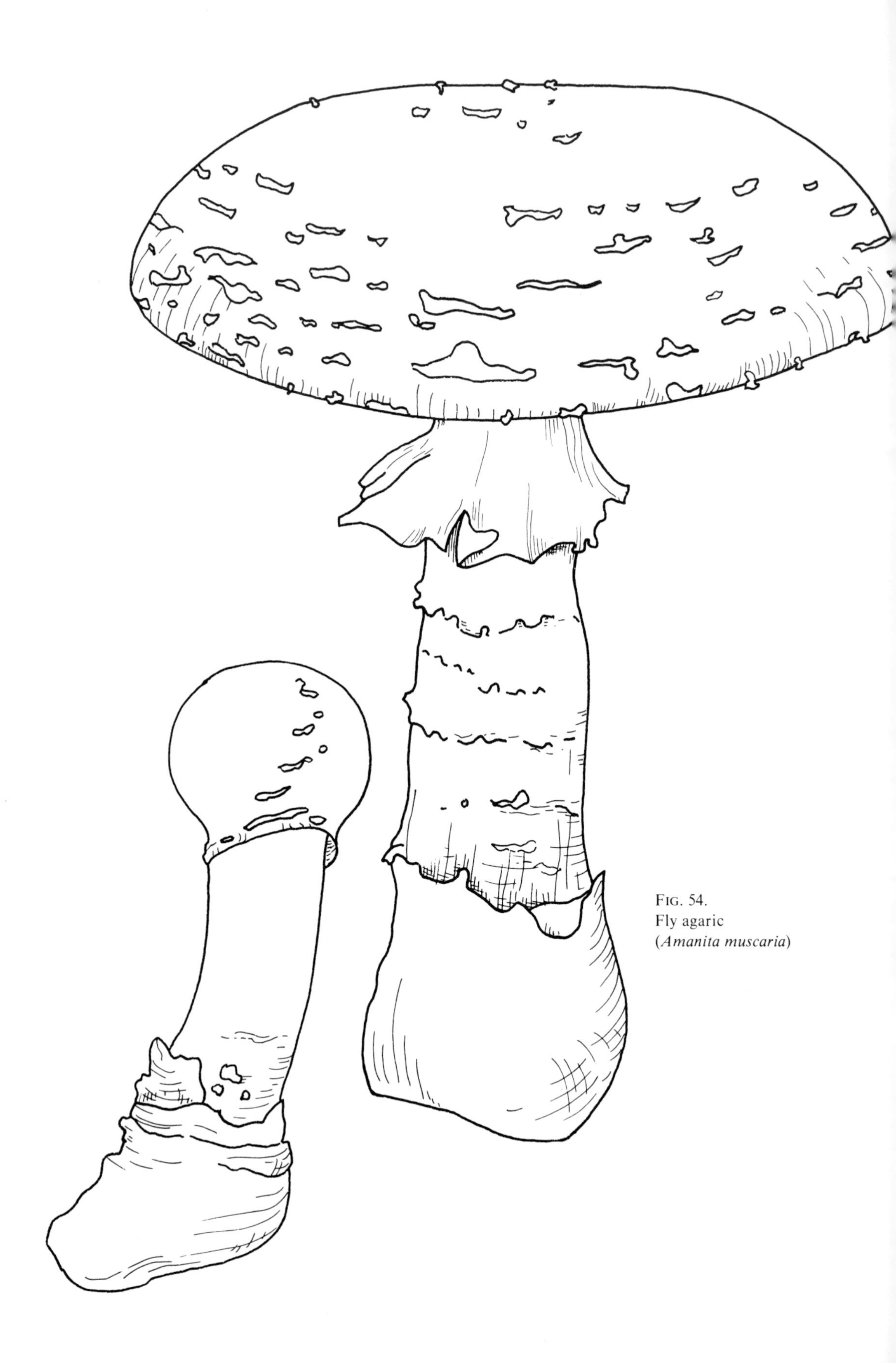

FIG. 54.
Fly agaric
(*Amanita muscaria*)

2 weeks. A dose of 10 mg muscimol produced dizziness, ataxia, euphoria, a slight change of color vision and myoclonic twitching. Elevation of the dose to 15 mg produced, after a 40 minute latent period, dizziness, slight anorexia, interference with concentration, visual echo pictures, auditory echo, and myoclonic cramps which lasted for about 4 hours. This higher dose produced hallucinations but these were not as vivid as those that are evoked by lysergic acid diethylamide.

Prognosis

The incidence of fatalities in this country has been negligible. In Germany, where such poisonings are more frequent, Alder (2) found a death rate of 5.5 per cent for *Amanita muscaria* and 1.54 per cent for *Amanita pantherina.*

Treatment

Usually nothing is required beyond simple gastric lavage. Chlorpromazine may be employed to terminate severe agitation or hallucinations.

Comment

Older works which give atropine as a specific antidote should be disregarded. This recommendation was founded before the isolation and pharmacological evaluation of ibotenic acid and muscimol (jointly called "pilzatropine" before their identity was known) and was based on the impression that small traces of muscarine in these species was responsible for their toxicity. Actually atropine will aggravate rather than ameliorate the symptoms produced by members of this group.

Poisonous Mushrooms of Group IV

Intoxications by mushrooms of this class may be accidental or deliberately self-inflicted in an attempt to elicit a hallucinogenic effect. This latter may involve dried mushrooms imported into the country for this purpose.

The mushrooms in Group III are also capable of producing delirium and hallucinations but are otherwise different in that none of the members of Group IV produce gastroenteritis.

Members of the Group

Conocybe cyanopus (Atk.) Kühn.
Conocybe smithii Watling
Psilocybe caerulescens Murr.
Psilocybe mexicana Heim
Psilocybe pelliculosa A. H. Smith
Psilocybe cyanescens Wakefield
Psilocybe baeocystis Singer & Smith
Psilocybe cubensis (Earle) Sing.
Pholiota spectabilis (Fr.) Gill.

The following species of *Panaeolus* have been reported to possess hallucinogenic activity: *P. sphinctrinus* (Fr.) Quél.; *P. campanulatus* (Fr.) Quél; *P. semiovatus* (Fr.) Lund.; *P. subbalteatus* (Berk & Br.) Sacc. (=*P. venenosus* Murr.). It can now be stated with reasonable certainty that these reports were based on erroneous identifications (65).

Hallucinogenic Constituents

The *Conocybe* and *Psilocybe* mushrooms contain psilocybin and psilocin as their active constituents. Chemical analysis, not yet reported in detail, indicates that some other material must be responsible for the activity of *Pholiota spectabilis* (11, 18).

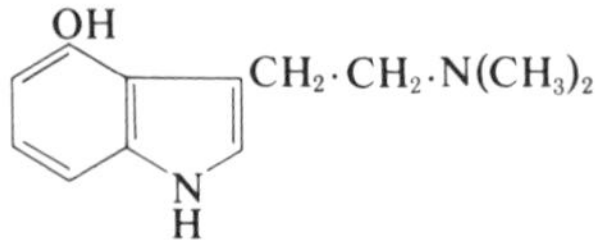

OH
$CH_2 \cdot CH_2 \cdot N(CH_3)_2$
N
H

Psilocin

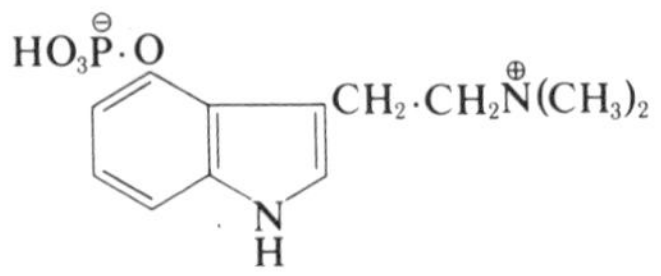

$HO_3\overset{\ominus}{P} \cdot O$
$CH_2 \cdot CH_2\overset{\oplus}{N}(CH_3)_2$
N
H

Psilocybin

Symptoms

The onset of effects for all varieties usually occurs within 3 hours of ingestion and is characterized by drowsiness, loss of ability to concentrate, dizziness, ataxia, and sometimes muscle weakness. Mydriasis, dyspnea, and skin parasthesias are relatively frequent findings for all of the above species. The hallucinogenic effects are dose dependent and may vary in their nature according to the personality of the patient. Both space and time distortion are reported together with visual and auditory imagery. Hilarity may be evoked and the hallucinations are usually described as pleasant (41, 53, 54, 66, 70).

Treatment

Recovery following ingestion of a mushroom is normally uneventful. The period of intoxication is generally of short duration, usually about 3 to 6 hours, after which the patient is asymptomatic.

There is a danger that patients may undertake destructive behavior during the hallucinatory period, and thus their movements should be restricted. In those patients who deliberately inflict self-intoxications, there is always the possibility of precipitating long-term psychoses.

The phenothiazine drugs may be employed to terminate the psychosis if extreme agitation is present. The comments under the treatment section for hallucinogenic plants, Chapter VI, should be consulted.

Poisonous Mushrooms of Group V

The mushrooms in this group are responsible for 90 per cent of the fatal mushroom intoxications in the United States. Poisoning by members of the *Amanita phalloides* type is of extremely grave consequence, the mortality rate being in excess of 50 per cent.

Members of the Group

Amanita phalloides (Fr.) Secr.	Death cup, Death cap (fig. 55)
Amanita verna (Fr.) Vitt. s Boud.	Spring Amanita
Amanita virosa Secr.	The Destroying Angel

Amanita bisporigera Atk.

(Possibly *Amanita brunnescens* Atk.; *A. tenuifolia* Murr.; *A. verniformis* Murr.; and *A. virosiformis* Murr. The toxicity of these species requires verification.)

Galerina marginata (Fr.) Kühn

Galerina autumnalis (Peck) Smith & Sing.

Galerina venenata A. H. Smith

Toxic Principles

Eight toxic peptides have been isolated from *A. phalloides* and their structures characterized by Wieland and Wieland (72, 73) and more recent reports indicate that there are at least 4 more. Alpha amanitin is probably responsible for the primary actions exhibited by these mushrooms. These compounds are thermostable and are not affected by either cooking or drying. Dried *Amanita phalloides* mushrooms examined after 9 years storage retained nearly full toxic activity. The toxicity is such that fatalities have resulted from eating a small fragment from a single mushroom cap. According to Tyler, *A. bisporigera* has been found to be the most toxic of the American mushrooms thus far chemically analyzed.

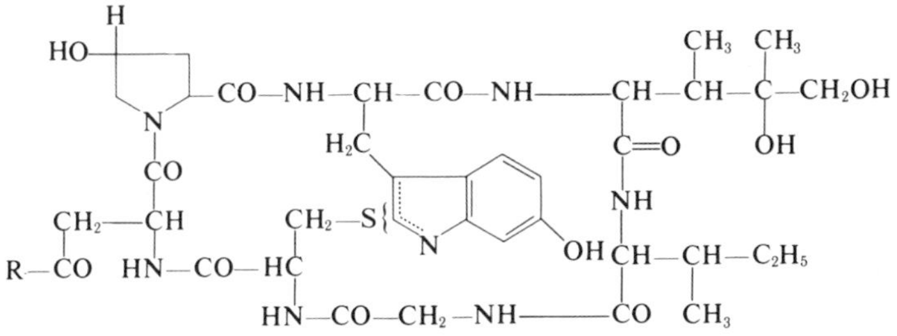

α-Amanitin ($R = NH_2$)
β-Amanitin ($R = OH$)

The toxic principles of *Galerina* have been studied and identified as Amanita toxins (62, 63), and have been produced in fermentative culture (4).

Differential Diagnosis

The sudden onset of gastroenteritis in not less than 6 and usually about 12 hours after ingestion of mushrooms is characteristic only for members of these species and those of Group VI. A differential diagnosis may be accomplished by the demonstration of Amanita toxins in specimens of the ingested mushrooms or from the stomach washings by the simple laboratory procedure of Block, *et al.* (6) or Sullivan, *et al.* (58).

As a generalization, poisonings with this symptomology appearing in May or June are probably due to *Helvella* species while those in July or later are of the *A. phalloides* variety. Frequently the patient can indicate the difference if shown the text illustrations (figs. 55, 56) since only the *Amanita* mushrooms have gilled caps.

Symptoms

The first symptoms appear suddenly about 6 to 15 hours after ingestion and usually consist of profound gastroenteric irritation, with vomiting, violent and painful abdominal cramps and continuous diarrhea, often with blood and mucus in the stools. There is extreme thirst reflecting the loss in body fluids which may amount to 2 to 3 liters/day. Albuminuria, hematuria or anuria should be anticipated. Jaundice is a typical and constant feature and becomes apparent 2 to 3 days after the onset of symptoms. Cyanosis with coldness and pain in the extremities may occur. Increasing prostration, peripheral circulatory collapse, and hepatic coma finally lead to death, usually within 3 to 8 days after ingestion.

Not all cases of poisoning present evidence of central nervous system involvement. The variety of reactions which may be seen are suggestive of random destruction of the brain together with secondary effects due to hepatic destruction, renal failure and hypotension. In a survey made by Marcovitz and Alpers (40), the most common neurologic manifestations are those indicating generalized cerebral involvement, for example, prostration, confusion, delirium, convulsions, somnolence and coma. In addition, a number of rather heterogeneous signs have been recorded indicating widespread involvement of the nervous system. Visual disturbances, such as amblyopia and rarely blindness, pupillary disorders, such as miosis, anisocoria and sluggish reactions, and ocular palsies occur. Involuntary movements, such as tremors and twitchings, increased or decreased tonus with weakness or paralysis of the extremities, and loss or exaggeration of reflexes with a Babinski sign, may be found. Incontinence, paralysis of the bladder and spasm of the sphincter are sometimes observed. Meningeal signs, such as stiffness of the neck and opisthotonos, occur. Finally, there is vasomotor collapse, with cyanosis, a fall in blood pressure, sweating and a rapid, weak, irregular pulse. There seems to be no consistent relationship in the appearance of these signs, or in their combinations, and no definite nervous symptomatology can be outlined. In any particular case almost any of the signs may appear, singly or in combination, depending on the degree and extent of generalized and focalized involvement of the nervous system. A discussion of acute psychoses has been reported by Helbig (27).

Cardiac involvement is seen only rarely. The classic case reported by Hyman (31) of right bundle branch block and right ventricular extrasystoles,

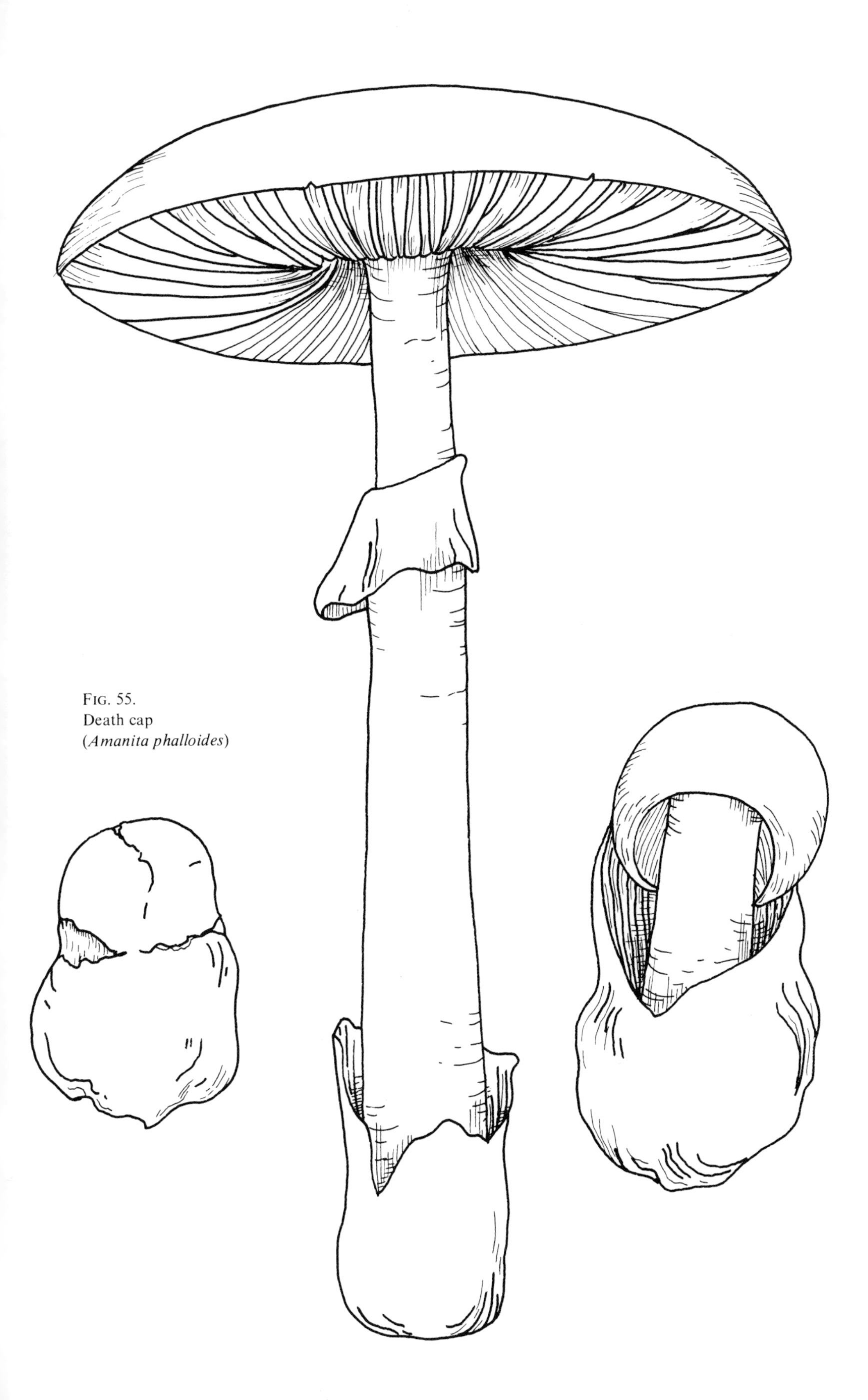

FIG. 55.
Death cap
(*Amanita phalloides*)

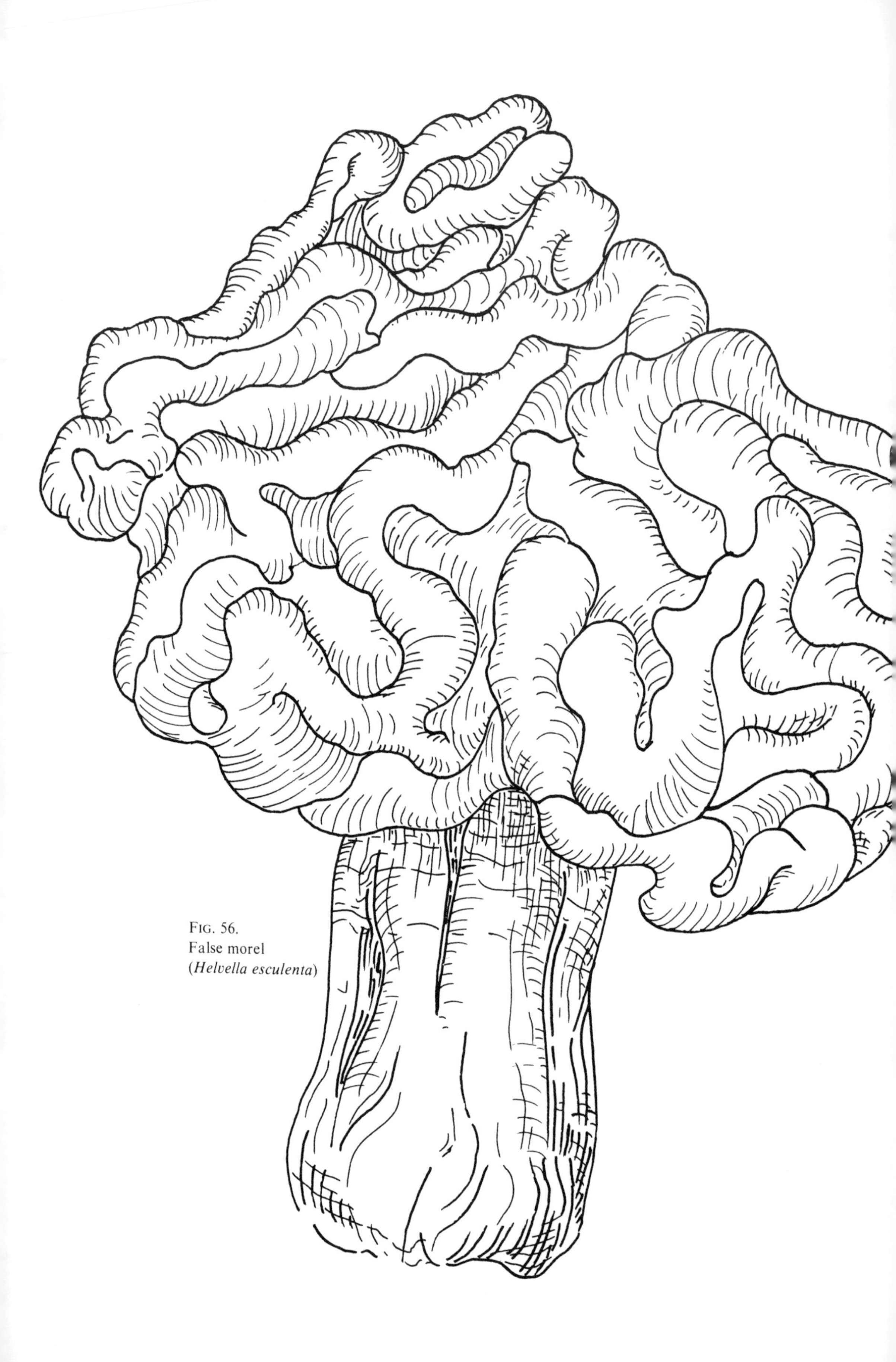

FIG. 56.
False morel
(*Helvella esculenta*)

is consistent with an hemorrhagic lesion in the conduction tissue but doubt has been expressed on the identification of the offending mushroom (5). Better established cases of *Amanita phalloides* poisoning illustrating myocardial damage are presented by Boch (7) and by Debiec, *et al.* (16).

Extensive details of clinical biochemistry measurements in 2 cases of *Galerina venenata* poisoning are given by Grosman and Malbin (24). Essentially, these reveal the anticipated changes in hepatic and renal function.

Pathology

The mucous membrane of the whole gastrointestinal tract is profoundly congested and degenerated. The stomach shows a severe degree of hemorrhagic gastritis; the ileum and colon undergo inflammatory changes with petechial hemorrhages and some free blood.

The liver is reduced in size, and is a pale yellow and very friable. Acute fatty degeneration is marked. Microscopic examination shows all the tissue to be abnormal. The cells are pale and empty looking. The nuclei are hydropic and often distorted in shape. All degrees of karolysis are present, many scattered cells having undergone necrosis, and dead cells containing yellow pigment can be seen.

The kidneys are enlarged and whitish in color with petechial hemorrhages on the surface. Section of the kidney shows much parenchymatous degeneration and congestion, especially in the medulla. Yellow pigment is abundant, particularly at the base of the cells of the tubular epithelium. There is a cloudy swelling of the tubules, with engorgement of the glomeruli with some escape of red cells into the tubules. Electron microscopy of the kidney following fatal human poisoning is given by Myler, *et al.* (43).

The lungs may be congested and edematous with consolidation and petechial hemorrhages in the apices.

The brain may show a widespread edema, congestion, punctate hemorrhages and erosion of cortical areas. The ganglion cells exhibit degenerative changes, and there is fatty infiltration in the ganglion cells, neuroglia, microglia, ependyma and endothelium.

Small petechial lesions may be seen on the heart and pericardium. All chambers, particularly the right side, may be dilated. A few cases have been reported of fatty degeneration of the heart muscle.

Treatment

Despite the prolonged latent period between the mushroom ingestion and the appearance of symptoms, an attempt should be made to remove unabsorbed matter from the stomach and colon by lavage, saline cathartics and enema.

There is no specific antidote for deadly *Amanita* poisoning. The most attractive regime appears to be the establishment of hemodialysis as early as possible. Although less rapid in action, peritoneal dialysis could be instituted in hospitals which do not have the facilities or staff for hemodialysis. Thereafter scrupulous attention must be given to electrolyte and fluid balance. Appropriate measures should also be initiated on evidence of impending renal or hepatic failure. Prophylactic measures undertaken toward minimizing hepatic degeneration, such as the administration of methionine, enzyme preparations, glucose, and so on, are of questionable value.

In a series of 4 cases presented by Tholen, *et al.* (59), hemodialysis was initiated 24 to 36 hours after ingestion of *Amanita phalloides* and was maintained over 8 to 16 hours. None of these patients had renal failure and only one experienced hepatic coma (which occurred prior to initiation of therapy). All were saved, apparently without permanent pathological alteration. Another severe case illustrating successful therapy with hemodialysis is given by Elliott (19) and with intermittent peritoneal dialysis by Myler, *et al.* (43).

Because of its reported usefulness in hepatic coma, thioctic (α-lipoic) acid was tried and proved to be an effective antidote in 39 out of 40 cases of human phalloides intoxication. It was administered by a slow, prolonged infusion up to levels of 300 mg/day, in conjunction with electrolytes and dextrose in water, until serum transaminase decreased (35, 36). Its antidotal value in phalloides poisoning has been verified in animal experiments (46).

Additional useful discussions on deadly *Amanita* poisoning are given by a number of authors (1, 3, 17, 23, 26, 55).

Poisonous Mushrooms of Group VI

Helvella esculenta Fr. (= *Gyromitra esculenta* Fr.; *Physomitra esculenta* Boudier) — False Morel; Lorel; Lorchel (fig. 56)

Toxicity

Symptoms appear 6 to 12 hours after ingestion and are generally similar to those seen in *A. phalloides* poisoning (Group V). These are characterized by severe abdominal pain, emesis, vertigo, convulsions and coma. During the early phase of the intoxication the temperature is elevated and tachycardia is usually present (12, 28, 57).

Differential Diagnosis

See Poisonous Mushrooms of Group V, page 161.

Prognosis

In one series of 151 cases of *Helvella* poisoning in Germany (2), the fatality rate was 40 per cent but the usual mortality rate is closer to 4 per cent. At least 7 fatal cases attributed to *H. esculenta* have been reported in the United States since 1924.

Comment

The toxicity of this and other related *Helvella* species presents a very great problem which is just now beginning to be resolved. There can be no doubt that *H. esculenta* is ordinarily toxic in Europe. It is frequently eaten, however, after being rendered safe by parboiling or drying. Other species, such as *H. gigas* Krbh. are also poisonous in Europe.

There is at least one reliable report that *H. esculenta* is toxic in the Eastern United States, but it (and *H. gigas* and related species) are commonly collected and eaten in the West (Rocky Mountains to the coast) without previous parboiling, and no single case of poisoning has been reliably reported. In our present state of knowledge, we must assume that there exist different chemical races of the mushrooms; the ones in the western United States lack the toxic principle.

Toxic Principle

The toxicity was originally ascribed to a thermostable, water soluble carbohydrate of unknown composition named helvellic acid. However, all of the old chemical data on helvellic acid are now known to be invalid (36). Prof. P. H. List, University of Marburg, has recently isolated the poisonous principle, which he has named gyromitrin, from *Helvella esculenta*. A brief note appeared (44) suggesting that this component was the ethylene imide of α,β-epoxyethylene dicarboxylic acid. However, more recent work from that laboratory (36) indicates that the structure is more probably the following osazone:

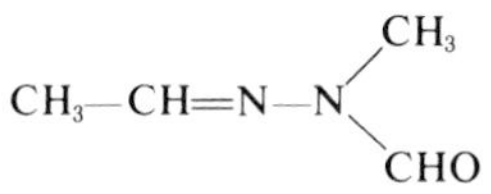

$$CH_3-CH=N-N\begin{matrix} \diagup CH_3 \\ \diagdown CHO \end{matrix}$$

Gyromitrin

It is quite volatile, which explains the edibility of the species after parboiling or long drying. Still unexplained is the variability in the toxicity of the species in different parts of the world.

Recommended Treatment

Ford suggested exchange transfusion but there is no recorded evidence of this having been tried. Either hemodialysis or peritoneal dialysis might be worthy of consideration. Attention must be given to electrolyte and fluid balance.

Poisonous Mushrooms of Group VII

Coprinus atramentarius (Fr.) Fr. Inky cap

This mushroom exhibits a disulfiram (Antabuse) like effect. Like disulfiram, 12 to 24 hours are required after ingestion of the mushroom before the individual is maximally sensitized to alcohol. According to List, the ingestion of uncooked *Coprinus* is ineffective in eliciting the alcohol reaction (37, 38). Tyler, in a personal communication, reports that recently dried specimens are active but to a somewhat lesser degree than freshly cooked mushrooms.

Symptoms

Within 5 to 10 minutes after the ingestion of alcohol the face feels hot and soon afterwards it is flushed and scarlet in appearance. As the vasodilation spreads over the whole body, intense throbbing is felt in the head and neck, and a pulsating headache may develop. Respiratory difficulties, nausea, copious vomiting, sweating, thirst, chest pain, considerable hypotension, orthostatic syncope, marked uneasiness, weakness, vertigo, blurred vision, and confusion are observed. The facial flush is replaced by pallor, and the blood pressure may fall to shock level.

The effect lasts between 30 minutes in mild cases to several hours. After the symptoms regress, the patient is exhausted and may sleep for several hours, after which he is asymptomatic (25, 48).

Prognosis and Treatment

The course of events in mushroom sensitization to alcohol is usually considered innocuous. Since the symptoms will be very alarming to the patient, he may require considerable reassurance and explanation, but no particular treatment is recommended.

Comment

Child (14) failed to elicit this response with three species of *Coprinus*, possibly because he did not allow for the sensitization latent period (33). Alcohol probably enhances the toxic effects of certain other mushrooms, but this action is distinct from the disulfiram-like response (52).

The report that disulfiram was isolated from *Coprinus atramentarius* is erroneous. The substance responsible for the alcohol-sensitizing response is not yet known (74).

REFERENCES

1. Abul-Haj, S. K., Ewald, R. A. and Lazyak, L. Fatal Mushroom Poisoning. New Eng. J. Med. *269:* 223 (1963).
2. Alder, A. E. Erkennung und Behandlung der Pilzvergiftunger. Dtsch. Med. Wschr. *86:* 1121 (1961).
3. Ahronheim, J. H. Acute Yellow Atrophy of the Liver Caused by Poisonous Mushrooms. J. Mich. State Med. Soc. *37:* 921 (1938).
4. Benedict, R. G., Tyler, V. E. Jr., Brady, L. R. and Weber, L. J. Fermentative Production of Amanita Toxins by a Strain of *Galerina marginata*. J. Bact. *91:* 1380 (1966).
5. Bickford, J. A. R. "Mushroom" Poisoning Due to *Amanita phalloides*. Brit. Med. J. *2:* 498 (1948).
6. Block, S. S., Stephens, R. L., Barreto, A., Murrill, W. A. Chemical Identification of the Amanita Toxin in Mushrooms. Science *121:* 606 (1955).
7. Bock, H. E., Nieth, H., Zysno, E., Gayer, J., and Fröhlich, C. Die Knollenblätterschwamn-Vergiftung. Dtsch. Med. Wschr. *89:* 1617 (1964).
8. Bowden, K. and Mogey, G. A. The Story of Muscarine. J. Pharm. Pharmacol. *10:* 145 (1958).
9. Brown, J. K., Malone, M. H., Stuntz, D. E. and Tyler, V. E. Jr. Paper Chromatographic Determination of Muscarine in Inocybe Species. J. Pharm. Sci. *51:* 853 (1962).
10. Bschor, F., Kohlmeyer, J. and Mallach, H. J. Neue Vergiftungsfälle durch *Paxillus involutus* (Batsch) Fr. Ztschr. Pilzkunde *29:* 1 (1963).
11. Buck, R. W. Psychedelic Effect of *Pholiota spectabilis*. New Eng. J. Med. *276:* 391 (1967).

12. Buck, R. W. Mushroom Toxins—A Brief Review of the Literature. New Eng. J. Med. *265:* 681 (1961).
13. Charles, V. K. Mushroom Poisoning Caused by *Lactaria glaucescens*. Mycologia *34:* 112 (1942).
14. Child, G. P. The Inability of Coprini to Sensitize Man to Ethyl Alcohol. Mycologia *44:* 200 (1952).
15. Dearness, J. The Personal Factor in Mushroom Poisoning. Mycologia *3:* 75 (1911).
16. Debiec, B., Bielinska, W., Romer, T. E. Modifications de l'Electrocardiogramme au cours d'un empoisonnement par des *Amanites phalloides*. Pediatrie *19:* 451 (1964).
17. Dubash, J. and Teare, D. Poisoning by *Amanita phalloides*. Brit. Med. J. *1:* 45 (1946).
18. (Editor) Champignons toxiques au Japon. Bull. Soc. Mycol. France *80*(I): IV–V (1964).
19. Elliott, W., Hall, M., Kerr, D. M. S., Rolland, C. F., Smart, G. A., Swinney, J. Mushroom Poisoning. Lancet *2:* 630 (1961).
20. Eugster, C. H. Über den Fliegen pilz. Neujahrsblatt Naturforsch. Ges. Zurich. *169:* (1967).
21. Eugster, C. H. Psychoactive Principles in *Amanita muscaria* in *Ethnopharmacologic Search for Psycho-Active Drugs*, Proc. Symposium, San Francisco, Calif. Jan 28–30, 1967. Editor-in-chief, D. H. Efron; co-editors, B. Holmstedt and N. S. Kline. U.S. Dept. Health, Education and Welfare; U.S. Gov. Printing Office 1967.
22. Ford, W. W. in Peterson, F. *Legal Medicine and Toxicology*. Saunders, Philadelphia, 1923. Pp. 817–856.
23. Gaultier, M., Orcel, L., Fournier, E., Benhamou, J. P., Gervais, P., and Sicot, C. L'Hepatite Phalloidienne. A propos de quatorze observations. Presse méd. *73*, Part 4: 2349 (1965).
24. Grossman, C. M., Malbin, B. Mushroom Poisoning: A Review of the Literature and Report of Two Cases Caused by a Previously Undescribed Species. Ann. Int. Med. *40:* 249 (1954).
25. Groves, J. W. Poisoning by Morels when taken with alcohol. Mycologia *56:* 779 (1964).
26. Harrison, D. C., Coggins, C. H., Welland, F. H., Nelson, S. Mushroom Poisoning in Five Patients. Am. J. Med. *38:* 787 (1965).
27. Helbig, H. Beitrag zur Psychopathologie der Knollenblätterpilzvergiftung (*Amanita phalloides*). Nervenarzt *27:* 219 (1956).
28. Hendricks, H. V. Poisoning by False Morel (*Gyromitra esculenta*). J. Am. Med. Assoc. *114:* 1625 (1940).
29. Hotson, J. W. and Lewis, E. *Amanita pantherina* of Western Washington. Mycologia *26:* 384 (1934).
30. Hughes, D. W., Genest, K. and Rice, W. B. The Occurrence of Muscarine in *Clitocybe dealbata*. Lloydia *29:* 328 (1966).
31. Hyman, A. S. The Heart in Mushroom Poisoning. Bull. Johns Hopkins Hosp. *42:* 8 (1928).
32. Jelliffe, S. E. Some Notes on Poisoning by *Clitocybe dealbata* (Sow.) var. *Sudorifica* (Peck). N.Y. State J. Med. *37:* 1357 (1937).
33. Josserand, M. The Ability of Coprini to Sensitize Man to Ethyl Alcohol. Mycologia *44:* 829 (1952).
34. Kubicka, J. New Possibilities in the Treatment of Poisoning by the Deadly Amanita—*Amanita phalloides*. Mykologisches Mitteilungsblatt *7:* 92 (1963).
35. Kubica, J. Prevention and Therapy of Intoxications by *Amanita phalloides* in South Bohemia Region. Prakt. Lekar. *44*(18): 702 (1964).
36. List, P. H. and Luft, P. Gyromitrin, Das Gift der Fruehjahrlorchel, *Gyromitra* (Helvella) *esculenta* Fr. Tetrahedron Letters No. 20, 1893–4 (1967).
37. List, P. H. and Hetzel, H. Chemie der Höhreren Pilze. Planta Med. *7:* 310 (1959).
38. List, P. H. and Reith, H. Basische Pilzinhaltsstoffe, X Imidazolderivate im Faltentintling, *Coprinus atramentarius* Bull. Ztsch. Physiol. Chemie *319:* 17 (1960).
39. Malone, M. H., Robichaud, R. C., Tyler, V. E. Jr., Brady, L. R. A Bioassay for Muscarine Activity and its Detection in Certain Inocybe. Lloydia *24:* 204 (1961).
40. Marcovitz, E. and Alpers, B. J. The Central Nervous System in Mushroom Poisoning. Report of Two Cases with Toxic Encephalitis. Arch. Neurol. Psychiat. *33:* 53 (1935).
41. Marmo, E. Psilocibina e Psilocina: Principi Attivi Dei Funghi Allucinogeni Messicani. Cl. Terap. (Italian) *18:* 464 (1960).
42. Miyata, J. T., Tyler, V. E. Jr., Brady, L. R. and Malone, M. H. The Occurrence of Norcaperatic Acid in *Cantharellus floccosus*. Lloydia *29:* 43 (1966).
43. Myler, R. K., Lee, J. C. and Hopper, J. Jr. Renal Tubular Necrosis Caused by Mushroom Poisoning. Arch. Int. Med. *114:* 196 (1964).

44. Neuhoff, W. Gyromitrin, ein neuentdeckter Giftstoff in der Frühlorchel. Ztsch. Pilzkunde *31:* 69 (1965).
45. Nishihara, M., Lin, C-C., Furukawa, I. and Nakanishi, S. Chemical Studies on Poisonous Mushroom. (I) A Preliminary Experiment on the Isolation of Poisonous Ingredients in *Hypholoma fasiculare*. Doshisha Eng. Rev. *9:* 36 (1958).
46. Obauer, G. and Schön, H. *Amanita phalloides* poisoning. Arzneimittel-Forsch. *14:* 1257 (1964).
47. Picchioni, A. L. Mushroom Poisoning. Am. J. Hosp. Pharm. *22:* 634 (1965).
48. Reynolds, W. A. and Lowe, F. H. Mushrooms and a Toxic Reaction to Alcohol. New Eng. J. Med. *272:* 630 (1965).
49. Roch, M. and Mach, J-P. Délire grave et prolongé causé par un empoisonnement par *Amanita muscaria* (fausse oronge). Praxis *49:* 226 (1960).
50. Rogers, D. P. Identification of Edible and Poisonous Mushrooms. Trans. N.Y. Acad. Sci. Ser. II, *19:* 545 (1957).
51. Schmidt, O. Kremplingsvergiftung in meiningen. Ztchr. Pilzkunde *29:* 54 (1963).
52. Shaffer, R. L. Poisoning by *Pholiota squarrosa*. Mycologia *57:* 318 (1965).
53. Singer, R., Stein, S. I., Ames, R. W. and Smith, A. H. Observations on Agarics Causing Cerebral Mycetisms. Mycopath. Mycol. App. *9:* 261–284 (1958).
54. Stein, S. I. Observations on Psychoneurophysiologically Significant Mushrooms. Mycopath. Mycol. App. *11:* 205 (1959).
55. Stevenson, J. A. *Scleroderma* Poisoning. Mycologia *53:* 438 (1961).
56. Steyn, D. G. The Treatment of Cases of *Amanita phalloides* and *Amanita capensis* Poisoning. South African Med. J. *40:* 405 (1966).
57. Stuhlfauth, K. and Jung, F. Vergiftung mit Lorcheln (*Helvella esculenta*). Arch. Tox. *14:* 86 (1952).
58. Sullivan, G., Brady, L. R., and Tyler, V. E. Jr. Identification of α- and β-Amanitin by Thin-Layer Chromatography. J. Pharm. Sci. *54:* 921 (1965).
59. Tholen, H., Frolich, T., Huber, F. and Massini, M.-A. Frühzeitige Hämodialyse bei Vergiftungen mit *Amanita phalloides*. Deutsche Med. Wschr. *90:* 1364 (1965); (English trans.) Ger. Med. Monthly *11:* 89 (1966).
60. Tyler, V. E. Jr. Recent Studies of the Chemical Constituents of the Agaricales. Beiträge zur Biochemie und Physiologie von Naturstoffen, Festschrift Kurt Mothes zum 65, Geburtstag, Gustav Fischer Verlag, Jena, 1964. P. 501.
61. Tyler, V. E. Jr. Poisonous Mushrooms. Progr. Chem. Toxic. *1:* 339 (1963).
62. Tyler, V. E. Jr., Brady, L. R., Benedict, R. G. Chromatographic and Pharmacologic Evaluation of Some Toxic *Galerina* Species. Lloydia *26:* 154 (1963).
63. Tyler, V. E. Jr. Chromatographic Detection of Amanita Toxins in *Galerina venenata*. Mycologia *55:* 358 (1963).
64. Tyler, V. E. Jr. and Brady, L. R. Chemotaxonomic Significance of Isoxazole Derivatives in *Amanita* Species. Lloydia *29:* 333 (1966).
65. Tyler, V. E. Jr. and Groger, D. Occurrence of 5-Hydroxytryptamine and 5-Hydroxytryptophan in *Panaeolus sphinctrinus*. J. Pharm. Sci. *53:* 462 (1964).
66. Walters, M. B. *Pholiota spectabilis*, a Hallucinogenic Fungus. Mycologia *57:* 837 (1965).
67. Waser, P. G. The Pharmacology of *Amanita muscaria* in *Ethnopharmacologic Search for Psycho-Active Drugs*, Proc. Symposium, San Francisco, Calif. Jan. 28–30, 1967. Editor-in-chief, D. H. Efron; co-editors, B. Holmstedt and N. S. Kline. U.S. Dept. Health, Education and Welfare; U.S. Gov. Printing Office 1967.
68. Wasiljkow, B. P. Die Vergiftungsfälle des Büscheligen Schwefelkopfes, *Hypholoma fasiculare* (Fr.) Quél. Schweiz. Ztsch. Pilzkunde, *41:* 117 (1963).
69. Wasson, R. G. Fly Agaric and Man in *Ethnopharmacologic Search for Psycho-Active Drugs*, Proc. Symposium, San Francisco, Calif. Jan. 28–30, 1967. Editor-in-chief, D. H. Efron; co-editors, B. Holmstedt and N. S. Kline. U.S. Dept. Health, Education and Welfare; U.S. Gov. Printing Office 1967.
70. Wasson, R. G. The Hallucinogenic Mushrooms of Mexico and Psilocybin: A Bibliography. Bot. Museum Leaflets Harvard Univ. *20:* 25 (1962).
71. Wells, V. L. and Kempton, P. E. *Togaria aurea* in Alaska. Mycologia *57:* 316 (1965).
72. Wieland, T. and Wieland, O. Chemistry and Toxicology of the Toxins of *Amanita phalloides*. Pharmacol. Rev. *11:* 87 (1959).

73. Wieland, T. Peptides of *Amanita phalloides*. Pure App. Chem. *9:* 145 (1964).
74. Wier, J. K. and Tyler, V. E. Jr. An Investigation of *Coprinus atramentarius* for the Presence of Disulfiram. J. Am. Pharm. Assoc. *49:* 426 (1960).
75. Yaffee, H. S. Individual Toxic Reactions to Mushrooms. J. Am. Med. Assoc. *188:* 328 (1964).

X MISCELLANEOUS POISONOUS PLANTS

The poisonous plant literature contains hundreds of species which have not been included in this text. In many instances these names are derived from the veterinary literature wherein toxicity may depend upon chronic ingestion or on the consumption of grasses and weeds which would not be utilized by humans. Other plants are included on the basis of the presence of known toxic constituents without consideration of their concentration or their localization in the plant. The roots of the common barberry (*Berberis vulgaris*), for example, contain significant quantities of berberine, yet the attractive red seeds are swallowed without harm by hundreds of children each year. Finally, there were a great number of plants once used as home remedies and in the medical practice of half a century ago, decoctions of which did indeed sometimes produce serious intoxications and fatalities. Many of these were extremely bitter, then a measure of their value, but neither the fresh plant nor its galenical derivative would be acceptable today. The following comment concerning the bloodroot (*Sanguinaria canadensis*) is illustrative: "(It) is not at all liable to be eaten, on account of its peculiar blood red color, which is forbiddingly suspicious, and more especially because of exceedingly acrid taste which would render the chewing and swallowing of a poisonous quantity an act of heroism" (12).

One basis for exclusion from our text was rarity of intoxication. All of the six plants treated in this chapter came under that category, yet they each present some particular feature of interest. The differing fates of children who ate *Lantana* berries, for example, demonstrates forcefully the importance of immediate gastric lavage following the ingestion of plant parts of unknown toxic potential. The case of mistletoe poisoning is one of many examples given throughout the text of the continuing source of intoxications resulting from the use of plant preparations in an attempt to secure an abortion.

Lantana camara

The major part of the literature concerning *Lantana* poisoning deals with chronic ingestion of the whole plant by grazing animals. The active constituent in this type of poisoning is the triterpenoid Lantadene A, which may exert its effect by preventing the formation of bilirubin glucuronide. As the kidney can excrete only conjugated bilirubin, retention jaundice with ensuing photosensitivity results (6). Neither this compound nor this mechanism is involved in the acute human intoxications produced by ingestion of the immature berry.

The symptoms of intoxication are usually delayed for a few hours. They include emesis, diarrhea, weakness, lethargy, cyanosis, labored slow respiration, mydriasis, photophobia, ataxia, coma and depressed deep tendon reflexes.

Wolfson (21) presents 4 cases of *Lantana* poisoning in children which are summarized in the following table:

Age and Sex	Approx. Time between Ingestion & Symptoms	Symptoms	Treatment
$2\frac{1}{2}$ years Female	6 hours	Weakness; ataxia; lethargy; vomiting; slow deep respirations; dilated pupils then became pinpoint; cyanosis; comatose state; death	Adrenal steroids I.M.; epinephrine 1:1,000 S.Q.; oxygen; (not lavaged)
3 years Male	5 hours	Vomiting; diarrhea with green berries present in stool; lethargy; cyanosis; labored, slow, deep respirations; dilated pupils; depressed deep tendon reflexes	Gastric lavage; adrenal steroids, I.M.; oxygen with croupette for 24 hr
4 years Female	$3\frac{1}{2}$ hours	Weakness; lethargy; vomiting; slow, deep respirations; ataxia; photophobia; dilated pupils; depressed deep tendon reflexes	Gastric lavage; clear liquids for 24 hr
$2\frac{1}{4}$ years Female	$2\frac{1}{2}$ hours	Vomiting; lethargy; dilated pupils	Gastric lavage

In 13 other instances given in Wolfson's report in which children ate the berries, gastric lavage was instituted within 30 minutes to $1\frac{1}{2}$ hours of ingestion. None of these children developed any signs of intoxication. Of the entire 17 cases, the only fatality occurred in the single instance in which gastric lavage was omitted. Thus this procedure is definitely indicated in all instances of *Lantana* berry ingestion whether or not signs of toxicity are present. The management of the intoxication thereafter is symptomatic.

Botanical Description

Lantana camara (figure 57). The lantana is a shrub reaching a height of 3 to 5 feet. The stems are widely branched, brittle at the joints, sometimes prickly. The leaves are serrated, about 5 inches long and are borne in pairs or, less commonly, in groups of three. The flowers are creamy white, yellow or pink changing to orange or scarlet and emerge in clusters on the ends of long, bare stems. The fruits are green to blue turning black, about $\frac{1}{4}$ inch in diameter and contain a single, hard seed. It is occasionally cultivated but primarily a weed in southern Florida and Hawaii. Family: Verbenaceae.

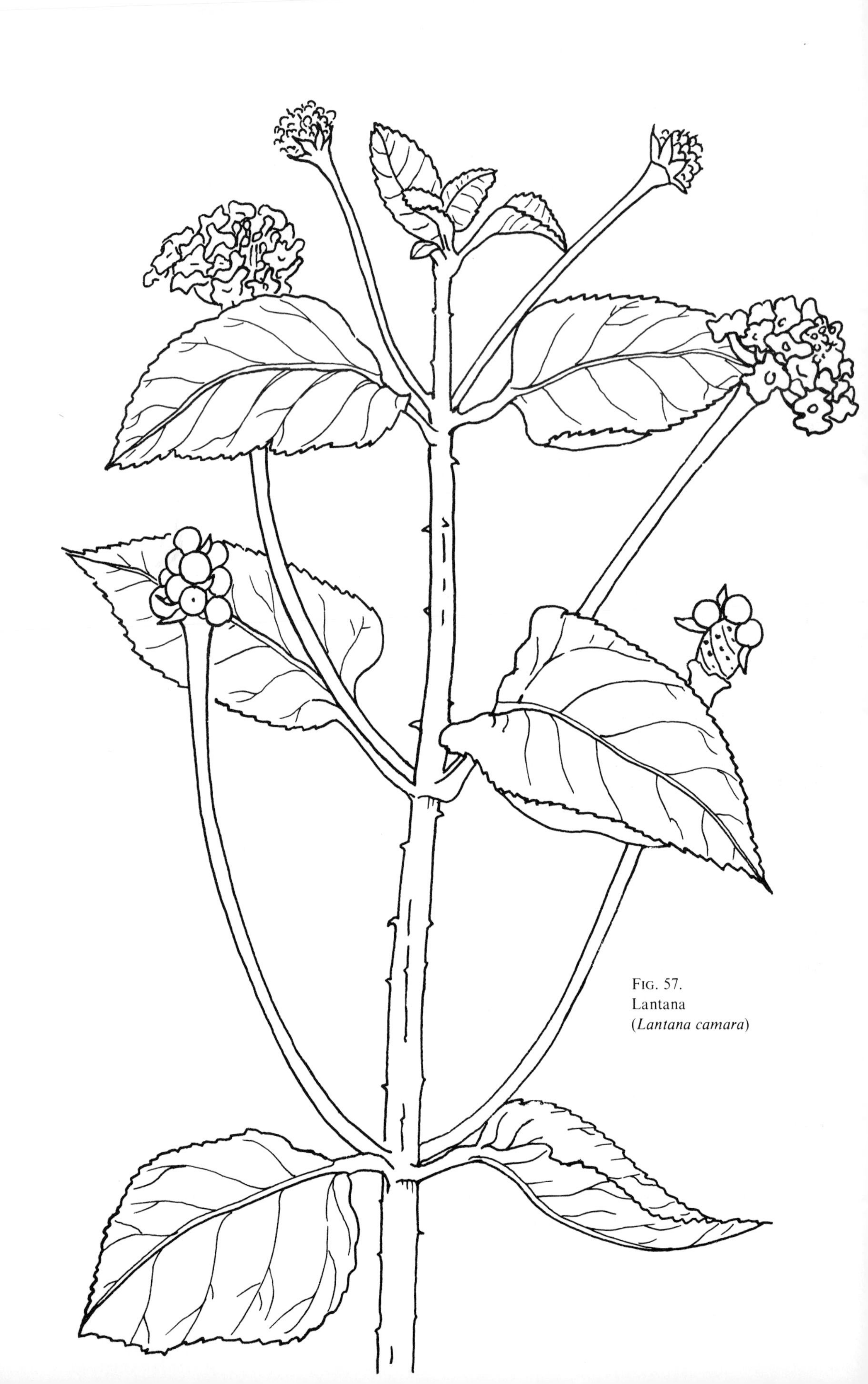

Fig. 57.
Lantana
(*Lantana camara*)

Mistletoe

The American mistletoe (*Phoradendron flavescens*) should be distinguished from the European variety (*Viscum album*) which has completely dissimilar pharmacological properties (15, 19). Hanzlick and French (5) found that the American mistletoe contained sympathetic amines of the tyramine class, choline, and that it also exhibited direct smooth muscle stimulating and marked oxytocic properties.

Fatalities have been reported from the popular use of a decoction of the berries as an abortifacient. Lethal intoxications in children from eating the berries is noted in the earlier literature.

The principal symptoms given are nausea, emesis, drastic catharsis, hypertension, tachypnea and dyspnea, delirium and hallucinations, mydriasis, and cardiovascular collapse (11). Reports of a digitalis-like activity (4) are presumably due to confusion with *Viscum album*, since the American mistletoe has been shown to be devoid of any cardiac activity (5).

Case Report

A 28 year old patient drank a tea made from mistletoe berries in an apparent attempt to secure an abortion. About one to two hours later she became suddenly ill. Vomiting and abdominal cramps with copious diarrhea and frequent voiding occurred for 8 to 10 hours prior to seeking medical aid. By this time the patient was in severe shock, extremely pale, sweating profusely and mydriatic. She was confused and apathetic, but sufficiently conscious to complain of severe abdominal discomfort and nausea. She appeared to be moderately dehydrated, with a subnormal temperature, an unobtainable blood pressure and barely perceptible pulse. No cardiac arrythmias were noted. Death ensued some 10 to 15 minutes after arrival at the hospital approximately 12 hours after ingestion of the tea (11).

This case suggests that serious intoxications are the result of dehydration and electrolyte imbalance as a consequence of acute gastroenteritis rather than that of a systemic toxin. Therefore treatment of early intoxications should be initiated by gastric lavage followed by appropriate measures to prevent shock.

Botanical Description

Phoradendron flavescens. Mistletoe. This is the species of mistletoe of the North American holiday market. It is parasitic on deciduous trees from New Jersey to Florida west to southern Indiana for its northern extreme and New Mexico in the south. It has elongated oval leaves 1 to $2\frac{1}{2}$ inches long. At the base of the leaf there is a short spike covered with white berries. Family: Loranthaceae.

Rhodotypos tetrapetala

An interesting case simulating diabetic coma from the ingestion of the berries ("jet beads") of *Rhodotypos tetrapetala* is presented by Rascoff and

Wasser (14). This appears to be the only recorded case of such poisoning in the United States.

Case Report

A 5 year old girl was admitted with the chief complaints of emesis, abdominal pain and fever. "The child was apparently well until the night before admission, when she complained of pain in the abdomen and vomited. The temperature was normal. The next morning the pain became more intense and localized mostly about the umbilical region. The vomiting continued and the vomitus was bile stained; the temperature rose to 102°F. A blood count and urinalysis were found to be within normal limits. In the next few hours the child's general condition grew worse, and she was hospitalized.

"On admission, the picture presented was that of an acutely ill child who was semicomatose and had a temperature of 105°F. The pulse was rapid but regular, and the respirations were not labored. The skin was hot, dry, and free of any discoloration. The pupils were somewhat dilated but reacted to light. There was no neck rigidity; no abnormal reflexes were elicited. The heart and lungs were normal. There was some spasm and rigidity of the recti muscles, but no abdominal tenderness. A 5 per cent solution of glucose in sodium chloride solution was given intravenously, but before this was done blood was drawn for chemical studies, and the child was catheterized for urine specimen. The urine specimen was free of albumin but showed 4+ glucosuria and acetonuria. The blood chemical findings disclosed a glucose content of 290 mg. per 100 cc. and a carbon dioxide combining power of 14 vol. per cent.

"After we received this report, our impression was that we were dealing with some overwhelming infection and diabetic coma. In view of the report that the urine was normal prior to hospitalization, it was decided to withhold insulin therapy until further laboratory study. Intravenous administration of fluid in the form of $1/6$ molar lactate and distilled water instead of glucose solution was begun. Antibiotic therapy was given, consisting of one million units of penicillin intramuscularly every 3 hours and 100 mg. of oxytetracycline (Terramycin) in 50 cc. of distilled water intravenously every 4 hours. Adrenal cortical extract was administered, with 10 cc. given initially and 5 cc. every 4 hours.

"At 8:20 that evening the temperature rose to 106°F. and the child began to have tonic and clonic convulsions. Phenobarbital was given intramuscularly to control the seizures. At 9:20 p.m. the blood glucose level fell to 210 mg. per 100 cc., without insulin therapy; there was 3+ glucosuria, but the twitchings and seizures still persisted and the temperature remained high. A spinal tap done at this time revealed normal fluid content. After continuous antipyretic and hydrotherapy, the temperature fell to 103°F. at midnight and the glucosuria was 2+. The convulsions were diminishing. At 6 a.m. the child called for its mother and began taking fluids by mouth. At 10 a.m. the temperature was 100.2°F. and the child sat up. The following day, 48 hours after admission the child was afebrile, and all the laboratory findings were within normal limits. The child was discharged on the fifth day of hospitalization."

Botanical Description

Rhodotypos tetrapetala (*R. scandens*, *R. kerrioides*) (figure 58). Jetbead. This is a rose, growing shrub-like from 3 to 6 feet tall. It is the only rose cultivated in the United States which has opposite leaves. The flowers are white and up to 2 inches across. The fruit is a shining black berry about $^1/_4$ inch in diameter. It is hardy in New York and throughout New England. Family: Rosaceae.

Gelsemium sempervirens

Children have been poisoned by chewing the flowers of this plant; however, most intoxications have resulted from the use of galenical preparations of the root. A number of toxicologically related alkaloids are present, of which 2, gelsemine and gelsemicine, have been fully characterized.

Symptoms of *Gelsemium* intoxication are: headache, dizziness, dimness of vision or diplopia, mydriasis, ptosis, dryness of the mouth, dyspagia and inability to enunciate. In severe cases, the patient may display muscular weakness as evidenced by falling of the jaw. However, there may be signs of a mixed intoxication due to a weak strychnine-like action of one of the components. Thus one may see muscular rigidity, particularly trismus, and convulsions. Dyspnea, orthopnea, cyanosis and loss of consciousness have been reported (9).

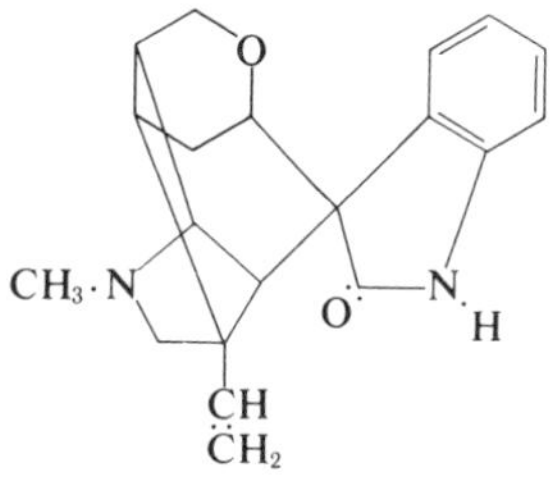

Gelsemine

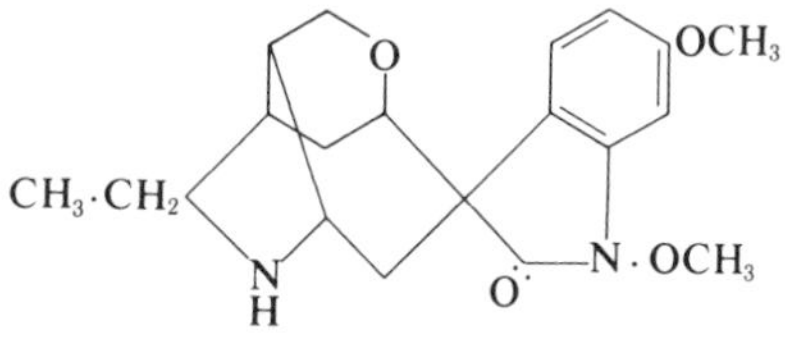

Gelsemicine

Despite rather numerous instances of poisoning which occurred during the medicinal application of plant extracts for neuralgia around 1900, no useful system of management was developed. It appears that gastric lavage followed by symptomatic management of respiratory complications or of strychnine-like activity if present is indicated. The use of drugs such as ammonia, digitalis, morphine, atropine, and strychnine which appear in the literature are obviously contraindicated.

In non-fatal cases the visual disturbances may persist for several days.

Botanical Description

Gelsemium sempervirens (figure 59). The Carolina yellow jessamine. This is an evergreen climber. The leaves are lance-shaped, paired, 4 inches long. The flowers are bright yellow, fragrant, to 1 $^1/_2$ inches long. The fruit is a capsule slightly under an inch in length. It is found in woods from southeastern Virginia to Tennessee and Arkansas south to Florida and Mexico. Family: Loganiaceae.

FIG. 58.
Jetbead
(*Rhodotypos tetrapetala*)

FIG. 59.
Carolina yellow jessamine
(*Gelsemium sempervirens*)

Hippomane mancinella

The manchineel tree has considerable reputation as an extremely toxic plant. Several historical reviews of its manifestations, both real and fanciful, have been prepared (1, 3, 7). Without a doubt it is a potent direct irritant (see Chapter XI) producing severe contact dermatitis (3, 16, 18) and intense conjunctivitis (3, 18). Inhalation of sawdust causes cough, rhinitis, laryngitis and bronchitis. Dermal reactions to the dried wood presumably depend upon a sentization reaction.

Chewing on the fruit, without swallowing, may produce, after a delay of 1 to 2 hours, severe pain, profound salivation and dysphagia. The lips are blistered and swollen and the mouth can be opened only with difficulty. The tongue, gums, buccal mucosa and palate desquammate in large patches. Ingestion usually produces emesis, an extremely painful gastritis and bloody diarrhea. Many case reports contain symptoms of shock (3).

The oral lesions and gastroenteritis are consistent with those which might be anticipated from the ingestion of any severe irritant. Nevertheless the feeling persists that specific systemic toxins may be present. A series of investigations (2, 8, 17) failed to disclose any substances which would account for the signs of animal toxicity or the symptoms encountered in human poisoning.

The treatment recommended for internal involvement is that given at the end of Part A, Chapter II, page 12.

Botanical Description

Hippomane mancinella (figure 60). Manchineel. This is a handsome, deciduous tree from 30 to 50 feet in height which may form a large trunk with a thick gray bark. The leaves are elliptic and glossy green. The fruit resembles a small crabapple and has a pleasant odor. When the tree is cut, it oozes a white latex which thickens and darkens on exposure to air. It is now found only in the remoter parts of the Florida Everglades. Family: Euphorbiaceae.

Cycads

The cycads are primitive plants. Their dark green coarse palm-like leaves fan out from the ground or from a stalky trunk. Species of *Zamia*, which is the only cycad genus indigenous to the United States, are found in Florida. Many other members of the cycad family, particularly *Cycas circinalis* and *Cycas revoluta*, are cultivated in Florida, the extreme south, California and Hawaii. The slow growing cycads are becoming more popular as house plants elsewhere.

The cycads are of considerable importance in certain tropical areas where their roots are used for the production of edible flour. Improper preparation of this flour is associated with neurological toxicity resembling amyotrophic lateral sclerosis. With the recognition of the carcinogenic and hepatotoxic

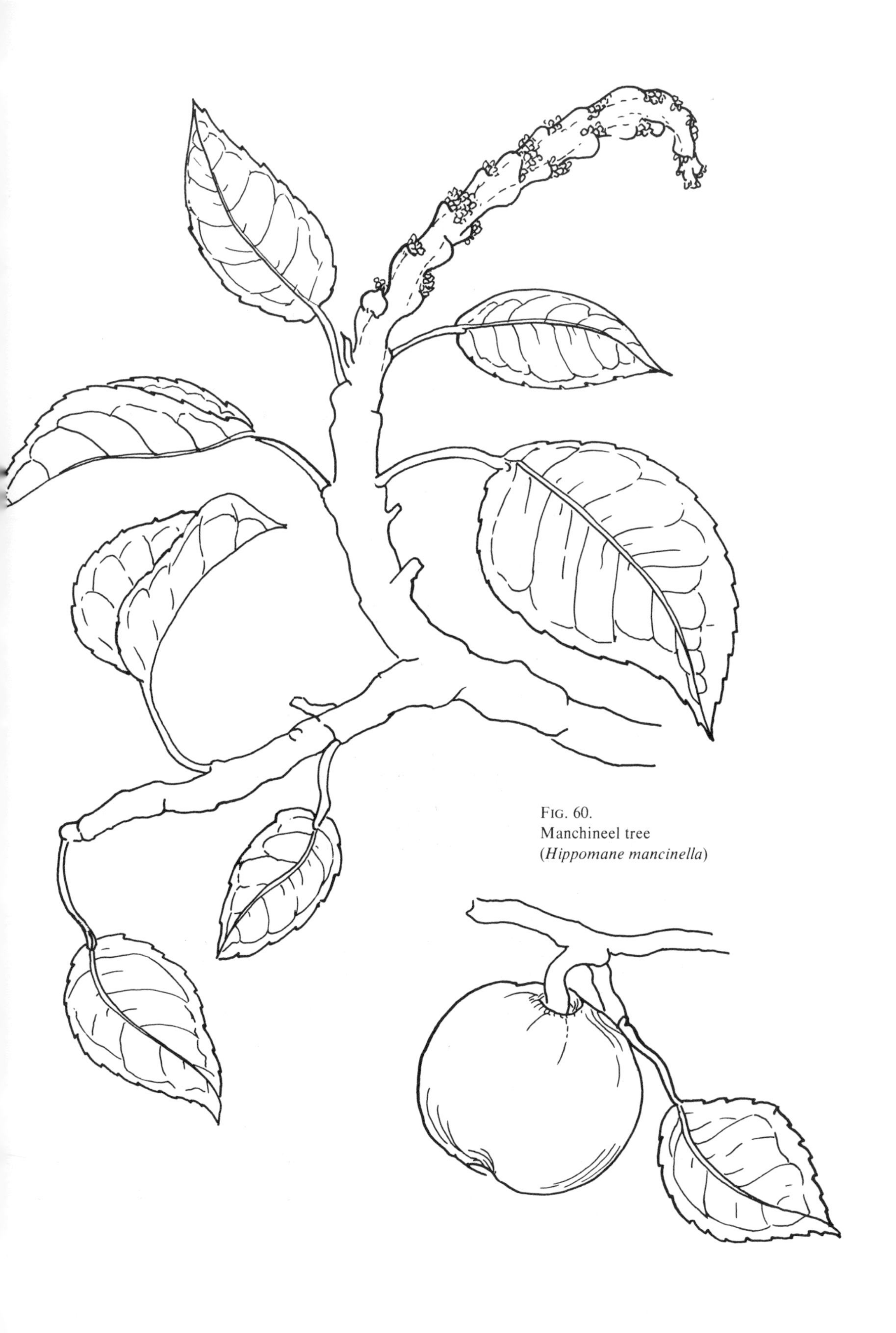

Fig. 60.
Manchineel tree
(*Hippomane mancinella*)

glucoside cycasin, methylazoxymethanol-β-D-glucoside, a great deal of work has been done on these plants (13).

$$\begin{array}{c} \mathrm{O} \\ \uparrow \\ \mathrm{CH_3{-}N{=}N{-}CH_2O{-}glucose} \end{array}$$

Cycasin

The incidence of acute intoxications from single exposures to cycad seeds or roots throughout the world is extremely low. They have been summarized by Whiting (20). The only two cases in the United States involved the ingestion of *Zamia* roots (10, 20).

Intoxications from cycads range in severity from minor and vague complaints to severe and often fatal illnesses. The symptoms may include: headache, emesis, diarrhea, colic, depression to coma, and muscular paralysis (20).

Unfortunately, there is no specific treatment which can be recommended for cycad intoxications at this time.

REFERENCES

1. Allen, P. H. Poisonous and Injurious Plants of Panama. Am. J. Trop. Med. Hyg. *23*, suppl. 1 (1943).
2. Carroll, M. N. Jr., Fox, L. E. and Ariail, W. T. Investigation of the Toxic Principles of *Hippomane mancinella* L. III. Toxic Actions of Extracts of *Hippomane mancinella* L. J. Am. Pharm. Assoc. *46:* 93 (1957).
3. Earle, K. V. Toxic Effects of *Hippomane mancinella.* Trans. Roy. Soc. Trop. Med. Hyg. *32:* 363 (1938).
4. Haggerty, R. J. Christmas Holiday Poison Hazards. Mass. Med. Soc. *29:* 1277 (1958).
5. Hanzlik, P. J. and French, W. O. The Pharmacology of *Phoradendron flavescens* (American Mistletoe). J. Pharm. Exp. Therap. *23:* 269 (1924).
6. Lampe, K. F., McAnally, J. S., Katzen, M. Mechanisms of Lantadene-Induced Jaundice. Am. Chem. Soc. 133d Nat'l Meeting, San Francisco, 1958. Abstr. 10M-17.
7. Lauter, W. M., Fox, L. E. and Ariail, W. T. Investigation of the Toxic Principles of *Hippomane mancinella* L. I. Historical Review. J. Am. Pharm. Assoc. *41:* 199 (1952).
8. Lauter, W. M. and Foote, P. A. Investigation of the Toxic Principles of *Hippomane mancinella* L. II. Preliminary Isolation of a Toxic Principle of the Fruit. J. Am. Pharm. Assoc. *44:* 361 (1955).
9. Lewin, L. *Gifte und Vergiftungen.* Karl Haug, Ulm/Donau, 1962. Pp. 787–9.
10. Miami News (Florida), July 18, 1963.
11. Moore, H. W. Mistletoe Poisoning. J. South Carolina Med. Assoc. *59:* 269 (1963).
12. Pammel, L. H. *A Manual of Poisonous Plants.* Torch Press, Cedar Rapids, Iowa, 1911; Reprinted, Univ. Microfilms Inc., Ann Arbor, Mich., 1965. Pp. 476–7.
13. Proc. Conf. on the Identification of Toxic Elements of Cycads. L. T. Kurland, ed. Feb. 28, 1962. Nat'l Inst. Neurol. Dis. and Blindness, NIH. Mimeo.
    Proc. 2nd Conf. on the Identification of Toxic Elements of Cycads. L. T. Kurland, ed. Aug. 17, 1962. NINDB, NIH. Mimeo.
    Proc. 3rd Conf. on the Toxicity of Cycads. Chicago, Ill. April 17, 1964. Fed. Proc. *23:* 1337 (1964).
    Proc. 4th Conf. on Toxicity of Cycads. M. G. Whiting, ed. April 15, 1965. NINDB, NIH. Mimeo.
    Proc. 5th Conf. on Cycad Toxicity. G. L. Laqueur and H. Teas, ed. Miami, Fla. April 24, 1967. Mimeo.
14. Rascoff, H. and Wasser, S. Poisoning in a child Simulating Diabetic Coma. J. Am. Med. Assoc. *152:* 1134 (1953).
15. Samuelsson, G. Phytochemical and Pharmacological Studies on *Viscum album.* Svensk farm. tidskr. *66:* 237 (1962).

16. Satulsky, E. M. Dermatitis venenata Caused by the Manzanillo tree. Arch. Derm. Syph. *47:* 36, 797 (1943).
17. Schaeffer, H. J., Lauter, W. M. and Foote, P. A. A Preliminary Phytochemical Study of *Hippomane mancinella* L. J. Am. Pharm. Assoc. *43:* 43 (1954).
18. Snow, J. S. and Harley, R. D. Dermatitis Venenata and Keratoconjunctivitis Caused by the Manzanillo Tree. Arch. Derm. Syph. *49-50:* 236 (1944).
19. Thun, H. Pharmakologische Untersuchungen über die Eichenmistel und die amerikanische mistel. Arch. exp. Path. Pharm. *202:* 642 (1943).
20. Whiting, M. G. Toxicity of Cycads. Economic Botany *17:* 270 (1963).
21. Wolfson, S. L. and Solomons, T. W. G. Poisoning by Fruit of *Lantana camara.* Am. J. Dis. Children *107:* 109 (1964).

XI PLANT DERMATITIS

Of all the toxic manifestations due to plants, dermatitis is probably the most frequently encountered. Plants may produce injury to the skin by direct mechanical trauma, primary chemical irritation, allergic sensitization, photosensitization, or any combination of these, which, in turn, may be complicated by secondary infection or injudicious treatment. The proper identification of the plant etiology is important in order to prevent subsequent exposure.

For the purpose of this manual, a discussion of only the more important aspects of plant dermatitis will be given. Keratoconjunctivitis due to plant sap is also discussed. Tables of common dermatitis-producing plants are provided at the end of the chapter.

Mechanical Injury

Trauma to the skin by plants may be produced by contact with their specialized protective organs; these include thorns, bristles, spines, barbs, and sharp or serrate edges. Wounds of various kinds, including imbedding of plant parts, occur by injudicious contact. The barbs of the prickly-pear (*Opuntia* spp) for instance produce "sabra" dermatitis (99), a condition closely resembling scabies. Plant parts are often the vehicle by which bacteria and fungus spores are introduced into the skin; it is common, for example, to obtain a history of injury by the barberry thorn (*Berberis vulgaris*) in cases of sporotrichosis (38). Vegetable fragments and beards of barley have been found in lesions of actinomycosis. Laborers who handle jute (*Corchorus olitorius* and *C. capsularis*) frequently develop folliculitis (27).

Primary Chemical Irritation

Plants of this group contain substances, generally not chemically identified, which produce direct irritation to the skin. The chemicals may be present in the leaves, bark, sap, roots, stem, flowers, fruit, pollen, hairs or other appendages. Some substances are contacted on the plant surface, others are released only when the plant is bruised or crushed (36). The toxic potential of these primary irritants may vary with the season, stage of maturation, weather, locality grown, etc.

Primary chemical irritants have the ability to affect most, if not all, persons who contact the substance. Allergic tendencies or sensitivities of the

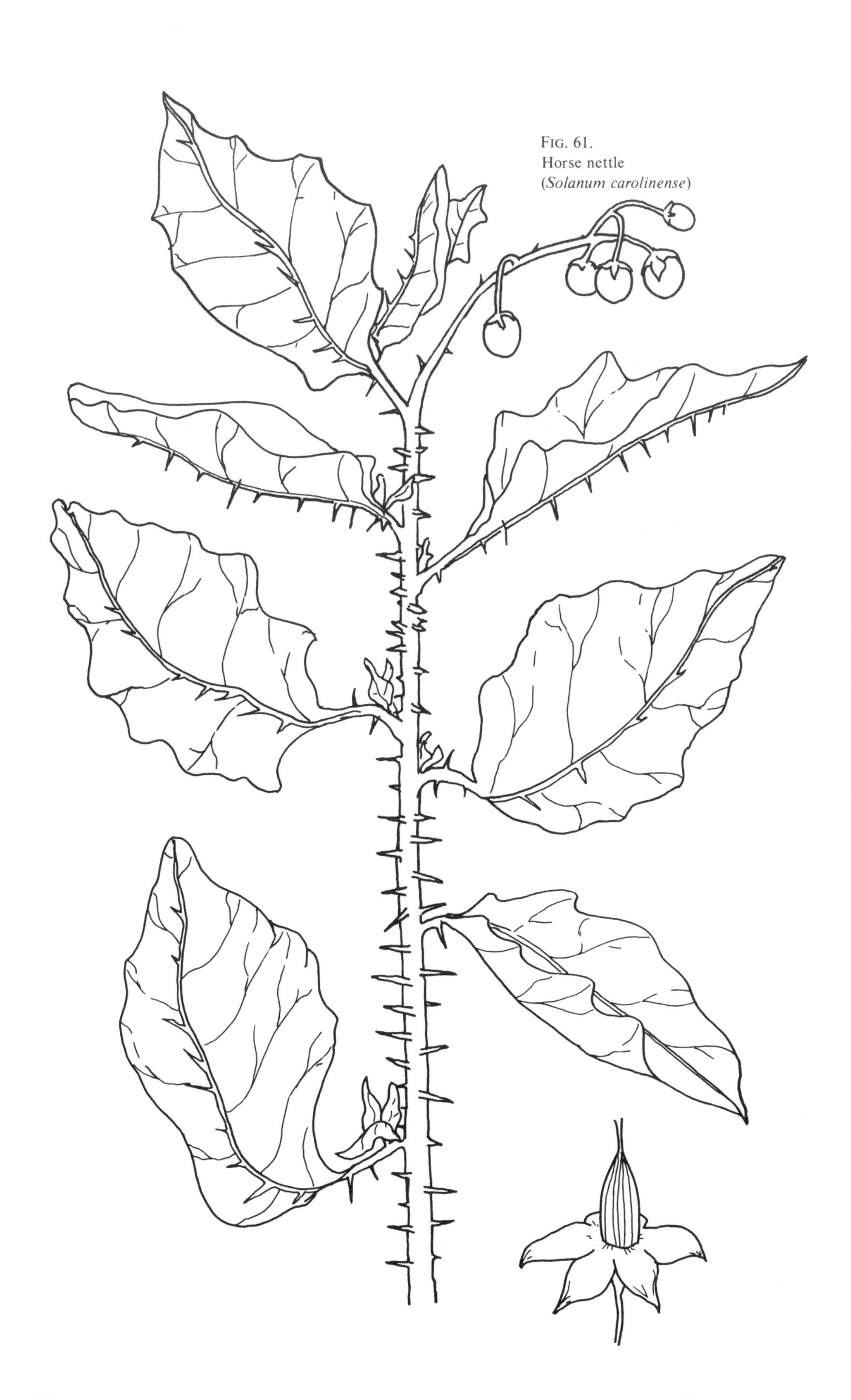

FIG. 61.
Horse nettle
(*Solanum carolinense*)

FIG. 62.
Nettle
(*Laportea canadensis*)

FIG. 63.
Bull nettle
(*Cnidoscolus stimulosus*)

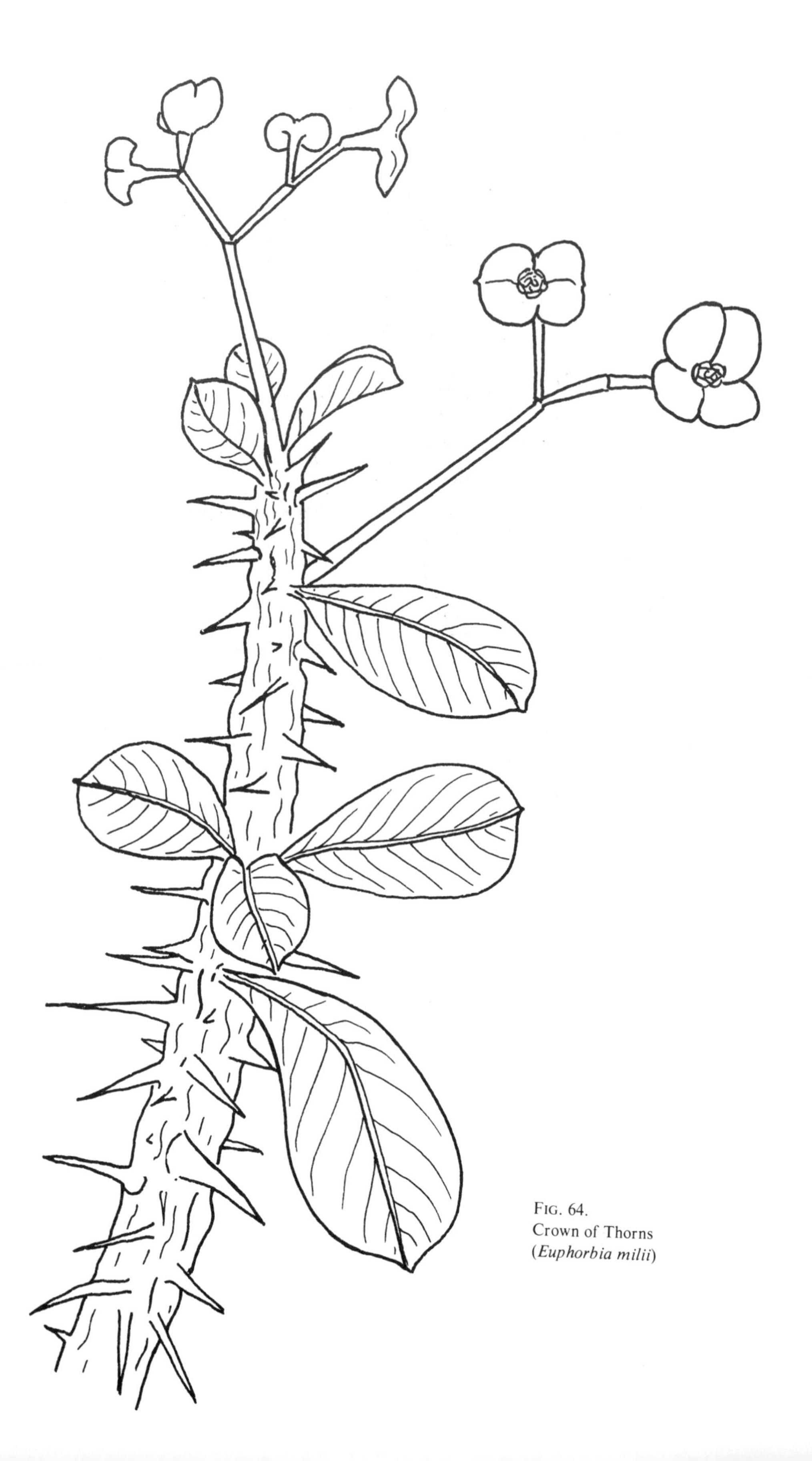

Fig. 64.
Crown of Thorns
(*Euphorbia milii*)

individual do not play any role. Reactions of the skin to primary irritants usually take place within a short time after exposure. Allergic reactions, on the other hand, usually do not occur for at least 24 hours after contact. The degree of reaction of the skin is mainly dependent on the concentration of the irritant and duration of contact with the skin and lesions are limited to the exposed areas. Skin regions in which the horny layer is thickened, such as the palms and soles, are less susceptible than areas where the stratum corneum is thin (96).

Some plants commonly associated with this type of reaction may produce irritation by both mechanical and chemical injury. These are the nettle types: (figure 61) *Solanum carolinense*, *Urtica dioica*, *Laportea canadensis* (figure 62), and *Cnidoscolus stimulosus* (figure 63) and the stinging hairs as in certain species of *Primula* and *Jatropha* (71).

Other prominent sources of chemical irritants include the milky sap of many species of *Euphorbia* (figures 64, 65), the peel oil from lemons (35, 95) and other citrus fruits, the buttercups (115, 122) (*Ranunculus*, figure 13), the daisy (*Chrysanthemum*) (44), and the fruit of the maiden hair tree (17, 92) (*Ginkgo biloba*, figure 66). Mild dermatitis may be produced by the proteolytic enzyme bromelin present in pineapple juice (84). Calcium oxalate crystals contained in tulip bulbs (79) and other plants are irritating.

Swimmers in Hawaii have developed severe contact dermatitis from the salt water alga *Lyngbya majuscula*. The plant parts act as primary irritants when they are imbedded in bathing suit areas which rub the skin (47).

The vesicant sap of *Euphorbia tirucalli* (figure 67), *Euphorbia lactea* (figure 68), *Hippomane mancinella* (figure 60) and *Hura crepitans* (figure 22) of the family Euphorbiaceae produce keratoconjunctivitis as well as severe dermatitis (3, 16, 25, 34, 46, 109).

Allergic Sensitization

Plant dermatitis also results from the exposure of an individual to a plant substance to which he is allergic. The plants which contain primary chemical irritants may produce sensitization. Inflammation of the skin is a predisposing factor in the production of contact allergies, consequently primary irritation and sensitization may occur simultaneously.

Allergic dermatitis is produced after a latent period in which immunologic changes in the patient specific for the allergen have taken place. This incubation period is usually 5 or more days after the initial contact with the offending substance (96). The skin therefore may not react on the first contact with the allergen, though there may be continual exposure to the substance from the first contact, through the incubation period, to the onset of dermatitis.

There are considerable differences among sensitizing plants in their ability to induce allergic dermatitis. This is due to variations in their content of allergens and also on the capacity of the individual to react. Although there is a definite tendency for some individuals to become more easily

FIG. 65.
Snow-on-the-Mountain
(*Euphorbia marginata*)

FIG. 66.
Maidenhair tree
(*Ginkgo biloba*)

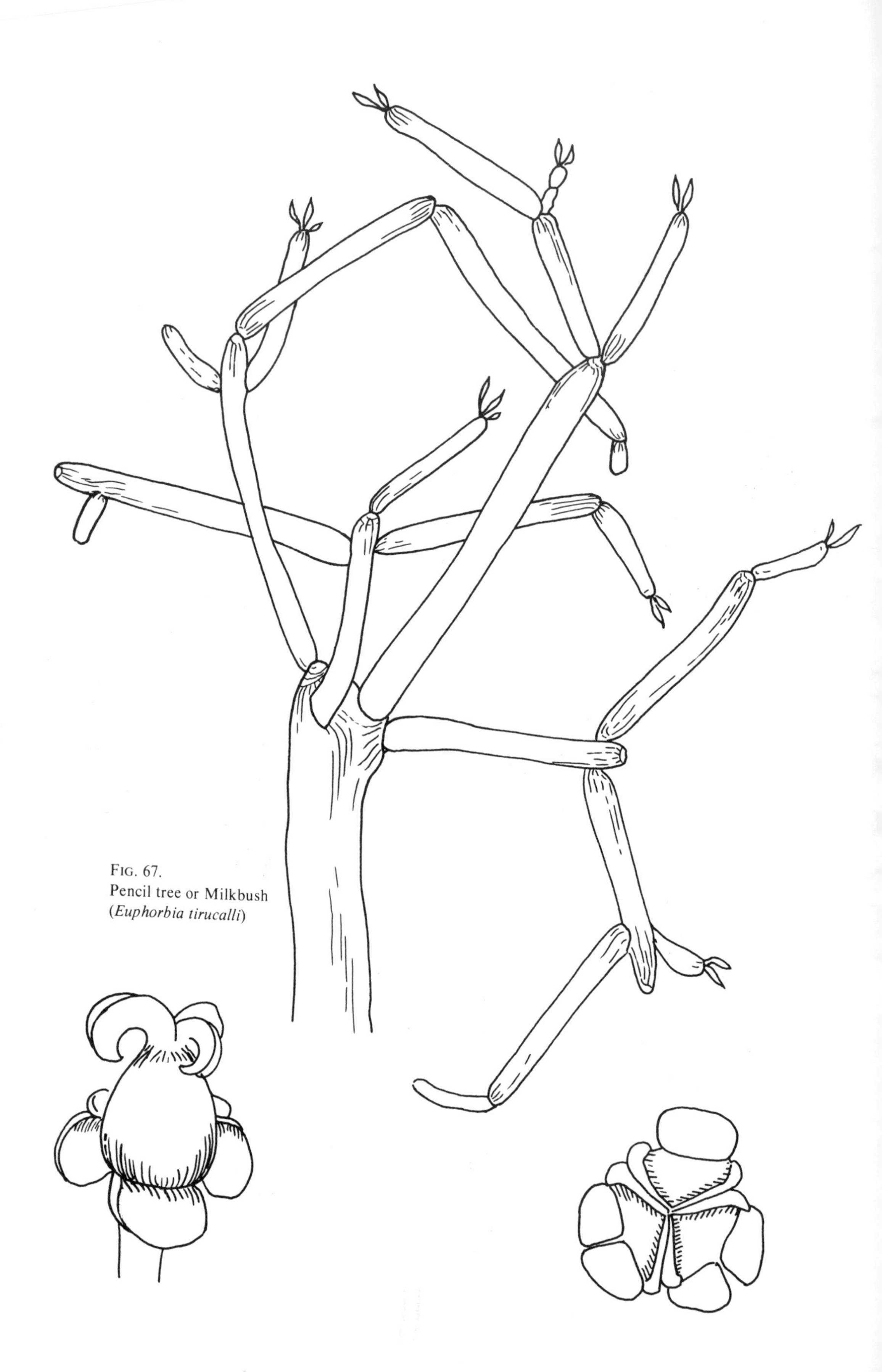

FIG. 67.
Pencil tree or Milkbush
(*Euphorbia tirucalli*)

FIG. 68.
Candelabra cactus
(*Euphorbia lactea*)

sensitized than others, no correlation can be drawn between allergic contact dermatitis and the presence of systemic allergies of the hay fever type (36). No potential sensitizer can be ignored on the grounds of previous exposure without deleterious effects. From a practical viewpoint it is proper to conclude that the offender is an agent recently reencountered.

Differential Diagnosis

Acute allergic contact dermatitis is characterized by itching and vesiculation of varying degrees. The involved skin may be erythematous, edematous and large bulla, weeping and crusting may be observed. After variable periods, the chronic lesions become progressively less angry-looking, thickened, perhaps fissured, and sometimes pigmented. The lesions are similar in appearance to several other types of eczematous reactions, e.g., bacterial and fungal infections, so-called nummular eczema, seborrheic dermatitis, atopic dermatitis, and especially primary irritant contact dermatitis.

Diagnostic patch testing is a valuable tool in the investigation of allergic contact dermatitis. However it should be employed by those who are thoroughly familiar with accepted technics. Patch testing should not be done during the acute phase of any dermatitis. Established procedures, concentrations, vehicles, and interpretations are well described for the most part, and should be followed (65, 102). It must be considered that substances used for patch testing may sensitize the patient in the process of performing the test; this may have medico-legal implications (57). New procedures, unknown substances, and potential primary irritants should be investigated only by a qualified dermatologist. Positive and negative results of patch testing are not, in themselves, diagnostic, but are properly interpreted in light of the history, physical findings, laboratory evidence, and the clinical experience of the physician.

Plants Producing Allergic Reaction

Some specific plants which are commonly associated with sensitizing the skin to cause allergic contact dermatitis belong to the following families:

Anacardiaceae	Poison ivy, Poison wood, Mango, Florida holly
Compositae	Dog fennel, Chrysanthemums, Daisies
Liliaceae	Tulips, Hyacinth, Garlic, Onions
Amaryllidaceae	Daffodil, Narcissus
Primulaceae	Primrose
Umbelliferae	Carrots, Celery
Gramineae	Grasses, Cereal grains
Euphorbiaceae	Spurges, Castor plant
Rutaceae	Citrus fruits

By far the most important of these families is the Anacardiaceae (18, 59, 60) (figures 69 to 73). Any part of these plants may contain the dermatitis producing compounds, which are monohydric or polyhydric phenols (urushiol,

FIG. 69.
Poison wood
(*Metopium toxiferum*)

cardol, etc. (29) but the leaves, which often have short sharp spines, are the common sources of contact. Often there is seen a linear pattern of vesicles or papules on the skin, "scratch marks", where the leaf has been brushed, which is a helpful sign of Rhus dermatitis. This characteristic pattern is absent if the dermatitis results from contact with objects contaminated with sap, such as clothing, dogs, fishing rods, smoke containing particulates of the oleoresin (52), or from diffuse direct contacts; diffuse contacts usually result in erythematous eczematous eruptions. Edema, blistering and other signs of inflammation may be present.

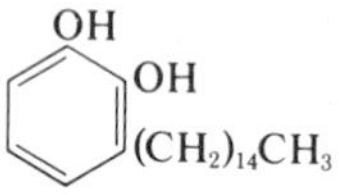

OH
OH
$(CH_2)_{14}CH_3$

3-n-Pentadecylcatechol
(Poison ivy urushiol)

A common conception is that the vesicle fluid is also antigenic and is responsible for spread of dermatitis. This is untrue. However, contact with antigen still present under the fingernails may be the source of continued exposure.

The inflammatory reaction of the skin usually begins several hours to days after contact with *Toxicodendron* (*Rhus*) antigen and, if no complications supervene, the case heals in 7 to 14 days (64, 73, 83).

Other ivy "poisonings", such as those due to contact with Algerian ivy (*Hedera canariensis*) (30, 31) and English ivy (*Hedera helix*) (43) are identical to the dermatitis of poison ivy.

In Great Britain and Western Europe, primrose dermatitis due to the sensitizing chemical primulin is more common then that from poison ivy (87,100). Three species of *Primula* (*P. obconica*, *P. cortusoides*, *P. sieboldii*) have been recognized as sensitizing plants in the United States (37).

"Tulip Fingers" or "Lily Rash" are syndromes commonly encountered among those engaged in the floral industry (13, 45, 56, 76, 85). The first is characterized by tenderness and reddening of the fingers which later become thickened and fissured due to the oleoresins present in the Liliaceae and Amaryllidaceae families. The second is an eruption associated primarily with varieties of *Narcissus* such as the jonquil and daffodil.

Workers in other occupations which deal with the constant handling of plants or plant products have a high incidence of sensitivity reactions. Housewives and greenhouse workers develop dermatitis from Philodendron (9, 32, 50). Cases have been noted in those who either manufacture or use insecticides containing pyrethrum which is derived from certain chrysanthemums (36, 98). Agricultural workers involved with such plants as *Humulus lupulus* develop "hop-pickers itch" from the oleoresin myrcene (24). Other common produce, such as onions (19) (*Allium cepa*), carrots (63, 118) (*Daucus carota*), tomatoes (68) (*Lycopersicon esculentum*), potatoes (81) (*Solanum*

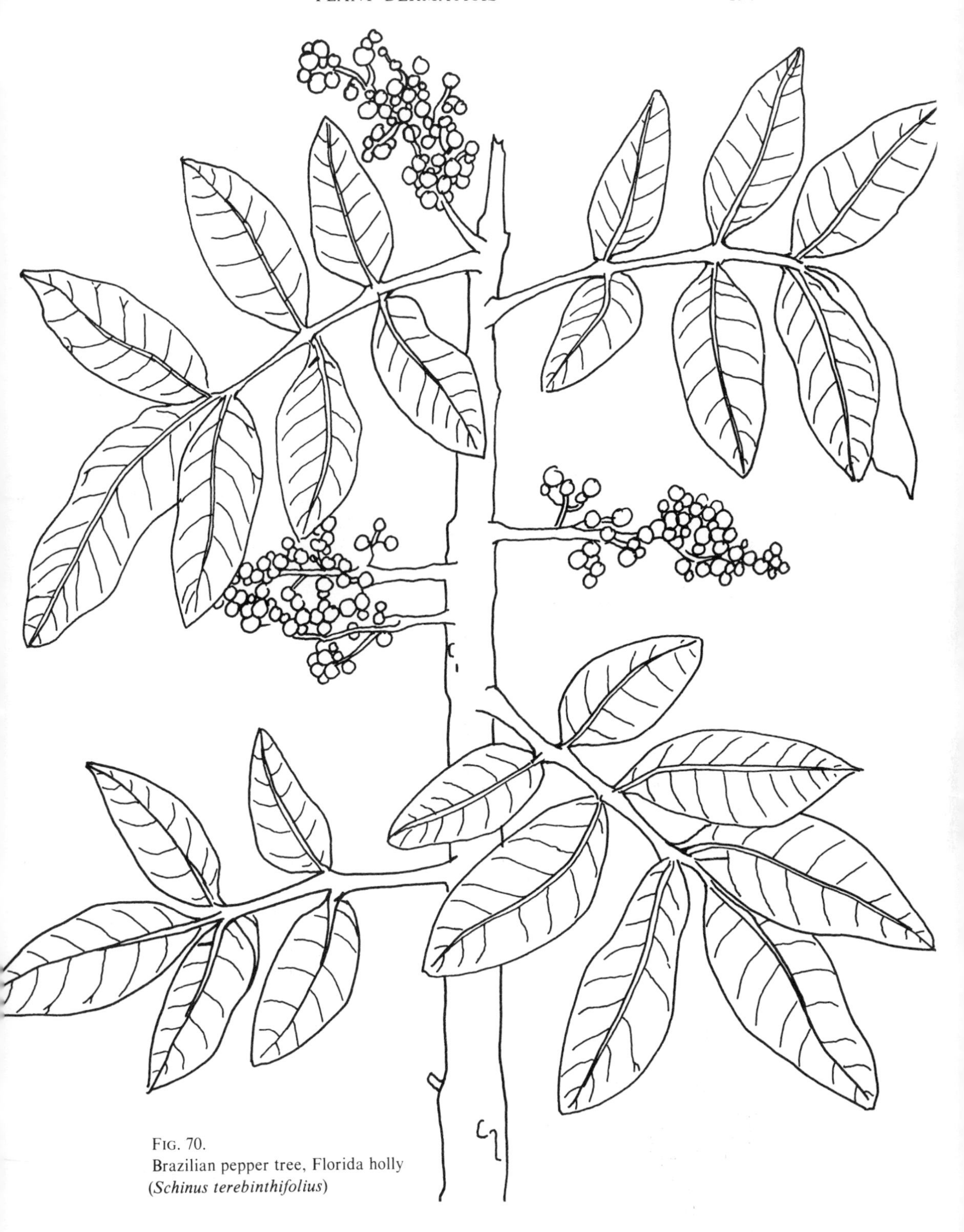

Fig. 70.
Brazilian pepper tree, Florida holly
(*Schinus terebinthifolius*)

FIG. 71.
Eastern Poison Oak
(*Toxicodendron quercifolium*)

FIG. 72.
Poison ivy
(*Toxicodendron radicans*)

Fig. 73.
Poison sumac
(*Toxicodendron vernix*)

tuberosum) and garlic (*Allium sativum*) are capable of producing allergic contact dermatitis.

Amateur as well as professional gardeners may develop sensitivity to commonly cultivated ornamentals belonging to the families Compositae, Liliaceae, Amaryllidaceae, Primulaceae (44, 88, 101). A genus of the orchid family, *Cypripedium* (figure 74) or Lady Slipper is a source of dermatitis from wild flowers (115). Weeds, particularly of the family Compositae, and the grasses, Gramineae, are a common but often unsuspected etiology.

Carpenters, lumber millers, woodsmen and hobbyists have often been sensitized by both rare and common woods with which they work (28, 39, 41, 42, 58, 67, 94, 96, 113). Most of these reactions may be attributed to oleoresins. Wood dermatitis in the United States has been associated most frequently with the poplar, which contains an irritant glucoside as well as an oleoresin (119).

Plants, not usually considered in reviewing possibilities for allergic contact dermatitis, are the lichens, which are probably the important agents in "cedar poisoning" or "woodcutters disease" (21). Usnic acid may be the specific sensitizer. A fresh water blue-green alga, the *Anabena* spp of the family Nostocaceae was identified as the allergen responsible for producing dermatitis in a child (23).

Pollen Dermatitis

Certain pollens contain an oleoresin and a water soluble antigen both of which are capable of producing dermatitis but by different mechanisms. The water soluble portion responsible for the usual Hay-fever syndrome may cause an urticarial reaction due to inhalation of the protein allergen. However an eczematous dermatitis is most frequently encountered as the result of contact of the skin with the pollen oleoresin (36, 72).

This condition is characterized by a sheet-like subacute eruption covering the exposed areas of the skin such as the eyelids, face, the "V" of the neck, arms, ankles, etc. Often these involve the same areas of distribution as photodermatitis and may in fact be aggravated by sunlight.

Since, in most instances, the pollen is airborne, there is usually no history of direct contact with the plant. Occasionally this condition may be confused with neurodermatitis. The occurrence is normally seasonal but may be due to different pollen sources at various times of the year (22, 40, 88, 105, 114).

Ragweed dermatitis is the most prevalent form of pollen dermatitis in the United States and is in no way associated with the individual's sensitivity to the rhinitis or asthma producing antigen present in some members of the *Ambrosia* spp.

Certain trees (70), for example the box elder (*Acer negundo*), poplar (*Populus* spp), maple (*Acer* spp), ash (*Fraxinus* spp), and elm (*Ulmus* spp), are reported to be associated with pollen sensitization. Other possible etiologies are weeds such as the cocklebur (*Xanthium* spp) (figure 75), mares tail

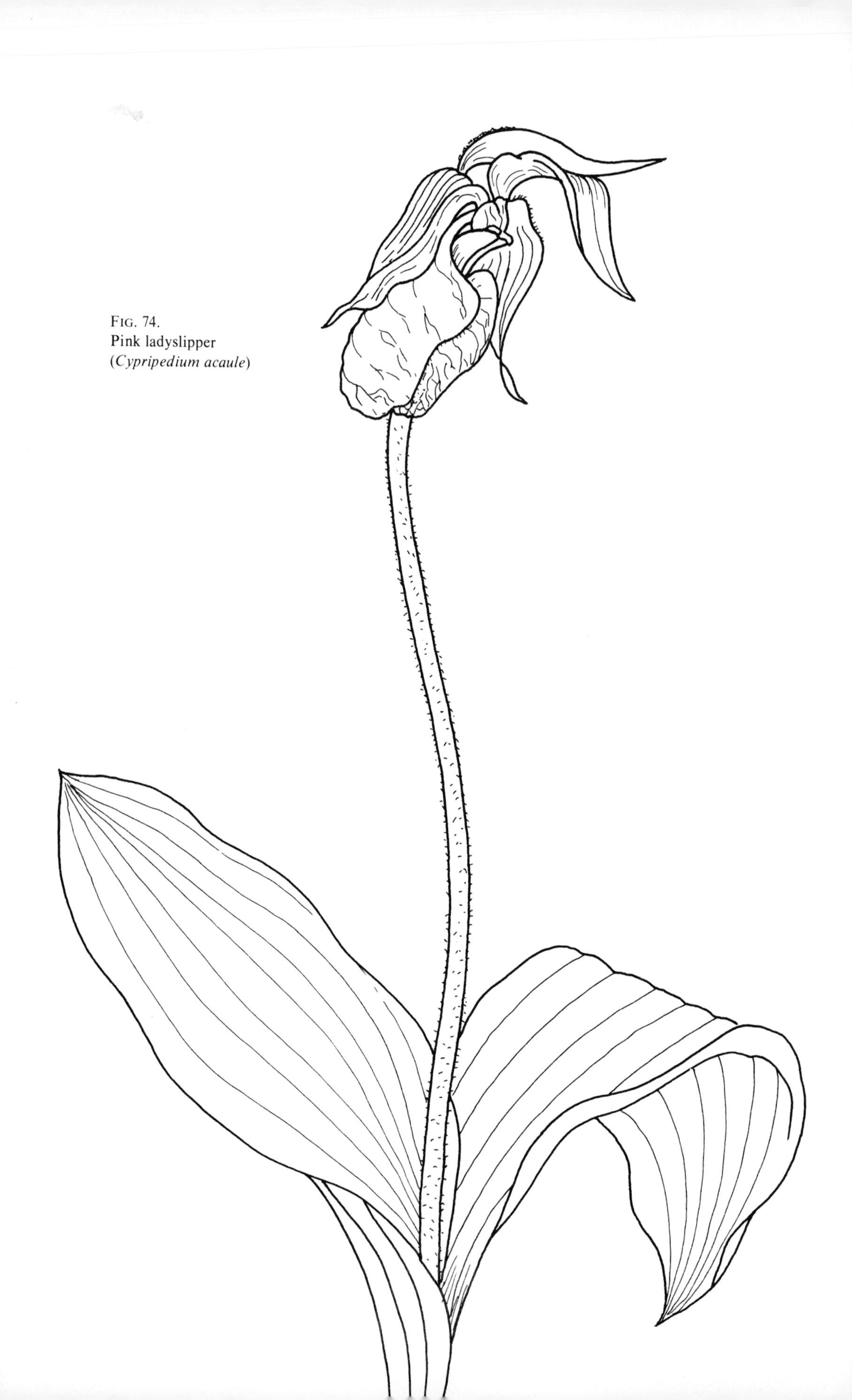

FIG. 74.
Pink ladyslipper
(*Cypripedium acaule*)

Fig. 75.
Cocklebur
(*Xanthium strumarium*)

FIG. 76.
Marsh elder
(*Iva xanthifolia*)

(*Erigeron canadenses*) and marsh elders (108) (*Iva angustifolia*; *Iva xanthifolia*, figure 76).

It is rather interesting to note that the pollen of poison ivy does not contain the oleoresin antigen. Shellmire reported that he was unable to elicit a positive patch test with the pollen in 6 patients sensitized to poison ivy (102).

Photodermatitis

Furocoumarins (psoralens) present in certain plants produce dermatitis by a phototoxic mechanism which makes the skin hypersensitive to sunlight. This condition is characterized by an eruption which becomes hyperpigmented about 48 hours after contact with the plant and subsequent exposure to sunlight (11, 15, 26, 55, 62, 77, 93). The area may remain pigmented for a prolonged period after the erythema has disappeared. The classic berloque dermatitis (49) from toiletries containing oil of bergamot presents the same symptoms. Reactions of this nature are not associated with allergic sensitivity.

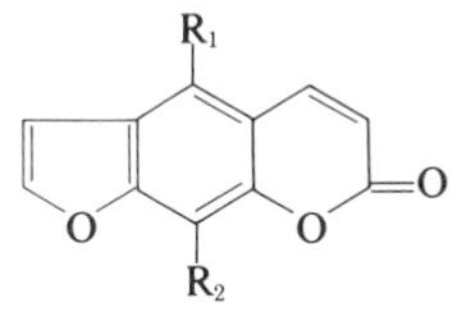

	R_1	R_2
Psoralene	—H	—H
Bergapten	$—OCH_3$	—H
Xanthotoxin	—H	$—OCH_3$

The following plants are considered phototoxic on the basis of experimental as well as clinical evidence (117):

Pastinaca sativa	Parsnip (figure 77)
Pastinaca urens	
Heracleum mantegazzianum	Giant hog weed, Wild parsnip
Heracleum dulce	
Ficus carica	Fig
Psoralea carylifolia	Scurfy pea
Daucus carota	Carrot
Anthriscus sylvestris	Wild chervil
Schinopsis lorentzii	Quebracho
Dictamnus albus	Gas plant, Burning bush (figure 78)
Citrus aurantifolia	Persian lime
Apium graveolens	Celery

Systemic and other Involvements

For the most part there is no substantiated evidence of systemic involvement due to external exposure to these plants. Shock may follow a trauma, such as rolling in a field of nettles or an unusually severe and extensive contact with a primary irritant. In retrospect the study of cases of nephrotic syndrome and glomerular nephritis supposedly associated with the long term incidence of poison oak dermatitis are inconclusive (91).

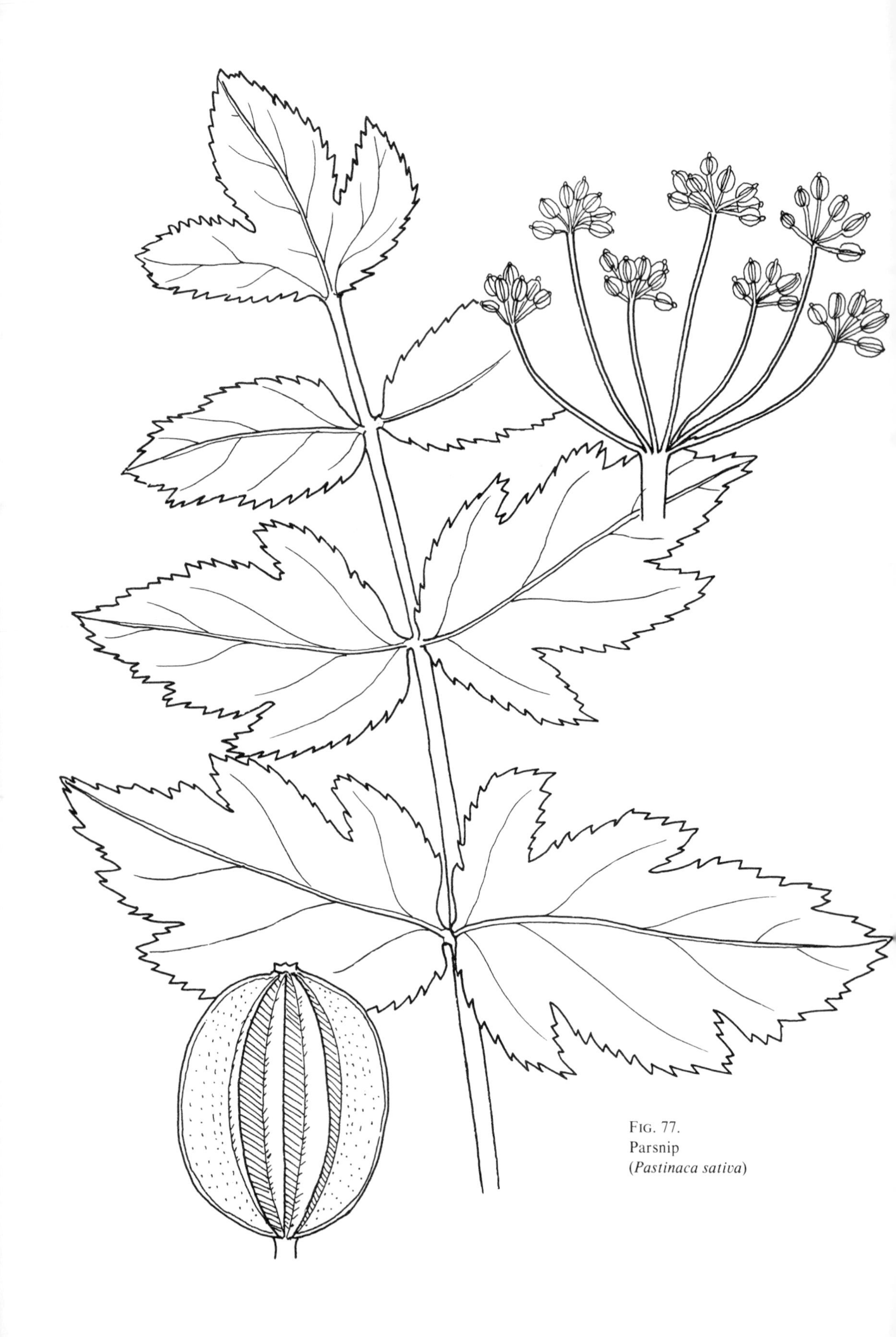

FIG. 77.
Parsnip
(*Pastinaca sativa*)

Fig. 78.
Gas plant or Burning bush
(*Dictamnus albus*)

The ill-advised practice of ingesting *Toxicodendron* plants (*Rhus*) to produce an immunity to dermatitis may result in the following: after a delay of about 48 hours, edematous swelling and pain in the tongue, cheeks, palate and pharynx. About 2 days thereafter the anal region becomes red, swollen and extremely tender (104). In women, the urethral orifice and vulvae may become affected since the oleoresin is partially excreted in the urine. Gastroenteritis with emesis and diarrhea may develop, but this is not a constant finding. Central nervous system disturbances, resembling atropine poisoning and suggestive of anaphylactic reactions, particularly fever, but also stupor, mydriasis, delirium and convulsions may develop in an occasional patient.

Most of the primary irritant containing plants certainly produce drastic symptoms upon ingestion or contact with the eye, nose, throat or other sensitive areas (25, 34, 46, 121). Management of eye injury will be discussed in the treatment section of this chapter. For possible poisoning following the ingestion of dermatitis producing plants other than species of *Toxicodendron*, the reader should consult the index.

Treatment of Dermatitis Produced by Plants

In general the management of acute contact dermatitis is to identify the source and to provide relief of inflammation and itching, while protecting the skin from further abuse. The treatment should be simple, safe, and conservative since contact dermatitis is usually self limiting in the absence of repeated exposure to the offending material. In severe cases a short course of 3 to 5 days systemic corticosteroid therapy is indicated. Cool compresses of plain water applied to the affected area at half hour intervals are of great value during the acute stages.

Special considerations in regard to the treatment of mechanical injury with imbedding of plant parts would be the removal of foreign and necrotic material and, if indicated, appropriate treatment for the type of secondary infection involved.

In the case of pollen dermatitis, although systemic corticosteroid therapy will relieve the severe acute stage, the only practical answer lies in identification of the source and removal of the patient from the region where he is likely to encounter that specific pollen during the flowering season.

Photodermatitis is treated as other forms of dermatitis. Exclusions of the causative factor is, again, important. The patient should be advised, as should all patients suffering from acute contact dermatitis, to avoid undue exposure to direct sunlight.

Since itching is a consistent symptom, the primary complication in children is secondary infection, usually of the impetigo type, which is superimposed on the contact dermatitis. It is wise, therefore, to advise the parent to keep the child's fingernails trimmed and the hands clean.

"Overtreatment dermatitis" (116) is most usually encountered in cases of allergic contact dermatitis in which the affected individual does not recognize the source of his eruption. It is due, in his mind, to fungus, bacterial infection, poisonous insect bites, or worse and must be treated accordingly. His family, friends, the local pharmacists, and even the physician (often by telephone) will prescribe topical medication for the self-diagnosed condition. Sensitization to the medication may result, further complicating the existing dermatitis.

Bacterial infections should be managed by the use of the proper systemic antibiotic.

Immunization procedures against antigens that produce allergic contact dermatitis, including those for poison ivy and its relatives, are not recommended for general use by this author.

Treatment of Keratoconjunctivitis

The eye should be irrigated immediately to remove the vesicant material. A mydriatic agent should be instilled followed by an ophthalmic preparation of corticosteroids. Sufficient relief of pain is usually accomplished by the corticosteroid but, if persistent, local anesthetics may be used.

Treatment of Oral Self-Immunization Reactions

Management of conditions produced by ingestion is usually symptomatic. Acute inflammatory reactions may respond to corticosteroids.

TABLE OF DERMATITIS-PRODUCING PLANTS

The following list is composed of plants for which actual incidents of dermatitis or positive sensitivity reactions have been reported. Often the plants were merely identified by genus. Members of the extensive lists in the literature available of plants suspected of, or likely to produce dermatitis were omitted. Plants or plant products not likely to be encountered in the United States were also deleted.

Aceraceae		
Acer negundo	Box elder	(70)
Amaryllidaceae		
Agave spp	Agave	(33)
Narcissus spp	Daffodil, Narcissus	(33, 88)
Narcissus jonquilla	Jonquil	(96)
Anacardiaceae		
Anacardium occidentale	Cashew	(29)
Mangifera indica	Mango	(18, 59)
Metopium toxiferum	Poison wood	(54)
Schinus terebinthifolius	Brazilian pepper tree, Florida holly	
Toxicodendron diversilobum (*Rhus diversiloba*)	Western poison oak	(73)
Toxicodendron quercifolium (*Rhus quercifolia*)	Eastern poison oak	(60, 77, 83)
Toxicodendron radicans (*Rhus radicans*)	Poison ivy	(60, 77, 83)

Toxicodendron vernix (*Rhus vernix*)	Poison sumac, Swamp sumac	(60, 77, 83)
Annonaceae		
Asimina triloba	Paw paw	(10)
Apocynaceae		
Nerium oleander	Oleander	(33)
Araceae		
Arum maculatum	Cuckoo pint, Lords-and-Ladies	(96)
Dieffenbachia spp	Dumbcane	(32, 50)
Philodendron cordatum (*P. oxycardium, P. Scandens cardatum*)		(9)
Philodendron selloum		(9)
Philodendron speciosum		(9)
Araliaceae		
Hedera canariensis	Algerian ivy	(30, 31)
Hedera helix	English ivy	(43)
Asclepiadaceae		
Calotropis gigantea	Crown flower	(121)
Bignoniaceae		
Jacaranda spp		(113)
Bromeliaceae		
Ananas comosus	Pineapple	(84)
Chenopodiaceae		
Sarcobatus vermiculatus	Greasewood	(33)
Commelinaceae		
Rhoeo spathacea (*R. discolor*)	Oyster plant, Boat-lily	(123)
Setcreasea purpurea	Purple-queen	(123)
Compositae		
Achillea lanulosa		(72)
Achillea millefolium	Milfoil, Yarrow	(77, 117)
Ambrosia spp	Ragweeds	(22, 40, 53, 70, 105, 112, 114)
Ambrosia artemisiifolia (*A. elatior*)	Ragweed	(72, 101)
Ambrosia bidentata	Lance-leaved ragweed	(101)
Ambrosia psilostachya	Western ragweed	(101)
Anthemis cotula	Stinking mayweed	(70, 88)
Artemisia ludoviciana	Western mugwort	(72)
Artemisia vulgaris	Mugwort	(72)
Aster spp		(33)
Chrysanthemum spp		(44)
Chrysanthemum cinerariaefolium	Dalmatian Chrysanthemum	(76)
Chrysanthemum coccineum	Pyrethrum, Painted daisy	(88, 112)
Chrysanthemum leucanthemum	Marguerite, Whiteweed, Ox-eye daisy	(72, 76, 88)
Chrysanthemum marshallicarneum		(76)
Chrysanthemum maximum	Shasta daisy	(88)
Chrysanthemum x morifolium	Chrysanthemum of florists	(88)
Chrysanthemum parthenium	Feverfew	(88)
Chrysanthemum roseum		(76)
Encelia californica		(33)
Erigeron canadensis (*Leptilon canadense*)	Fleabane, Marestail	(70)
Franseria acanthicarpa	Poverty weed	(72)

Gaillardia spp	Gaillardia	(89)
Helenium autumnale	Sneezeweed	(72)
Helenium microcephalum		(101)
Iva angustifolia	Marsh elder	(101, 108)
Iva xanthifolia	Marsh elder	(53, 72)
Lactuca sativa	Lettuce	(86)
Oxytenia acerosa	Copper weed	(97)
Parthenium argentatum	Guayule	(107)
Parthenium hysterophorus	Parthenium	(101)
Rudbeckia hirta (*R. serotina*)	Black-eyed Susan	(70, 72)
Tanacetum vulgare	Tansy	(53, 88)
Xanthium spp	Cocklebur	(72)
Xanthium spinosum		(90, 101)
Xanthium strumarium		(101)
Convovulaceae		
Dichondra repens		(33)
Cornaceae		
Cornus sanguinea	Bloodtwig Dogwood	(122)
Euphorbiaceae		
Cnidoscolus stimulosus (*Jatropha stimulosa*)	Bull nettle, Spurge nettle, Tread-softly	(61)
Euphorbia lactea	Candelabra cactus	(25)
Euphorbia lathyrus	Caper spurge, Mole plant	(25)
Euphorbia marginata	Snow on the mountain	(60)
Euphorbia pulcherrima	Poinsettia	(33)
Euphorbia tirucalli	Milk bush, Pencil cactus	(25)
Jatropha spp		(3, 16)
Jatropha urens		(72)
Hippomane mancinella	Manchineel tree	(34, 46, 109)
Hura crepitans	Sandbox tree	(3, 16)
Ricinus communis	Castor bean	(33)
Fumariaceae		
Dicentra spectabilis	Bleeding heart	(57)
Geraniaceae		
Geranium spp		(5)
Ginkgoaceae		
Ginkgo biloba	Maiden hair tree	(17, 92, 110)
Gramineae		
Agropyron repens	Quack grass, Dog grass	(70)
Cynodon dactylon	Bermuda grass	(101)
Oryza sativa	Rice	(2)
Secale cereale	Rye	(53)
Digitaria sanguinalis (*Syntherisma sanguinale*)	Crab grass	(101)
Hydrophyllaceae		
Phacelia crenulata		(12)
Phacelia parryi		(12)
Phacelia viscida		(12)
Phacelia whitlavia (*P. grandifolia*)	California bluebell	(12)
Wigandia caracasana		(6, 33)
Juglandaceae		
Juglans nigra	Black walnut	(103)
Lecythidaceae		

Bertholletia excelsa	Brazil nut	(74)
Leguminosae		
Prosopis juliflora var. *glandulosa*	Mesquite	(39, 111)
Psoralea spp	Scurfy pea	(117)
Liliaceae		
Allium cepa	Onion	(19)
Allium sativum	Garlic	(19)
Hyacinthus spp		(56)
Hyacinthus orientalis var. *albulus*	Roman hyacinth	(79)
Tulipa spp	Tulip	(13, 20, 45, 79, 85)
Loranthaceae		
Phorandendron flavescens (incorrectly identified as *Viscum album* in the United States)	Mistletoe	(78)
Magnoliaceae		
Magnolia grandiflora	Bull bay	(42)
Moraceae		
Ficus carica	Fig	(33)
Ficus pumila (*F. repens*)		(33, 117)
Humulus spp	Hop	(24)
Myrtaceae		
Eucalyptus globulus	Blue gum	(41)
Oleaceae		
Fraxinus spp	Ash tree	(70)
Orchidaceae		
Cypripedium acaule	Pink ladyslipper	(115)
Cypripedium calceolus	Yellow ladyslipper	(115)
Cypripedium candidum	Small white ladyslipper	(115)
Cypripedium reginae	Showy ladyslipper	(115)
Pinaceae		
Abies balsamea	Balsam fir	(58)
Primulaceae		
Primula farinosa	Birdseye primrose	(100)
Primula obconica	Primrose	(37, 87, 88)
Proteaceae		
Grevillea banskii	Kahili flower	(7)
Grevillea robusta	Australian silk oak	(33, 75)
Ranunculaceae		
Anemone patens (*Pulsatilla patens*)	Wind flower, Prairie Crocus	(1)
Clematis spp	Virgins-bower	(69)
Ranunculus acris	Tall field buttercup	(60)
Ranunculus bulbosus	Bulbous buttercup	(60)
Ranunculus sceleratus	Cursed crowfoot	(60)
Rosaceae		
Agrimonia spp	Beggar-ticks	(117)
Agrimonia eupatoria		(77)
Rosa odorata	Tea rose	(33)
Rutaceae		
Citrus spp		(95)
Citrus aurantifolia	Lime	(93)
Citrus aurantium	Sour orange	(117)
Citrus limonia	Lemon	(35)
Dictamnus albus	Gas plant, Burning bush, Fraxinella	(26)

Ruta graveolens	Rue	(62)
Salicaceae		
Populus spp	Poplar	(70, 119)
Solanaceae		
Lycopersicon esculentum	Tomato	(68)
Solanum carolinense	Horse nettle, Bull nettle	(61)
Solanum tuberosum	Potato	(81)
Thymelaeaceae		
Daphne mezereum	Daphne	(96)
Ulmaceae		
Ulmus glabra (*U. montana*)	Wych elm, Scotch elm	(42)
Ulmus procera (*U. campestris*)	English elm	(42)
Ulmus spp		(70)
Umbelliferae		
Anthriscus sylvestris	Cow parsley, Wild chervil	(88)
Apium graveolens var. *dulce*	Celery	(15, 120)
Daucus carota var. *sativa*	Carrot	(63, 82, 117, 118)
Heracleum spp	Cow parsnip	(117)
Heracleum mantegazzianum	Giant hogweed, Wild parsnip	(14, 88)
Pastinaca sativa	Parsnip	(55, 88, 117)
Urticaceae		
Laportea canadensis	Nettle	(60)
Urtica chamaedryoides	Nettle	(61)
Urtica dioica	Stinging nettle	(60)
Urtica urens	Nettle	(60)
Verbenaceae		
Tectona grandis	Teak	(28, 67)
Vitaceae		
Vitis vinifera	Wine grape	(4)
Zygophyllaceae		
Larrea tridentata var. *glutinosa* (*Covillea glutinosa*)	Creosote bush	(106)

REFERENCES

1. Aaron, T. H. and Muttitt, E. L. Vesicant Dermatitis Due to Prairie Crocus (Anemone Patens L.). Arch. Dermat. *90:* 168, (1964).
2. Alderson, H. E. and Rawlins, A. G. Rice Workers' Dermatitis. Calif. and Western Med. *23:* 42 (1925).
3. Allen, P. H. Poisonous and Injurious Plants of Panama. Am. J. Trop. Med. Hyg. *23*, suppl. 1 (1943).
4. Anderson, J. M. Dermatitis from Grapes. Arch. Dermat. Syph. *31:* 658 (1935).
5. Anderson, J. W. Geranium Dermatitis. Arch. Dermat. Syph. *7:* 510 (1923).
6. Anderson, N. P. Dermatitis Venenata Due to *Wigandia Caracasana.* Calif. and Western Med. *34:* 278 (1931).
7. Arnold, H. L. Dermatitis Due to the Blossom of *Grevillea Banksii.* Arch. Dermat. Syph. *45:* 1037 (1942).
8. Ayres, S. Jr. Dermatitis Venenata. Calif. and Western Med. *46:* 183 (1937).
9. Ayres, S. Jr. and Ayres, S. III. Philodendron as a Cause of Contact Dermatitis. A.M.A. Arch. Dermat. *78:* 330 (1958).
10. Barber, M. A. Poisoning Due to the Papaw (*Asimina triloba*). J. Am. Med. Assoc. *45:* 2013 (1905).
11. Bellringer, H. E. Phyto-Photo-Dermatitis. Brit. Med. J. *1:* 984 (1949).
12. Berry, C. Z., Shipiro, S. I., Dahlen, R. F. Dermatitis Venenata from *Phacelia crenulata.* Arch. Dermat. *85:* 737 (1962).
13. Bertwistle, A. P. "Tulip Fingers". Brit. Med. J. *2:* 255 (1935).

14. Binnie, G. A. C. Wild Parsnips. Lancet *2:* 533 (1964).
15. Birmingham, D. J., Key, M. M., Tubich, G. E. and Perone, V. B. Phototoxic Bullae Among Celery Harvesters. Arch. Dermat. *83:* 127 (1961).
16. Blohm, H. *Poisonous Plants of Venezuela.* Harvard Univ. Press, Cambridge, Mass. 1962.
17. Bolus, M. Dermatitis Venenata Due to Ginkgo Berries. Arch. Dermat. Syph. *39:* 530 (1939).
18. Brown, A. and Brown, F. R. Mango Dermatitis. J. Allergy *12:* 310 (1940).
19. Burks, J. W. Classic Aspects of Onion and Garlic Dermatitis in Housewives. Ann. Dermat. *12:* 592 (1954).
20. Caulfield, A. H. W. Report of the Investigation and Successful Treatment (Preventive) of Dermatitis. J. Allergy *8:* 181 (1937).
21. Champion, R. H. Wood-cutter's Disease: Contact Sensitivity to Lichen. Brit. J. Dermat. *77:* 285 (1965).
22. Cohen, S. G. Seasonal Ragweed Dermatitis. A.M.A. Arch. Dermat. *79:* 118 (1959).
23. Cohen, S. G. and Reif, C. B. Cutaneous Sensitization to Blue-Green Algae. J. Allergy *24:* 452 (1953).
24. Cookson, J. S. Hop Dermatitis in Herefordshire. Brit. Med. J. *2:* 376 (1953).
25. Crowder, J. I., Sexton, R. R. Keratoconjunctivitis Resulting From the Sap of Candelebra Cactus and the Pencil Tree. Arch. Ophthal. *72:* 476 (1964).
26. Cummer, C. L. and Dexter, R. Dermatitis Caused by *Dictamnus Albus* (Gas Plant). J. Am. Med. Assoc. *109:* 495 (1937).
27. Curjel, D. F. and Acton, H. W. Jute Dermatitis. Indian J. Med. Res. *12:* 257 (1924).
28. Davidson, J. M. Toxic Effects of Iroko. Lancet *1:* 38 (1941).
29. Dawson, C. R. The Toxic Principle of Poison Ivy and Related Plants. Rec. Chem. Prog. *15:* 39 (1954).
30. Dorsey, C. S. Contact Dermatitis from Algerian Ivy. A.M.A. Arch. Dermat. *75:* 671 (1957).
31. Dorsey, C. S. Algerian Ivy Dermatitis. Calif. Med. *90:* 155 (1959).
32. Dorsey, C. S. Philodendron Dermatitis. Calif. Med. *88:* 329 (1958).
33. Dorsey, C. S. Plant Dermatitis in California. Calif. Med. *96:* 412 (1962).
34. Earle, K. V. Toxic Effects of Hippomane Mancinella. Roy. Soc. Trop. Med. Hyg. *32:* 363 (1938).
35. Fanburg, S. J. and Kaufman, J. G. Eczema Due to Lemon Peel. J. Am. Med. Assoc. *97:* 390 (1933).
36. Fisher, A. A. *Contact Dermatitis.* Chapter 5, Pp. 67–90, Contact Dermatitis Due to Plants. Lea & Febiger, Philadelphia, 1967.
37. Foerster, O. H. Primula Dermatitis. J. Am. Med. Assoc. *55:* 642 (1910).
38. Foerster, H. R. Sporotrichosis, An Occupational Dermatosis. J. Am. Med. Assoc. *87:* 1605 (1926).
39. Fox, E. C. Mesquite Wood Dermatitis. Arch. Dermat. Syph. *44:* 1098 (1941).
40. Fromer, J. L. and Jenkins, W. S. Ragweed Oil Dermatitis. Lahey Clinic Bulletin *11:* 75 (1959).
41. Galewsky, Dr. Über Eucalyptus-Dermatitiden. Dermat. Ztschr. *12:* 36 (1904).
42. Genner, V. and Bonnevie, P. Eczematous Eruptions Produced by Leaves of Trees and Bushes. Arch. Dermat. Syph. *37:* 583 (1938).
43. Goldman, L., Preston, R. H. Muegel, H. R. Dermatitis Venenata from English Ivy (*Hedera Helix*). A.M.A. Arch. Dermat. *74:* 311 (1956).
44. Goldstein, M. B. Dermatitis Venenata Due to Chrysanthemum Leaves. J. Am. Med. Assoc. *96:* 1680 (1931).
45. Gore, H. C. Jr. "Tulip Fingers" (Dermatitis Venenata Due to Constituent in Tulip Bulb). Arch. Dermat. *85:* 798 (1962).
46. Grana, P. C. Clinical Notes. Conjunctivitis and Dermatitis Due to "Beach Apple". Arch. Ophthal. *35:* 421 (1946).
47. Grauer, F. H. and Arnold, H. L. Jr. Seaweed Dermatitis. Arch. Dermat. *84:* 621 (1961).
48. Greenhouse, C. A. and Sulzberger, M. B. The Common Weed Tansy (*Tenacetum vulgare*) as a Cause of Eczematous Dermatitis. J. Allergy *4:* 523 (1933).
49. Harber, L. C., Harris, H., Leider, M. and Baer, R. L. Berloque Dermatitis. Arch. Dermat. *90:* 572 (1964).
50. Harris, J. H. Dermatitis of the Eyelids Due to Philodendron (*Scandens cardatum*) Plants. Arch. Dermat. Syph. *45:* 1066 (1942).
51. Harville, C. H. Contact Dermatitis Due to a Common Plant. J. Allergy *4:* 527 (1933).

52. Howell, J. B. Poison Ivy Smoke. Arch. Dermat. Syph. *50:* 306 (1944).
53. Huber, H. L. and Harsh, G. F. A Summer Dermatitis Caused by a Common Weed. J. Allergy *3:* 578 (1932).
54. Jackson, W. P. U. Plant Dermatitis in the Bahamas. Brit. Med. J. *2:* 298 (1946).
55. Jensen, T. and Hansen, K. G. Active Spectral Range for Phytogenic Photodermatosis Produced by *Pastinaca sativa.* Arch. Dermat. Syph. *40:* 566 (1939).
56. Johnson, D. W. Dermatitis Due to Hyacinth Bulbs. Arch. Dermat. Syph. *32:* 289 (1935).
57. Kanof, N. B. Permanent Disability from Industrial Dermatitis. Arch. Environ. Health *4:* 622 (1962).
58. Kappes, L. O. Balsam as a Cause of Contact Dermatitis in a Florist. Ann. Allergy *6:* 21 (1948).
59. Keil, H., Wasserman, D. and Dawson, C. R. Mango Dermatitis and its Relationship to Poison Ivy Hypersensitivity. Ann. Allergy *4:* 268 (1946).
60. Kingsbury, J. M. Poison Ivy, Poison Sumac, and other Rash-Producing Plants. Cornell Ext. Bull. 1154, N.Y. State College of Agri. 1966.
61. Kingsbury, J. M. *Poisonous Plants of the United States and Canada.* Prentice-Hall, Inc., Englewood Cliffs, N.J., 1964.
62. Klaber, R. Phyto-photodermatitis. Brit. J. Dermat. Syph. *54:* 193 (1942).
63. Klauder, J. V. and Kimmich, J. M. Sensitization Dermatitis to Carrots. A.M.A. Arch. Dermat. *74:* 149 (1956).
64. Kligman, A. M. Poison Ivy (*Rhus*) Dermatitis. A.M.A. Arch. Dermat. *77:* 149 (1958).
65. Kligman, A. M. The Identification of Contact Allergens by Human Assay. J. Invest. Dermat. *47:* 369, 375, 393 (1966).
66. Kirsch, N. An Unusual Case of Contact Dermatitis. Conn. State Med. J. *22:* 756 (1958).
67. Krogh, H. K. Contact Eczema Caused by True Teak. Brit. J. Ind. Med. *21:* 65 (1964).
68. Lain, E. S. Dermatitis *Lycopersicum esculentum* (Tomato Plant). J. Am. Med. Assoc. *71:* 1114 (1918).
69. Lancaster, A. H. Clematis Dermatitis. Southern Med. J. *30:* 207 (1937).
70. Lovell, R. G., Mathews, K. P. and Sheldon, J. M. Dermatitis Venenata from Tree Pollen Oils. J. Allergy *26:* 408 (1955).
71. Lutz, O. The Poisonous Nature of the Stinging Hairs of *Jatropha Urens.* Am. J. Pharm. *86:* 527 (1914).
72. Mackoff, S. and Dahl, A. O. A Botanical Consideration of the Weed Oleoresin Problem. Minn. Med. *34:* 1169 (1951).
73. Maibach, H. I. and Epstein, W. L. Plant Dermatitis: Fact and Fancy. Postgrad. Med. *35:* 571 (1964).
74. Markson, L. S. Dermatitis from Seed and Oil of *Bertholletia Excelsa* (Brazil Nut). Arch. Dermat. Syph. *46:* 831 (1942).
75. May, S. B. Dermatitis Due to *Grevillea Robusta* (Australian Silk Oak). Arch. Dermat. *82:* 1006 (1960).
76. McCord, C. P. The Occupational Toxicity of Cultivated Flowers. Ind. Med. Surg. *31:* 365 (1962).
77. O'Donovan, W. J. Dermatitis Bullosa Striata Pratensis. Agrimony Dermatitis. Brit. J. Dermat. Syph. *54:* 39 (1942).
78. O'Farrell, N. M. Dermatitis Venenata Due to Mistletoe. Arch. Dermat. Syph. *43:* 416 (1943).
79. Overton, S. G. Dermatitis from Handling Flower Bulbs. Lancet *211:* 1003 (1926).
80. Paschoud, J. M. Kontakekzen durch Chrysanthemen. Hautarzt *16:* 229 (1965).
81. Peck, S. M., Clare, H. C. Dermatitis from Dehydration of Potatoes. Arch. Dermat. Syph. *52:* 9 (1945).
82. Peck, S. M., Spolyar, L. W., Mason, H. S. Dermatitis from Carrots. Arch. Dermat. Syph. *49:* 266 (1944).
83. Perlman, H. H. Contact Dermatitis caused by Poison Ivy, Poison Sumac and Poison Oak. Med. Sci. *15*, No. 8: 31 (1964).
84. Polunin, I. Pineapple Dermatosis. Brit. J. Dermat. *63:* 441 (1951).
85. Rappaport, B. Z., Welker, W. H. Tulip Bulb Dermatitis. J. Allergy *8:* 379 (1937).
86. Rinkel, H. J. and Balyeat, R. M. Occupational Dermatitis Due to Lettuce. J. Am. Med. Assoc. *98:* 137 (1932).
87. Rook, A. and Wilson, H. T. H. Primula Dermatitis. Brit. Med. J. *1:* 220 (1965).

88. Rook, A. Plant Dermatitis. Brit. Med. J. *2:* 1771 (1960).
89. Rostenberg, A. Jr. and Good, C. K. Gaillardia Dermatitis. J. Am. Med. Assoc. *104:* 1496 (1935).
90. Rowe, A. H. Contact Allergy to Cocklebur (*Xanthium Spinosum*). Arch. Dermat. Syph. *39:* 149 (1939).
91. Rytand, D. A. Fatal Anuria, the Nephrotic Syndrome and Glomerular Nephritis as Sequels of the Dermatitis of Poison Oak. Am. J. Med. *5:* 548 (1948).
92. Saito, J. Poisoning from the fruit of ginkgo (maidenhair tree). Japan. J. Dermat. Urol. 1929, 29; Quart. J. Pharm. Pharmacol. *3:* 121.
93. Sams, W. M. Photodynamic Action of Lime Oil (*Citrus Aurantifolia*). Arch. Dermat. Syph. *44:* 571 (1941).
94. Schiff, B. L. Contact Dermatitis Caused by Bamboo. A.M.A. Arch Dermat. Syph. *64:* 66 (1951).
95. Schwartz, L. Cutaneous Hazards in the Citrus Fruit Industry. Arch. Dermat. Syph. *37:* 631 (1938).
96. Schwartz, L., Tulipan, L., Birmingham, D. J. *Occupational Diseases of the Skin.* Third Edition. Lea & Febiger, Philadelphia, 1957.
97. Schwartz, L. and Warren, L. H. Dermatitis Caused by Contact with Copperweed (*Oxytenia acerosa*). J. Allergy *12:* 63 (1940).
98. Sequeira, J. H. Pyrethrum Dermatitis. Brit. J. Dermat. Syph. *48:* 473 (1936).
99. Shanon, J. and Sagher, F. Sabra Dermatitis. A.M.A. Arch. Dermat. *74:* 269 (1956). See also Kirsch, N. An Unusual Case of Contact Dermatitis. Conn. State Med. J. *22:* 756 (1958).
100. Sharpe, H. A. Primula Dermatitis. Its Occurrence in Rural Districts. J. Am. Med. Assoc. *49:* 2148 (1912).
101. Shelmire, B. Contact Dermatitis from Vegetation. Southern Med. J. *33:* 337 (1940).
102. Shelmire, B. Contact Dermatitis from Weeds: Patch Testing with their Oleoresins. J. Am. Med. Assoc. *113:* 1085 (1939).
103. Siegel, J. M. Dermatitis Due to Black Walnut Juice. A.M.A. Arch. Dermat. Syph. *70:* 511 (1954).
104. Silvers, S. H. Stomatitis Venenata and Dermatitis of the Anal Orifice from Chewing Poison Ivy Leaves (*Rhus Toxicodendron*). J. Am. Med. Assoc. *116:* 2257 (1941).
105. Slater, B. J., Norris, J. L. and Francis, N. Ragweed Dermatitis. Ann. Dermat. *6:* 594 (1948).
106. Smith, L. M. Dermatitis Caused by Creosote Bush. J. Allergy *8:* 187 (1937).
107. Smith, L. M. and Hughes, R. P. Dermatitis Caused by Mexican Rubber Plant. Arch. Dermat. Syph. *38:* 780 (1938).
108. Smith, W. A., Prince, H. E. and Cole, M. L. Contact Dermatitis from the Narrow Leaf Marsh Elder (*Iva angustifolia*). J. Allergy *13:* 371 (1941).
109. Snow, J. S. and Harley, R. D. Dermatitis Venenata and Keratoconjunctivitis caused by the Manzanillo Tree. Arch. Dermat. Syph. *49:* 236 (1944).
110. Sowers, W. F., Weary, P. E., Collins, O. D. and Cawley, E. P. Ginkgo-Tree Dermatitis. Arch. Dermat. *91:* 452 (1965).
111. Stewart, C. D. Dermatitis Due to Mesquite Wood. Arch. Dermat. Syph. *42:* 937 (1940).
112. Sweitzer, S. E. and Rusten, E. M. Seasonal Contact Dermatitis. Arch. Dermat. Syph. *37:* 727 (1938).
113. Tottie, M. Jacaranda als Ursache von Dermatitiden. Acta Dermato-Venereologica *19:* 235 (1938).
114. Trilla, E. Dermatitis Venenata Due to Ragweed Pollen. A.M.A. Arch. Dermat. *75:* 905 (1957).
115. Ulbrich, A. P. Contact dermatitis caused by plants. J. Amer. Osteopath. Assn. *64:* 1023 (1965).
116. Underwood, G. B. and Gaul, L. E. Overtreatment Dermatitis in Dermatitis Venenata Due to Plants. J. Am. Med. Assoc. *138:* 570 (1948).
117. Van Dijk, E. and Berrens, L. Plants as an Etiological Factor in Phytophotodermatitis. Dermatologica *129:* 321 (1964).
118. Vickers, H. R. The Carrot as a Cause of Dermatitis. Brit. J. Dermat. *53:* 52 (1941).
119. Weber, L. F. Dermatitis Venenata Due to Native Woods. A.M.A. Arch. Dermat. Syph. *67:* 388 (1953).

120. Wiswell, J. G., Irwin, J. W., Guba, E. F., Rackemann, F. M. and Neri, L. L. Contact Dermatitis of Celery Farmers. J. Allergy *19:* 396 (1948).
121. Wong, W. W. Keratoconjunctivitis Due to Crownflower. Hawaii Med. J. *8:* 339 (1949).
122. Woods, B. Irritant Plants. Trans. St. John's Hosp. Dermat. Soc. (new series) *48:* 75 (1962).
123. Morton, J. F. Ornamental Plants with Poisonous Properties II. Proc. Florida Hort. Soc. *75:* 484 (1962).

INDEX

Page numbers in **bold** type refer to illustrations.

D

S

T

U

V

W